PRINCIPLES

OF

MINERALOGY

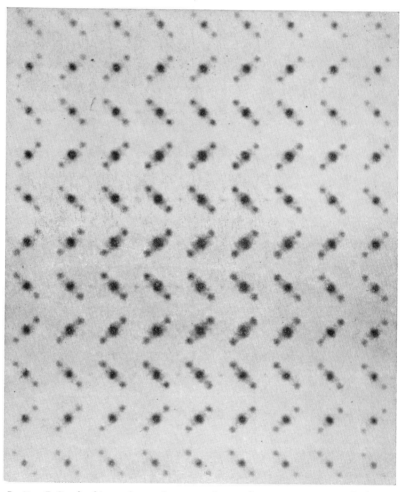

Pyrite, FeS$_2$, looking along the crystallographic a axis, magnified 2.3 million diameters.

PRINCIPLES
OF
MINERALOGY

WILLIAM H. DENNEN

ASSOCIATE PROFESSOR OF GEOLOGY
MASSACHUSETTS INSTITUTE OF TECHNOLOGY

REVISED PRINTING
with
Determinative Tables

THE RONALD PRESS COMPANY   ⁊   NEW YORK

Library of Congress Catalog Card Number: 60–16452
PRINTED IN THE UNITED STATES OF AMERICA

PREFACE

At the introductory level, mineralogy has traditionally been a study of the properties, appearance, use, occurrence, and techniques of identification of individual minerals. The fault of this descriptive approach is that it presents the student with a large amount of detailed information which he finds difficult to coordinate into a rational and useful body of knowledge.

This book, intended for an introductory college course in mineralogy, treats the subject as a study of phenomena that are common to all minerals. Emphasizing principles, it presents mineralogy as a study of the fundamental geometrical, chemical, and physical relationships of all matter rather than as a course in mineral recognition. It has a threefold goal: first, to provide students in geology and allied fields with a mineralogical background that will aid them in studies where the nature of the solid state is an important consideration; second, to provide a text, nonmathematical in treatment, which is broad enough to provide a base for continuing mineralogical studies and detailed enough to bridge the gap now existing between introductory mineralogical work and advanced studies in crystallography, crystal chemistry, petrology, and geochemistry; and finally, to provide convenient descriptive material covering the more common minerals and mineral groupings for examples and laboratory reference.

Mineralogy embraces so many aspects of geology, physics, and chemistry, including physical chemistry and thermodynamics, that in a textbook arbitrary choices of subjects and details are necessary. The six chapters of Part I cover phenomena of the solid state which are of direct and general concern in mineralogy, including symmetry, the nature of matter, chemical bonds, and such mineralogical relations as isomorphism and polymorphism, isostructure, and isotype, exosolution, and twinning, plus material on the physical properties and chemical testing of minerals. These chapters require only a knowledge of elementary chemistry; yet they provide the conceptual background necessary for understanding the geometrical and chemical parameters which determine the kind, number, variations, and stability of atomic arrangements which minerals assume. Part II is devoted to descriptions of individual mineral species or series, together with information applicable to appropriate mineral groups. The descriptions provide a basis for the student's laboratory identification of specimen material. An appendix Table of Atomic Parameters and a Mineral Index are also provided.

Professor Martin Buerger has long been a prominent figure in mineralogical studies. Grateful acknowledgment is made to him both as a teacher and for his sympathetic interest in the preparation of this book. The author is also indebted to his other colleagues and to his students, whose interest and cooperation have contributed materially to the presentation. Messrs. Charles Burham, Charles Prewitt, and Tibor Zoltai have been particularly helpful. His especial thanks go to Miss Edith Gould for making the sketches of minerals in Part II, and to Mrs. Martha Robes and Mrs. Eleanor Levingston for typing the manuscript. Last but not least, the author is grateful to his wife Charlotte for her constant and often much-needed encouragement.

WILLIAM H. DENNEN

Cambridge, Massachusetts
October, 1959

NOTE TO THE REVISED PRINTING

In response to suggestions from those using the book, this printing includes a new Appendix II of Determinative Tables. These tables have 265 entries in eight sections and cover 191 minerals. To show the progressive hardness of the minerals listed in each section, a graphic scale of hardness has been introduced along with hardness numbers. It is hoped that the tables will serve as a teaching tool as well as a reference source.

W. H. D.

September, 1960

CONTENTS

I. General Principles

II. Mineral Descriptions

Part I
GENERAL PRINCIPLES

1

SYMMETRY

Introduction

Nearly all minerals are crystalline solids composed of atoms held in an orderly three-dimensional array by interatomic forces. The geometry of the atomic arrangement, the kinds of atoms present, and the forces acting between the atoms differ from mineral to mineral and are the general categories for a study of mineralogy.

Three-dimensional arrays of atoms are called crystal structures and are characterized by the fact that each grouping of atoms is a duplicate of all other groupings. This regular and periodic arrangement of constituents is the most important feature of crystals. It allows physical examination of the structure by X rays; it allows geometrical analysis of possible and particular atomic arrangements; and it provides a means of identification, since internal structure is reflected in external shape and in certain physical properties.

The three-dimensional network of regularly arranged points to which atoms in a crystal may be related is called a *lattice*. It should be clearly understood that although lattice points may represent atom locations, it is not necessary that lattice points and atom centers be coincident. The atoms in a structure are symmetrically disposed with respect to a lattice, but the lattice itself is merely an imaginary geometrical framework to which their positions may be referred. The actual positions of atoms are properly termed *structure*. Figure 1–1 shows the relationship between the lattice and the structure for the mineral manganite, $MnO(OH)$. It should be noted that in this structure no atom lies on a lattice point.

ELEMENTS OF SYMMETRY

The idea of a pattern should be a familiar one because the world abounds with "arrangements or compositions that suggest or reveal a design." As examples, consider such things as orchards, crystals, flowers, and wallpaper, which are everyday examples of patterns. A pattern requires the presence of some basic element whose regular repetition produces the pattern. Such a basic element is a *motif*. The existence of repeated motifs necessitates, in turn, a "correspondence in size, shape, and

3

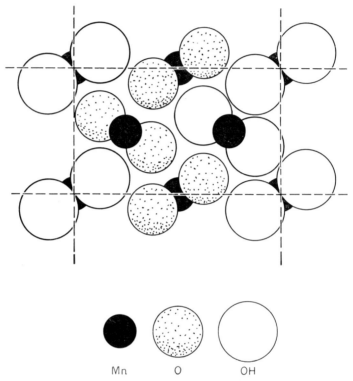

Fig. 1–1. View along the c axis of manganite, MnO(OH), showing its structure (atom locations) and lattice (dashed lines).

relative position of parts with respect to a point, line, plane, or axis." This correspondence of parts is called *symmetry*.

Crystals have external symmetry because identical faces are regularly repeated; they have internal symmetry because each grouping of the constituent atoms is a duplicate of each other grouping. Obviously, both internal and external symmetry are manifestations of the same set of symmetrical relations and can be described in the same terms.

The duplication of one motif by another implies that some geometrical movement connects them. A geometrical movement which will transform one motif into another is known as a *symmetry operation*, and any pattern can be built up by a few simple geometrical operations which alone or in combination produce the complete pattern from any motif. The positions of motifs moved by symmetry operations are symmetrically disposed with respect to some point, line, or plane; and these are called *elements of symmetry*.

The elements of symmetry are *translation*, which relates motifs moved by equal distances in some fixed direction; *reflection*, which relates motifs symmetrically disposed with respect to a mirror plane; *rotation*, which relates motifs moved by regular amounts around an axis; and *inversion*, which relates motifs which are repeated as by a simple lens. Inversion does not have the status of a fundamental element of symmetry since the same result may be obtained by operations of the first three elements.

The symmetry operations consistent with these elements of symmetry are shown diagrammatically in Figure 1–2. The symbols *t*, *m*, and *i* are the accepted notation for translation, reflection (*m* = mirror), and inversion.

Some combinations of symmetry elements are so common in crystalline matter that they have been given particular names. The more important of these are *glide reflection* or simply *glide*, whereby reflection is coupled with a translation parallel to the reflection plane, and a *screw axis*, whereby rotation is coupled with translation parallel to the rotation axis. These two combinations are shown in Figure 1–3.

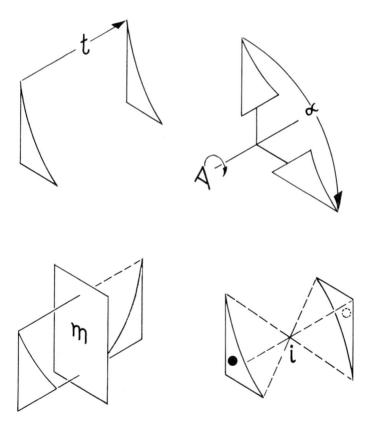

Fig. 1–2. Operation of symmetry elements.

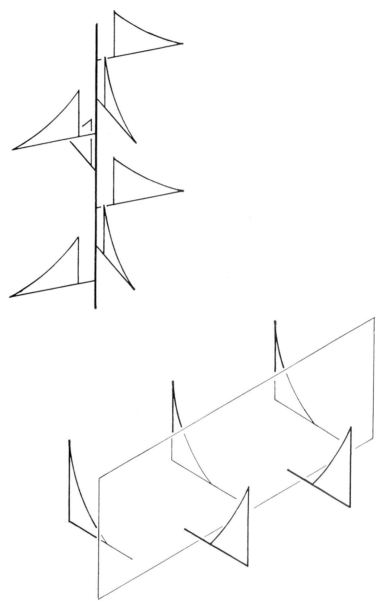

Fig. 1–3. Screw axis (above); glide reflection (below).

In this chapter the background of symmetry in crystalline solids will be developed by a consideration of the individual symmetry elements, the results of combining these elements, and especially the restrictions which are placed on symmetry operations when applied to crystalline matter.

CONGRUENCE AND ENANTIOMORPHISM

The repetition of an asymmetrical motif may be carried out in such a way that the repeated motif is no longer congruent. Such a relationship, for example, would be the symmetry existing between a left and right hand, which are obviously related but just as obviously different.

These figures ✋ ☞ 🖐 are all asymmetrical but they all have the same "handedness" and would run together when placed one on top of the other by movements in the plane of the paper. They are *congruent*. In contradistinction, these figures ✋ ☞ cannot be made congruent by any movement in the plane of the paper. Such figures are *enantiomorphous*. An analogous situation exists in three dimensions, and both enantiomorphic groups of atoms within a crystal and enantiomorphous crystals of the same mineral can exist.

Repetition of an asymmetrical motif by translation or rotation produces a sequence of congruent motifs, Figure 1–4a, whereas repetition by reflection or inversion produces a sequence of enantiomorphic pairs, Figure 1–4b.

Symmetry in a Plane

A space lattice to which a three-dimensional structure may be referred can be generated by successive translations of an initial point. The repeated application of a translation of given length and direction, t_1, to an initial point will generate a row of points:

$$\bullet - t_1 \rightarrow \bullet - t_1 \rightarrow \bullet - t_1 \rightarrow \bullet - t_1 \rightarrow \bullet$$

The repeated application of some other translation, t_2, to this row will generate a planar array of lattice points:

A third non-coplanar translation, t_3, when applied to such a plane lattice, generates a three-dimensional array of points called a *space lattice* or simply *lattice*.

Rational features of a lattice and its related structure are determined by the lattice points. A lattice point is itself a rational point, a rational line connects two lattice points, and a rational plane passes through at

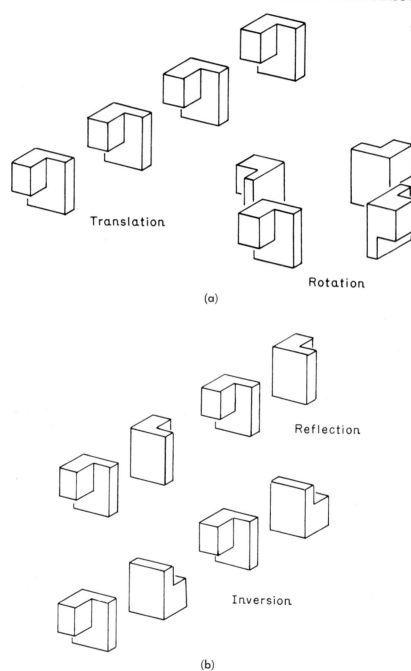

Translation

Rotation

(a)

Reflection

Inversion

(b)

Fig. 1–4. (a) Repetition of congruent motifs. (b) Repetition of enantiomorphous motifs.

least three lattice points not in a straight line. All other points, lines, or planes are irrational.

The structure of a crystal, being three-dimensional, must be referred to an appropriate space lattice. However, any space lattice may be derived by translation from a plane lattice and is hence a stack of plane lattices. It is the plan of the following discussion first to find the distinctively different plane lattice shapes and then to generate consistent space lattices from them. The total number of distinctively different symmetries found for these plane and space lattices must then represent all of those possible for crystalline matter.

The symmetrically different shapes of plane lattice meshes may be found by examining the consistent combinations of symmetry operations which may be used to generate motifs in a plane. Some of the results of this analysis, however, can be anticipated by a simple geometrical argument and are therefore stated briefly in advance of a more detailed study using the interaction of symmetry elements.

A plane lattice is generated by two noncoincident translations and, in consequence, must consist of points on the corners of identical (congruent) quadrilaterals having parallel sides. In turn, each quadrilateral may be divided by a diagonal into two congruent triangles having edges equal to t_1, t_2, and the vector sum of $t_1 + t_2$. If the geometrically distinct kinds of triangles are tabulated, their number should equal the number of distinctively different plane lattice meshes which can exist.

The geometrically different kinds of plane triangles are given in Table 1–1 below. When combined into quadrilaterals, these five different triangles yield the five distinct mesh shapes shown in Figure 1–5. No other plane lattice shapes are possible.

TABLE 1–1

Geometrically Different Triangles

Triangle	Sides	Angles
Scalene	Unequal	Unequal
Isosceles	Two equal	Two equal
Right	Unequal	Unequal; one is 90°
Equilateral	Three equal	Three equal
Right isosceles	Two equal	Two equal; the third is 90°

It is apparent from an examination of the plane lattice meshes in Figure 1–5 that all of them could be rotated around an axis normal to the page and returned to their initial position after some whole number of equal rotary operations. The rotary operations which are consistent with a plane lattice mesh are those which do not generate any new lattice

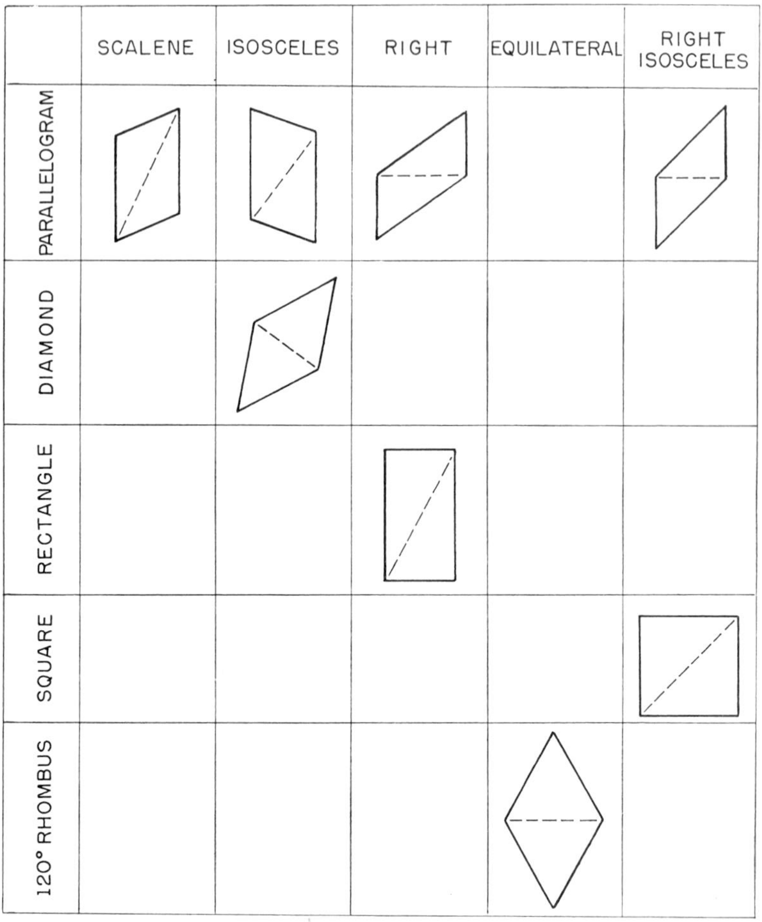

Fig. 1–5. The five distinct kinds of triangles and the five distinct mesh shapes.

points during the complete rotation. Rotations consistent with the five plane lattice shapes are shown in Figure 1–6. The central symbol is the conventional representation of the multiplicity of the axis, i.e., the number of times the rotary operation is performed to return the motif to its initial location.

It is also apparent on examination of the five plane lattice mesh shapes (Figure 1–5) that, with the exception of the generalized parallelogram, they are symmetrical with respect to selected planes normal to the mesh, as shown in Figure 1–7. Since these planes may be mirrors, some new symmetries can arise because of enantiomorphous repetition.

The mesh of a plane lattice is centrosymmetrical because every lattice point is necessarily midway between two other lattice points. This ar-

See fig 1-7

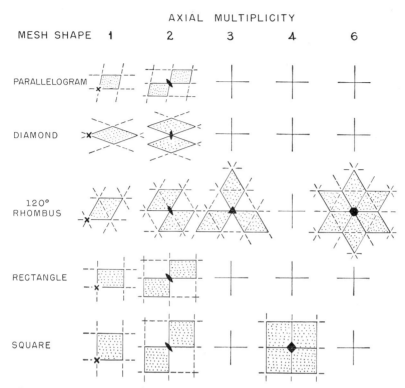

AXIAL MULTIPLICITY

MESH SHAPE   1   2   3   4   6

PARALLELOGRAM

DIAMOND

120°
RHOMBUS

RECTANGLE

SQUARE

Fig. 1–6. Consistency of rotation axes with the five plane mesh shapes.

rangement is consistent with inversion centers which, if present, could occasion new symmetries.

In order to determine all of the combinations of symmetry elements consistent with plane lattices it will be necessary to examine the interaction of various combinations of the elements since several may be simultaneously consistent with the same mesh. Some of these combina-

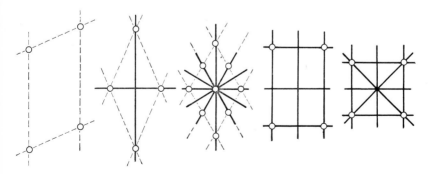

Fig. 1–7. Planes of symmetry consistent with the five plane lattice meshes.

tions will be found to be mutually exclusive while others will yield new symmetry sets. It may, however, be anticipated that the number of possible symmetries will be limited.

IDENTICAL OPERATIONS

The sequential operation of symmetry elements, alone or in combination, may generate an array of symmetrically disposed motifs. Most lattices are consistent with several different symmetry elements and may be considered to have been generated by an alternation of the several operations. The consistence of such operation sets may be shown by an *identical operation* in which the sequence of operations is tested to see that it returns a motif to some initial position. For example, a consistent combination of reflection and rotation is illustrated in Figure 1–8a. The

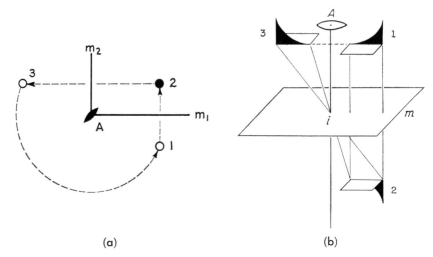

(a)   (b)

Fig. 1–8. (a) Consistent combination of two mirrors and a rotation axis. (b) Consistent combination of reflection, inversion, and rotation.

two mirrors, m_1 and m_2, are normal to the page and at right angles to each other. m_1 transforms an initial point, 1, into its enantiomorph, 2; and m_2 transforms point 2 into point 3, which is congruent with point 1. A two-fold axis, A, normal to the plane of the page at the intersection of the mirrors, can return point 3 to point 1 by a rotary operation of 180°. The particular sequence of reflection and rotation described is thus an identical operation and may be written analytically as $m_1 \cdot m_2 \cdot A_{180°} = 1$

$$\underbrace{}_{90°}$$

where the dot is read "followed by" and "1" indicates that the operation sequence returns a motif to its initial position.

Another identical operation is illustrated in Figure 1–8b.[*] The reflection of the motif at 1 by mirror m yields an enantiomorph at 2. Inversion of 2 through the center i lying in the mirror plane produces the motif at 3, which is congruent to the motif at 1. A two-fold axis, A, normal to the mirror and passing through the inversion center, can transform the motif at 3 to its initial position at 1. Analytically, $m \cdot i = A_{180°}$ or $m \cdot i \cdot A_{-180°} = 1$.

ROTATION

Motifs may be repeated by rotation through some angular distance around an axis. The number of times that the operation must be performed before the initial position is regained is used to describe the axis. A two-fold axis repeats the initial motif after two successive rotations of 180°, a six-fold axis repeats the initial motif after six rotations of 60°, etc. A one-fold axis may be inclined to the plane of the lattice, but all other axes must be normal to the lattice plane.

Rotary operations may be coupled with reflection (rotoreflection) or inversion (rotoinversion) to generate alternating congruent and enantiomorphous motifs. Such rotary operations are termed *improper* to distinguish them from *proper rotation*, in which only congruent motifs are generated.

The reflection plane of a rotoreflection axis is perpendicular to the axis. Its operation may be thought of as following the movement scheme in Figure 1–9a and letting the distance 2–3 shrink to nothing. A rotoinversion axis passes through the inversion center. The operation of such an axis may be thought of as following the movement scheme in Figure 1–9b and letting the distance 1–3 shrink to nothing.

Examples of proper and improper rotation are shown in Figure 1–10. Rotation is about an axis normal to the plane of the paper. Small dots and circles represent enantiomorphous motifs and may be thought of as lying above and below the plane of the page. The notation for a proper axis is an integer, n, of value equal to the number of operations required to repeat the initial motif, e.g., 4 for a four-fold axis. The notation for improper rotation axes is the same except that a wavy bar over the integer is added for rotoreflection axes ($\tilde{4}$), and a straight bar for rotoinversion axes ($\bar{4}$).

COMBINED OPERATIONS

Combined Rotations. Two axes of rotation can be coincident and therefore combined when the rotary operation of one is a submultiple of the rotary operation of the other. For example, the four-fold operation

---

[*] Figure 1–8b modified by permission from *Elementary Crystallography*, by M. J. Buerger. Copyright, 1956, by John Wiley & Sons, Inc., New York.

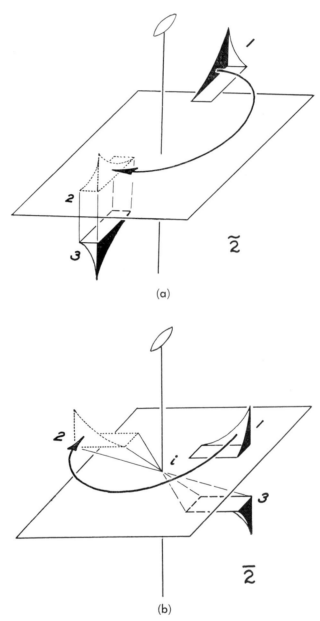

Fig. 1–9. (a) Movement schemes for rotoreflection axes. (b) Movement schemes for rotoinversion axes.

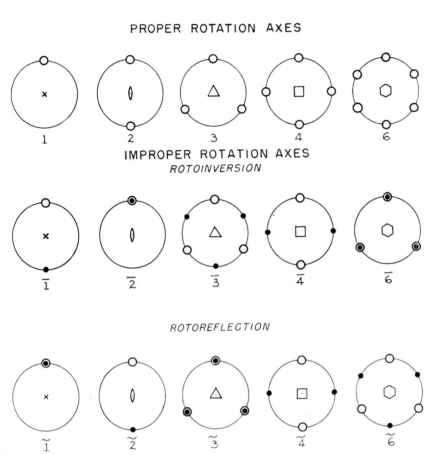

Fig. 1–10. Proper and improper rotation (after Buerger).

of 90° is a submultiple of the two-fold operation of 180°, and the two- and four-fold axes may be considered to be combined. Similarly, the six-fold rotary operation of 60° is a submultiple of three-, two-, and one-fold rotary operations. It follows that if an n-fold axis is consistent with a lattice and is also a submultiple of another n-fold axis, then both must be consistent with the mesh. n-fold axes and their submultiples are listed in Table 1–2.

New symmetries do not arise because of the combination of an axis and its submultiple, but the consistence of several different rotary operations with the same mesh is explained. The symmetry described is that of the highest multiplicity present.

Proper and improper axes of the same multiplicity may also be combined, since an axial location with respect to a lattice may be consistent

TABLE 1-2

Axial Submultiples

Axis	Rotary Operation	Submultiple
1	360°	2, 3, 4, 6
2	180°	4, 6
3	120°	6
4	90°	None
6	60°	None

with an n-fold proper axis, an n-fold improper axis, or simultaneously with both. This is because all lattices are inherently centrosymmetrical and must contain inversion centers.

The coincidence of proper and improper rotation axes is indicated by the notation $\frac{n}{n}$. Sets of coincident axes are represented in Figure 1–11.

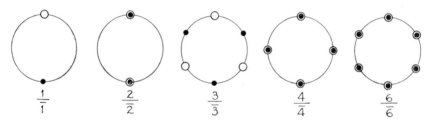

$$\frac{1}{\overline{1}} \qquad \frac{2}{\overline{2}} \qquad \frac{3}{\overline{3}} \qquad \frac{4}{\overline{4}} \qquad \frac{6}{\overline{6}}$$

Fig. 1–11. Combined proper and improper rotation (after Buerger).

By comparison with Figure 1–10,* it may be seen that the combination $\frac{1}{\overline{1}}$ equals $\overline{1}$ and that $\frac{3}{\overline{3}}$ is the equivalent of $\overline{3}$ so that no new rotational symmetries result from these combinations. The coincident combinations $\frac{2}{\overline{2}}$, $\frac{4}{\overline{4}}$, and $\frac{6}{\overline{6}}$, on the other hand, are new symmetries. The operation of such axial combinations, however, is equivalent to the combination of a proper axis and a mirror perpendicular to the axis (see Figure 1–10). In consequence, these three groups are usually designated $\frac{2}{m}$, $\frac{4}{m}$, and $\frac{6}{m}$.

The equivalence of improper axes, alone or coincident with proper axes, is given in Table 1–3.

Inspection of Table 1–3 shows that many axes and coincident combinations are identical. For example, all rotoreflections are equivalent to some

* Redrawn by permission from *Elementary Crystallography*, by M. J. Buerger. Copyright, 1956, by John Wiley & Sons, Inc., New York.

TABLE 1-3

Equivalence of Axes

Axis or Axial Combination	Decomposed into Rotation and Reflection or Inversion	Equivalent Axis	Usual Designation
$\bar{1}$	$1 \cdot i$	$\tilde{2}$	$\bar{1}$
$\bar{2}$	$1 \cdot m_\perp$	$\tilde{1}$	m
$\bar{3}$	$3 \cdot i$	$\tilde{6}$	$\bar{3}$
$\bar{4}$	$-$	$\tilde{4}$	$\bar{4}$
$\bar{6}$	$3 \cdot m_\perp$	$\tilde{3}$	$\dfrac{3}{m}$
$\tilde{1}$	$1 \cdot m_\perp$	$\bar{2}$	m
$\tilde{2}$	$1 \cdot i$	$\bar{1}$	$\bar{1}$
$\tilde{3}$	$3 \cdot m_\perp$	$\bar{6}$	$\dfrac{3}{m}$
$\tilde{4}$	$-$	$\bar{4}$	$\bar{4}$
$\tilde{6}$	$3 \cdot i$	$\bar{3}$	$\bar{3}$
$\dfrac{1}{\bar{1}}$	$\dfrac{1}{1 \cdot i}$	$\bar{1}$	$\bar{1}$
$\dfrac{2}{\bar{2}}$	$\dfrac{2}{1 \cdot m_\perp}$	$\dfrac{2}{m}$	$\dfrac{2}{m}$
$\dfrac{3}{\bar{3}}$	$\dfrac{3}{3 \cdot i}$	$\bar{3}$	$\bar{3}$
$\dfrac{4}{\bar{4}}$	$-$	$\dfrac{4}{m}$	$\dfrac{4}{m}$
$\dfrac{6}{\bar{6}}$	$\dfrac{6}{3 \cdot m_\perp}$	$\dfrac{6}{m}$	$\dfrac{6}{m}$

rotoinversion $(\tilde{2} = \bar{1})$ and rotoreflection notation need not be further used. The total of distinctively different symmetries for axial types $\bar{n}$, $\tilde{n}$, and $\dfrac{n}{n}$ is eight, and the total of distinctively different axial types, including proper rotation axes 1, 2, 3, 4, and 6, is thirteen.

Rotation and Translation. The discussion in the previous sections was limited to one-, two-, three-, four-, and six-fold axes. It is the purpose of the following section to show that rotation and translation combine to limit both the number of permissible axial kinds and the shape of the plane lattice nets with which they are consistent.

As an example of the limitations imposed on the angle through which rotation may occur when translation is also present, consider the interplay of a four-fold axis and a translation. The four-fold axis A is reproduced at A' by the translation t, Figure 1–12a. In turn, the four-fold axes A and A' require four-fold repetition about themselves of the translation t, Figure 1–12b. Each translation now requires the repetition of a four-fold axis at a distance t from A and A', Figure 1–12c.* Continued opera-

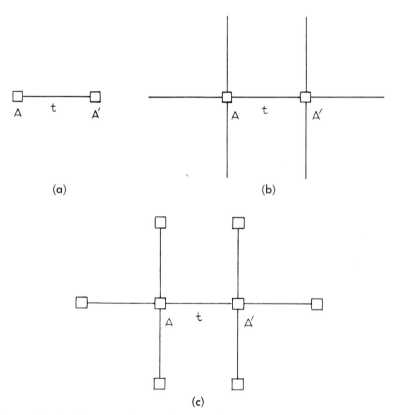

(a)   (b)

(c)

Fig. 1–12. Combination of translation and four-fold rotation (after Buerger).

tions of rotation and translation of this nature thus fix the plane lattice as being composed of squares, since $t_1 = t_2$ and the angle between these translations is 90°.

A similar situation is encountered for the interaction of a three-fold axis and a translation, Figure 1–13. Axis A is moved by translation t to A', the translation distance is reproduced three times around each axis, and

* Figures 1-12c and 1-13 modified by permission from *Elementary Crystallography*, by M. J. Buerger. Copyright, 1956, by John Wiley & Sons, Inc., New York.

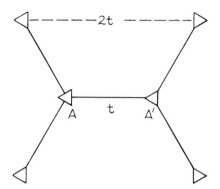

Fig. 1–13. Combination of translation and three-fold rotation (after Buerger).

the translation generates new three-fold axes separated by a rational line whose length is $2t$.

The generation of a mesh consistent with two-fold axes by the inter-action of two-fold rotation and translation must be accomplished by the interaction of both translations with rotation, since the two-fold operation generates motifs in a line only.

When the interaction of rotation and translation is such that the location of the axes generated by the symmetry operations are irrational, i.e., the axes do not fall on lattice points, then the combination cannot occur. Consider, for example, the interaction of translation and rotation for a five-fold axis A which is repeated by the translation t to A', Figure 1–14.[*] The five-fold symmetry about A and A' generates points such as 1 and 2 separated by the translation distance t from A and A'. The distance from 1 and 2, however, is not a translation of an integral multiple of the trans-

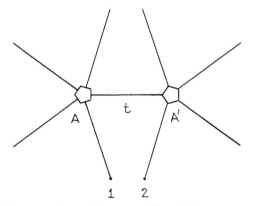

Fig. 1–14. Combination of translation and five-fold rotation (after Buerger).

[*] Figure 1–14 modified by permission from *Elementary Crystallography*, by M. J. Buerger. Copyright, 1956, by John Wiley & Sons, Inc., New York.

lation t and is, therefore, irrational. As a consequence, five-fold symmetry cannot occur in crystals since such symmetry is not consistent with a lattice.

A complete study of the interaction of rotation and translation shows that *plane lattice nets can be consistent only with one-, two-, three-, four-, and six-fold axes.* Crystals, therefore, have these and only these axes of rotational symmetry.

The combined operation of a rotation followed by a translation in a direction normal to the axis may be analyzed in greater detail in order to locate the position of all axes consistent with the plane mesh. The operation A_α (rotation through the angle α around the axis A) is selected so that lines 1 and 2 are symmetrically disposed with respect to the perpendicular to a translation t as shown in Figure 1–15.* The rotation of A_α

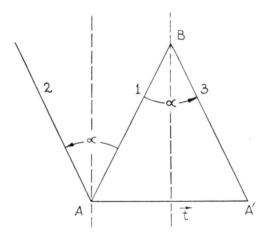

Fig. 1–15. Combination of rotation and perpendicular translation (after Buerger).

brings line 1 to line 2, and the translation t brings A to A' and line 2 to line 3. The initial and final positions of the line are 1 and 3, and obviously there has been no motion of the line at B. The net motion of the line as a result of rotation and translation is thus equivalent to a rotation of α about B. This rotation applies to all points on the line, and the operational sequence can be expressed analytically as $A_\alpha \cdot t_\perp = B_\alpha$ or $A_\alpha \cdot t_\perp \cdot B_{-\alpha} = 1$. A useful generalization from this construction is that an axis B of equal multiplicity to axis A lies on the perpendicular bisector of t.

The interaction of axes with translation can now be surveyed to locate the rotary operations consistent with the various plane meshes. In order

* Figure 1–15 modified by permission from *Elementary Crystallography*, by M. J. Buerger. Copyright, 1956, by John Wiley & Sons, Inc., New York.

to ensure that all possible axial locations have been examined, it will be necessary to consider the interaction of rotation with each of the different translations of the mesh. The distinct translations of a mesh are t_1, t_2, and the diagonal (vector sum of t_1 and t_2).

The combination of a two-fold axis with the translations of a plane lattice mesh is illustrated in Figure 1–16. In Figure 1–16a the rotation of

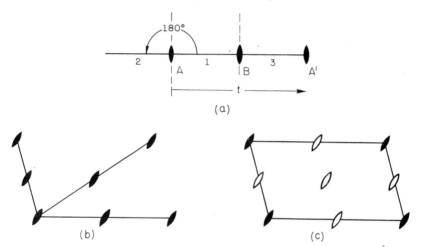

Fig. 1–16. The location of two-fold axes with respect to a parallelogram mesh.

line 1 through 180° by $A_{180°}$ generates line 2. Translation of line 2 to line 3 (and A to A') requires the presence of B on the perpendicular bisector of t at the "intersection" of lines 1 and 3. A two-fold axis must be present at B. Application of a similar argument to other translations in the cell yields axial locations as shown in Figure 1–16b. Successive operations of rotation or translation then generate all axial locations consistent with the general parallelogram plane lattice defined by t_1 and t_2, as shown in Figure 1–16c.

The solid symbols for a two-fold axis in this figure represent the position of the A axes and the open symbol the position of the B axes. All the A axes may be transformed into each other by lattice translations or by two-fold rotary operations around a B axis. The B axes on the edges may be transformed by rotary operation of the central B axis into similarly edge-located B axes, and vice versa. Axes which can be transformed into each other by the operation of another symmetry element are called *equivalent axes*. It is apparent that there must be four sets of equivalent axes consistent with a general parallelogram mesh located respectively at the plane cell corners, the midpoints of the t_1 and t_2 edges, and at the cell center.

The operation of a three-fold axis rotates a motif through an angle of 120°. Three-fold axes will therefore be consistent with a plane lattice mesh only if the angle between the translation directions is 120°. Using the construction in Figure 1–15, three-fold axes must exist at A and B locations, as shown in Figure 1–17a. All of the A axes may be transformed

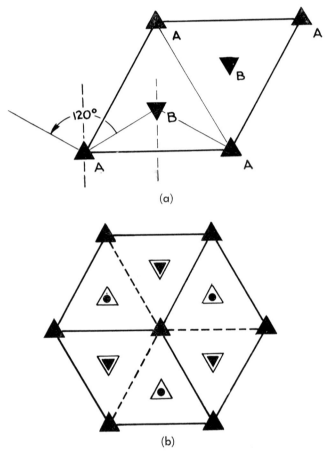

(a)

(b)

Fig. 1–17. The location of three-fold axes with respect to a mesh of equilateral triangles.

into each other by lattice translations or by three-fold rotary operations about a B axis. No such transformation, however, is possible between an A and a B axis, or indeed between the B axes shown. There must, therefore, be three sets of equivalent three-fold axes consistent with an equilateral triangular mesh—one equivalent set on the mesh corners and the other two in the centers of alternate triangles, as shown in Figure 1–17b by the different three-fold symbols. It is important to note that

the apparent six-fold symmetry of this mesh is destroyed by nonequiva-
lence of adjacent three-fold axes.

The four-fold operation is a rotation of 90°, and the position of four-
fold axes with respect to a square mesh may be found by following the
procedures in the previous paragraphs. One set of equivalent four-fold
axes will be located on the corners of the square mesh and another set at
the centers of the mesh squares, as shown in Figure 1–18a.

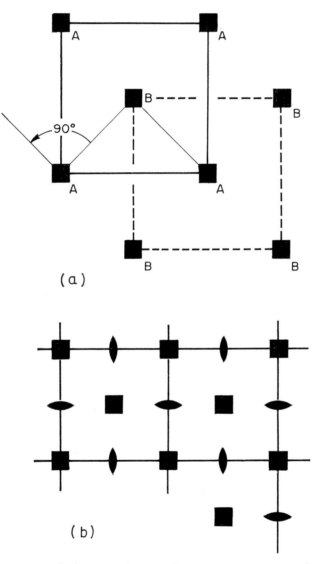

(a)

(b)

Fig. 1–18. The location of axes with respect to a square mesh.

Since the four-fold operation is a submultiple of the two-fold operation, each four-fold axis must have two-fold as well as four-fold symmetry. If two-fold axes are imagined to be coincident with the four-fold axes of Figure 1–18a, it is apparent that other two-fold locations must also be present by analogy with Figure 1–16c. Discrete two-fold axes will be found midway along each mesh side, as shown in Figure 1–18b. It should be noted that this location is consistent with the nonequivalent sets of four-fold axes present.

The operation of a six-fold axis is a rotation of 60°, and the position of six-fold axes with respect to an equilateral triangular mesh is evidently as shown in Figure 1–19a. The six-fold operation is a submultiple of both the two- and three-fold operations. Three- and two-fold axes must therefore also be consistent with this mesh. By analogy with the location of these axes with respect to other lattices, it may be seen that discrete three-fold axes will be located equidistant from three six-fold axes, i.e., the centers of the equilateral triangles and distinct two-fold axes will be located midway between six-fold axes along the translation directions, i.e., at the centers of the sides of the equilateral triangles, as shown in Figure 1–19b.

The locations of rotational elements of symmetry with respect to the five plane lattice meshes have now been described. The locations of mirrors consistent with these meshes must now be covered. A mirror will be consistent with a plane lattice mesh if it can be added in such a way that no additional lattice points are generated. The geometry of reflection requires the mirror to coincide with the perpendicular bisector of the line joining two points or to pass through a point. No consistent mirrors normal to the mesh of a general parallelogram can exist. Mirrors intersecting at 90° are consistent with rectangular and diamond meshes, mirrors at 45° to each other with a square mesh, and mirrors at 60° or 30° to each other with an equilateral triangular mesh, as shown earlier in Figure 1–7. Like axes, mirrors may be combined in certain consistent combinations, and, further, mirrors and axes may also exist in combination.

Combined Reflections. The effect of a combination of two mirrors is illustrated in Figure 1–20.[*] Two mirrors, m_1 and m_2, are normal to the page and intersect at an angle μ in a line A, which is also perpendicular to the page. An initial motif 1 is repeated as an enantiomorph 2 by the operation of m_1. The operation of m_2 on this enantiomorph then generates motif 3, which is congruent with motif 1. The distance from A to 1 equals the distance from A to 2, which in turn equals the distance from A to 3 because of the geometry of reflection. The angular separation of

[*] Figures 1–20 and 1–21 modified by permission from *Elementary Chrystallography*, by M. J. Buerger. Copyright, 1956, by John Wiley & Sons, Inc., New York.

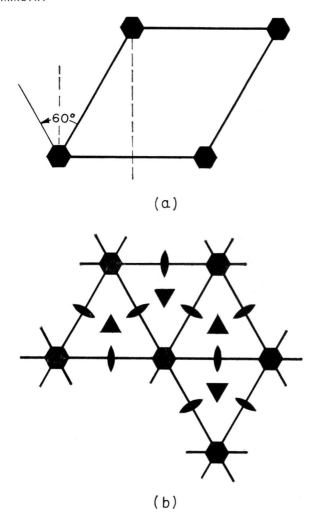

(a)

(b)

Fig. 1–19. The location of axes with respect to an equilateral triangular mesh.

motifs 1 and 3 ($\angle$ 1A3) is equal to 2μ, also from the geometry of reflection.

The successive operation of two mirrors intersecting at an angle μ thus produces the same result as a rotational operation around their intersection of 2μ, or $m_1 \cdot m_2 = A_{2\mu}$. Since A is a symmetry axis with an angular
$$\underset{\mu}{\smile}$$
period of α, $m_1 \cdot m_2 = A_\alpha$. Further, m_1 followed by m_2 followed by A_α in a
$$\underset{\alpha/2}{\smile}$$

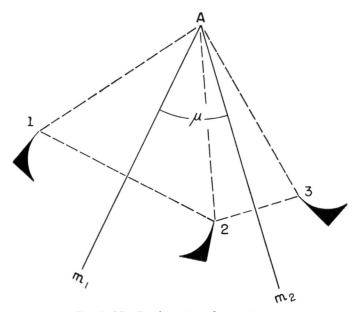

Fig. 1–20. Combination of two mirrors.

reversed sense is an identical operation which restores the initial motif to itself:

$$m_1 \bullet m_2 \bullet A_{-\alpha} = 1$$

$$\underbrace{\qquad}_{\alpha/2}$$

The locations of motifs 1 and 3 with respect to the mirrors are unaffected by the orientation of the mirror pair as long as the angle between the mirrors remains fixed.

Two sets of mirrors can be combined as shown in Figure 1–21 in order to examine the effect of three reflections. The mirrors m_1 and m_2 intersect at A with the angle $\alpha/2$, and the mirrors m_3 and m_4 intersect at B with an angle of $\beta/2$. The sequential operation of $m_1 \bullet m_2$ causes motif 1 to be reproduced as a congruent motif 2. The sequential operation of $m_3 \bullet m_4$ then causes motif 2 to be reproduced as motif 3. Motif 3 is congruent to motif 1, and the net effect of the sequential reflections would be accomplished by $m_1 \bullet m_4$ intersecting at C with the angle $\gamma/2$.

Rotation and Reflection. Periodic translations in a plane have been shown to be consistent with only five axial symmetries. Further, a reflection is the only operation in a plane needed to transform a motif into its enantiomorph. In consequence, all symmetries concerned with an alternating repetition of right- and left-handed motifs in a plane can be found by adding a mirror parallel to each of the permissible proper rotation axes.

In the preceding section it was shown that $m_1 \cdot m_2 = A_\alpha$, which may

$\overset{\displaystyle \diagdown\diagup}{\scriptstyle \alpha/2}$

be rewritten as $A_\alpha \cdot m_1 = m_2$. The addition of a mirror parallel to an axis

$\overset{\displaystyle \diagdown\diagup}{\scriptstyle \alpha/2}$

may thus be seen to require the presence of a new mirror at an angle of $\alpha/2$ with the original. The sequential operation of the axis on such a mirror pair then generates a symmetrical set. Symmetry collections which arise when a parallel mirror is combined with an n-fold axis are shown in Table 1–4.

TABLE 1–4 *

Plane Symmetries Resulting from the Combination of
a Parallel Mirror with an n-fold Axis

n	$n + m$	Designation
1		m
2		$2mm$
3		$3mm$ (called $3m$)
4		$4mm$
6		$6mm$

* Diagrams in Table 1–4, and Figure 1–22 are redrawn by permission from *Elementary Crystallography*, by M. J. Buerger. Copyright, 1956, by John Wiley & Sons, Inc., New York.

SUMMARY

Figure 1–22 represents the five distinct plane lattice meshes together with their consistent elements of symmetry (mirrors are shown with solid lines). A review of the permissible combinations shows these lattices to

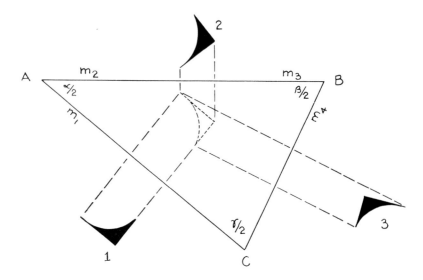

Fig. 1–21. Combination of three mirrors.

TABLE 1–5

Distinct Symmetries Consistent with Plane Lattice Meshes

Mesh Shape	Proper Rotation	Improper Rotation	Combined Rotations	Combined Rotation and Reflection
Parallelogram	1	$\bar{1}$	$\dfrac{1}{\bar{1}} = \bar{1}$	–
	2	$\bar{2} = m$	$\dfrac{2}{\bar{2}} = \dfrac{2}{m}$	–
Diamond	2	$\bar{2} = m$	$\dfrac{2}{\bar{2}} = \dfrac{2}{m}$	$2mm$
Rectangle	2	$\bar{2} = m$	$\dfrac{2}{\bar{2}} = \dfrac{2}{m}$	$2mm$
120° rhombus (equilateral triangle) ...	3	$\bar{3}$	$\dfrac{3}{\bar{3}} = \bar{3}$	$3mm$ (called $3m$)
	6	$\bar{6} = \dfrac{3}{m}$	$\dfrac{6}{\bar{6}} = \dfrac{6}{m}$	$6mm$
Square	4	$\bar{4}$	$\dfrac{4}{\bar{4}} = \dfrac{4}{m}$	$4mm$
Total number of different symmetries	5	5	3	4 (= 17)

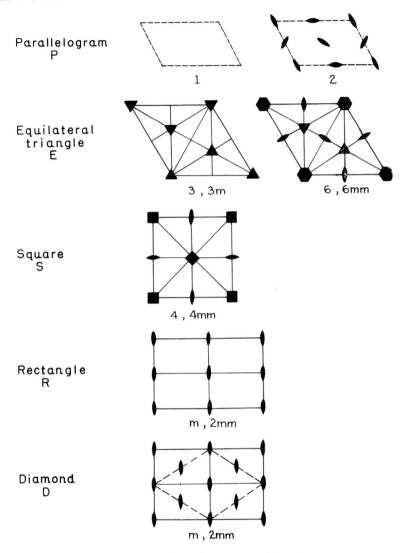

Fig. 1–22. The five plane lattice types (after Buerger).

be consistent with proper rotation axes 1, 2, 3, 4, and 6; improper rotation axes $\bar{1}$, $\bar{2}$ ($= m$), $\bar{3}$, $\bar{4}$, and $\bar{6} = \left(\dfrac{3}{m} \right)$; combined proper and improper rotation axes $\dfrac{2}{2} = \left(\dfrac{2}{m} \right)$, $\dfrac{4}{4} = \left(\dfrac{4}{m} \right)$, and $\dfrac{6}{6} = \left(\dfrac{6}{m} \right)$; and combined rotations and parallel mirrors $2mm$, $3mm$ (called $3m$), $4mm$, and $6mm$. Table 1–5 summarizes these symmetries.

Symmetry in Three Dimensions

Space lattices may be generated from plane lattices by the repeated application of translation, rotation, or reflection to the plane lattice, as shown in Figure 1–23. Since rotation and reflection do not yield meshes distinct from those which can be generated by specialized translations, however, only the latter need be considered.

The symmetry of a space lattice must be consistent with the elements of symmetry associated with the plane lattice upon which it is based.

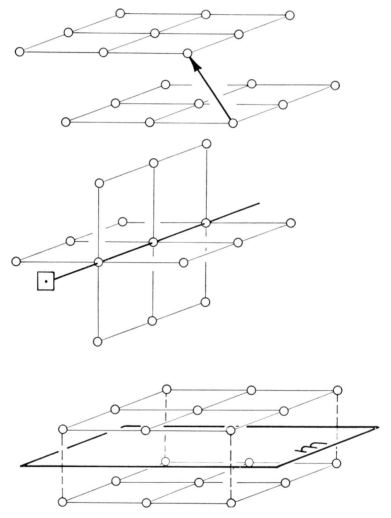

Fig. 1–23. Generation of a space lattice from a plane lattice.

Axes and mirrors associated with the plane lattice must pass through equivalent locations in each successive layer. This requirement drastically restricts the distinctively different kinds of space lattices.

The symmetry of a space lattice can be examined either by a study of the axial combinations consistent with it when using both proper and improper rotations, or by using combinations of proper axes with reflections and inversion centers.

CELLS

The repeated application of a translation, t_1, to some initial point generates a row of points or linear lattice. The repeated application of some other translation, t_2, to a linear lattice generates a two-dimensional array of points or plane lattice. Finally, a plane lattice may be periodically repeated by a third non-coplanar translation, t_3, to generate a three-dimensional array of points called a *space lattice* or simply *lattice*.

When three conjugate translations are chosen, a space lattice is uniquely defined. The volume enclosed by unit translations in each of the three directions provides a useful shape for geometrical analysis of a lattice and is called a *primitive cell*. The cell outlined by the three shortest translations is usually chosen. A primitive cell is outlined with heavy lines in Figure 1–24. Only one lattice point is associated with each primitive cell—each of the eight points on the corners of the cell belongs only one-eighth to the cell and seven-eighths to adjacent cells. This can be more readily appreciated if the parallelogram of a plane lattice cell is shifted slightly as shown in Figure 1–25.

Multiple cells may be outlined by other translations and are very useful in certain instances, especially in obtaining orthogonality. An orthogonal double cell is outlined in Figure 1–26.

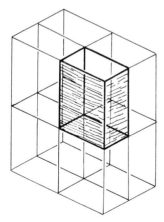

Fig. 1–24. A primitive cell.

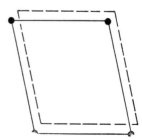

Fig. 1–25. Lattice points per cell.

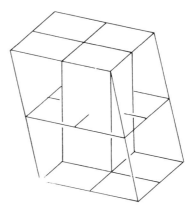

Fig. 1–26. Orthogonal multiple cell.

The *unit cell* of a crystal is that cell, either primitive or multiple, which is selected as the basic building unit in symmetry studies.

Rational Features of a Crystal. The three translation directions of a space lattice provide a natural coordinate system which may be used to describe the location of points, lines, or planes with respect to the lattice. These three translation directions need not be orthogonal to be used as coordinates, nor is it necessary that the same distance scales be used along the axes. The natural distance scale is that of the translation distance along the appropriate axis. Figure 1–27 shows the location of a point having *xyz* coordinates of 3, 2, 5 with respect to several coordinate systems.

Lattice translations provide a simple coordinate system for the location of rational lines. If a lattice point is chosen as an origin, any other lattice point may be reached by successive translations, as shown in Figure 1–28. The initial and final lattice points fix a rational line whose length is the vector sum of the translations in the t_1, t_2, and t_3 directions, and three integers, u, v, and w can be used to describe the number of unit translations in each translation direction.

The position of any line in any lattice may then be readily specified by use of the integers u, v, w which constitute the *indices* of the line. To indicate their sequence the form $[uvw]$ is used. For example, $[111]$ (read: one, one, one) is the diagonal of a primitive cell and is equal to $[222]$, $[333]$, etc. Other diagonals are $[\bar{1}11]$, $[1\bar{1}1]$, $[11\bar{1}]$, $[\bar{1}\bar{1}1]$, $[\bar{1}1\bar{1}]$, $[1\bar{1}\bar{1}]$, and $[\bar{1}\bar{1}\bar{1}]$.[*] Usually the smallest integral indices are used to designate the line; thus $[248]$ is the same as $[124]$, and the latter notation is used. Some other particular crystallographic directions are $[100]$, $[010]$, and $[001]$, which are parallel to the edges of a primitive cell, and $[110]$, $[011]$, and $[101]$, which are face diagonals of a primitive cell.

[*] A short bar over an index indicates a negative direction.

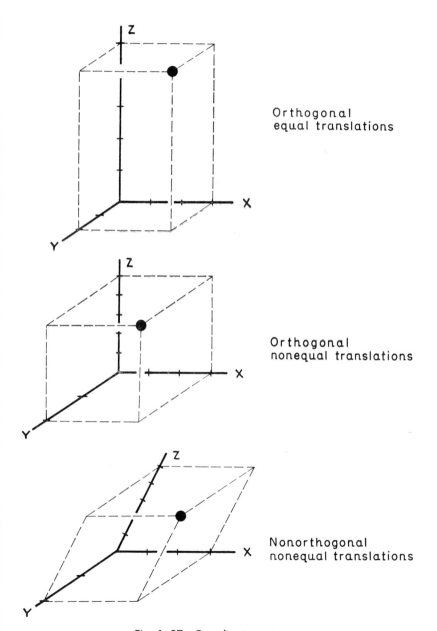

Orthogonal
equal translations

Orthogonal
nonequal translations

Nonorthogonal
nonequal translations

Fig. 1–27. Coordinate systems.

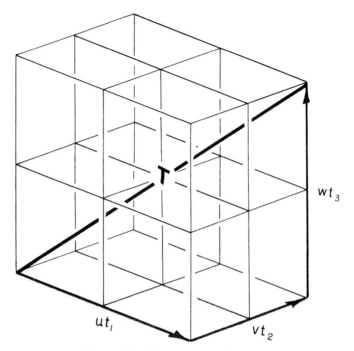

Fig. 1–28. Conjugate translations.

The position of a rational plane in a lattice may be designated by indices in a similar way to that of a rational line. The formula for a plane intersecting three axes is

$$\frac{x}{u} + \frac{y}{v} + \frac{z}{w} = 1$$

where u, v, and w are the unit translations on the x, y, and z axes. The fractions in this equation may be removed by multiplying through by uvw:

$$uvw\frac{x}{u} + uvw\frac{y}{v} + uvw\frac{z}{w} = uvw$$

and

$$vwx + uwy + uvz = uvw$$

If substitution of $h = vw$, $k = uw$, and $l = uv$ is now made, the formula becomes

$$hx + ky + lz = uvw$$

This is the equation of the rational intercept plane whose intercepts are ut_1, vt_2, and wt_3 translations along the x, y, and z axes, respectively.

The designation of a rational plane is accomplished by a set of integers, *hkl*, which constitute the (Miller) indices of the plane. When the exact indices are unknown, a type symbol, (*hkl*), in which *h*, *k*, and *l* each represent a simple whole number, is used. As examples of type symbols, the planes (100), (010), and (001) intersect the *x*, *y*, and *z* axes, respectively, and are parallel to the plane of the other two axes; the planes (110), (101), and (011) intersect two axes and are parallel to the third, and the plane (111) intersects all three axes.

The indices of lines and planes are related in a simple way—lines and planes with the same indices are approximately perpendicular and for equal orthogonal axes are exactly so.

SPACE LATTICES

Periodic repetition of a plane lattice in some non-coplanar direction generates a space lattice. A space lattice is thus a stack of identical plane lattices in parallel position separated by a translation, t_3. The location of the successive plane lattices in the stack must be consistent with the symmetry elements of the zero level. The number of space lattice types is therefore sharply limited, since axes and mirrors associated with the plane lattice must pass through an equivalent position in each successive layer.

A stack of plane lattices consistent with an *n*-fold axis can be devised by starting with a plane lattice having an *n*-fold axis location and adding successive levels in such a way as to have this axis intersect *n*-fold axial locations in the upper levels. The relative placement of the zero and first levels can be conveniently described by giving the horizontal components of t_3 in terms of the fractions *x* and *y* of the translations t_1 and t_2, respectively, plus the perpendicular distance *z* between the sheets. The loca-

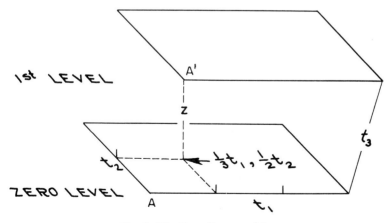

Fig. 1–29. Coordinates of t_3.

tion of A' with respect to A in Figure 1–29, using this system, is $x = \frac{1}{3} t_1$, $y = \frac{1}{2} t_2$, z, or simply $\frac{1}{3}$, $\frac{1}{2}$, z.

The general possibilities for location of successive levels with respect to a given zero level are illustrated in Figure 1–30. The zero level, Figure 1–29a, has axes normal to the page at positions represented by the

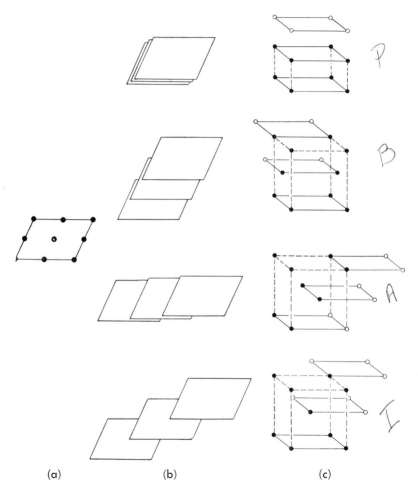

(a)   (b)   (c)

Fig. 1–30. General possibilities for stacking plane lattices.

solid circles. Distinct ways of stacking successive levels are shown by the plan views, Figure 1–30b (slightly offset for easier visualization), and in three-dimensional representations, Figure 1–30c. The x, y components of the t_3 coordinates which may be chosen are obviously the x, y components of one n-fold axis with respect to another on the zero level. The distinct possibilities in this instance are $0\,0$, $0\,\frac{1}{2}$, $\frac{1}{2}\,0$, and $\frac{1}{2}\,\frac{1}{2}$.

It is obvious, as successive levels are added, that some upper plane lattice must fall directly over the plane lattice of the zero level. If comparable points in these two levels are connected to outline a cell, the cell so delineated is a right prism. Such cells are outlined by dashed lines in Figure 1–30c. The orthogonality gained by the use of these multiple cells is of considerable aid in the visualization and description of space lattices.

Multiple cells have lattice points on their faces or in their interiors, in addition to those on their corners. Cells with interior points are termed *body-centered* (*I*) for space lattices based on parallelogram, square, rectangle, and diamond plane lattice meshes and *rhombohedral* (*R*) for space lattices based on an equilateral triangle. Cells with lattice points on their faces are termed *A*-, *B*-, or *C-centered* for point pairs on the front and back, side, or top and bottom faces or *face-centered* (*F*) if points are present on all six faces of the cell. The various cells which may be derived are listed in Table 1–6.

TABLE 1–6

General Space Lattice Types

Name	Symbol	Location of Additional Points	Total Number of Lattice Points per Cell
Primitive	*P*	–	1
Body-centered	*I*	Center of cell	2
Rhombohedral	*R*	Two points along the long body diagonal of the cell	3
A-centered	*A*	Center of (100) faces	2
B-centered	*B*	Center of (010) faces	2
C-centered	*C*	Center of (001) faces	2
Face-centered	*F*	Centers of all faces	4

Cell Shapes. CELLS BASED ON A GENERAL PARALLELOGRAM. A general parallelogram plane lattice mesh is consistent with plane symmetries 1 and 2 (Figure 1–22). In symmetry 1 the operation of a proper one-fold axis returns the motif to its initial position in a single operation so such an axis need not be perpendicular to the plane lattice. In consequence, t_3 coordinates are not restricted to simple fractional parts of t_1 and t_2, but may have any values between 0 and 1. The unit cell usually chosen in this instance is primitive, i.e., is a parallelepiped outlined by the t_1, t_2, and t_3 translations. This space lattice is designated as 1*P*. The angular difference from orthogonality is often slight, and a structure based on this cell may be easily mistaken for one of higher symmetry.

A general parallelogram consistent with plane symmetry 2 is that described in the previous section and illustrated by Figure 1–30. Two- or greater-fold axes consistent with a plane lattice must be perpendicular to the lattice plane. Possible distinct t_3 coordinates in this instance are $0\,0\,z$, $0\,\frac{1}{2}\,z$, $\frac{1}{2}\,0\,z$, and $\frac{1}{2}\,\frac{1}{2}\,z$. These give rise to right prisms with parallelogram bases which are, respectively, P, B, A, and I (see Table 1–6). However, the choice of an alternate cell, as shown in Figure 1–31 by

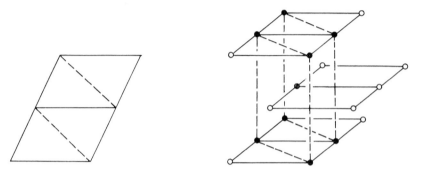

Fig. 1–31. Alternate choices of cells (after Buerger).

dashed lines, can transform a face-centered point to a body-centered point. The only distinct lattice types consistent with plane symmetry 2 are, consequently, primitive and body-centered cells. These are called $2P$ and $2I$, respectively.

CELLS BASED ON RECTANGLES AND DIAMONDS. Rectangular and diamond-shaped plane lattice meshes are consistent with plane symmetries m and $2mm$ (Figure 1–22). The possible t_3 coordinates for a rectangle are the same as for a parallelogram, namely $0\,0\,z$, $0\,\frac{1}{2}\,z$, $\frac{1}{2}\,0\,z$, and $\frac{1}{2}\,\frac{1}{2}\,z$. The coordinates $0\,0\,z$ define a primitive brick-shaped cell. The coordinates $0\,\frac{1}{2}\,z$ and $\frac{1}{2}\,0\,z$ define a space lattice from which orthogonal B-centered and A-centered cells may be chosen. These are, however, not distinct lattice types since a rotation of $90°$ around the z direction will transform one into the other. The coordinates $\frac{1}{2}\,\frac{1}{2}\,z$ define a space lattice from which a body-centered orthogonal cell may be chosen. Distinct space lattice types consistent with a rectangular plane lattice are thus composed of primitive, A- (or B-) centered, and body-centered cells which are designated as $222P$, $222A$, and $222I$, respectively.

The only possible t_3 coordinates consistent with the symmetry of a diamond-shaped plane lattice are $0\,0\,z$ and $\frac{1}{2}\,\frac{1}{2}\,z$ (see Figure 1–22). The first set defines a primitive cell having a diamond-shaped base. A more convenient cell, however, is C-centered, as shown in Figure 1–32. This is not a lattice type distinct from A- or B-centered cells because one can be derived from the other by a rotation of $90°$. The coordinates $\frac{1}{2}\,\frac{1}{2}\,z$ define a body-centered cell having a diamond base. This cell is

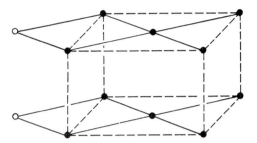

Fig. 1–32. Relation of a cell having a diamond base to one with a rectangular base (after Buerger).

geometrically difficult to deal with, and it is customary to choose a face-centered cell, as shown in Figure 1–33. This constitutes the only different space lattice from those derived from a rectangular plane lattice. It is designated 222F.

CELLS BASED ON A SQUARE. A square plane lattice is consistent with plane symmetries 4 and 4mm. The two permissible locations of four-fold axes with respect to the plane net are at $0\,0$ and $\frac{1}{2}\,\frac{1}{2}$. The two possible values of t_3 are then $0\,0\,z$ and $\frac{1}{2}\,\frac{1}{2}\,z$. The first defines an orthogonal primitive cell and the second a space lattice from which a body-centered orthogonal cell may be chosen. These two cells are identified as 4P and 4I, respectively.

A cubic space lattice may also be derived from a square plane lattice by setting t_3 equal to the translations of the latter. The possible coordinates of t_3 in this instance are $0\,0\,1$ and $\frac{1}{2}\,\frac{1}{2}\,\frac{1}{2}$, which define primitive and body-centered cubes designated 23P and 23I, respectively. Since consistent four-fold axis locations will also exist parallel to the plane mesh and passing through the centers of the vertical faces, a face-centered cell, 23F, may also be chosen. Figure 1–34 illustrates the cubic cells.

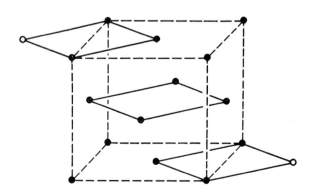

Fig. 1–33. 222F (after Buerger).

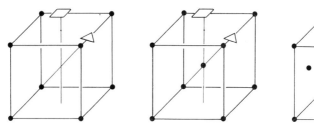

Fig. 1–34. 23P, 23I, and 23F.

CELLS BASED ON AN EQUILATERAL TRIANGULAR MESH. Plane symmetries 3, 3m, 6, and 6mm are consistent with a plane mesh composed of equilateral triangles. Permissible positions of three-fold axes consistent with this mesh are at $0\,0$, $\frac{2}{3}\frac{1}{3}$, and $\frac{1}{3}\frac{2}{3}$ (Figure 1–22). The coordinates of t_3 may therefore be $0\,0\,z$, $\frac{2}{3}\frac{1}{3}z$, and $\frac{1}{3}\frac{2}{3}z$. The first coordinate set defines a primitive cell, Figure 1–35a. This cell is designated 3P. The other two coordinate sets define cell types which can be transformed into one another by a rotation of $180°$ about a normal to the plane lattices. The only distinct cell is shown in Figures 1–35b and 1–35c. This cell contains two interior lattice points located on the long body diagonal of the cell. It is closely related to the little-used primitive rhombohedral cell and is designated as 3R.

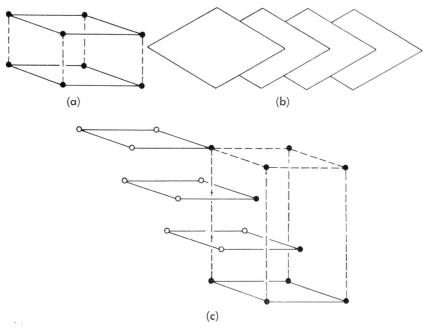

(a)   (b)

(c)

Fig. 1–35. 3P and 3R.

Six-fold axes do not occur at submultiples of t_1 and t_2 (Figure 1–22). The only possible t_3 coordinates are therefore $0\,0\,z$, and the cell is primitive. This cell is identical with $3P$ and is so designated.

Summary. A total of fourteen symmetrically specialized kinds of space lattices have now been described. (These are called the *Bravais Lattices* after the crystallographer who first showed that there are just fourteen.) These lattices represent all of the possible specialized space lattices. They are listed in Table 1–7, which summarizes the symmetrical groupings to this point.

The six primitive cells found are parallelepipeds whose faces are portions of plane lattices defined by t_1 and t_2, t_2 and t_3, and t_1 and t_3. In other words, these cells can be considered to be outlined by the intersection of three pairs of nonparallel plane lattices with the cell corners being the intersections of the sets. In a space lattice the plane symmetry sets associated with each face of the cell must interact. The only collections of symmetry elements consistent with a space lattice will then be combinations of plane symmetries in specialized positions and angular relationships which do not generate irrational lattice points.

TABLE 1–7

Summary of Specialized Space Lattices

Plane Lattice Type	t_3 Coordinates	Space Lattice Designation	Primitive Cell
Parallelogram	$x\,y\,z$	$1P$	$1P$
Parallelogram	$0\,0\,z$	$2P$	$2P$
Parallelogram	$\frac{1}{2}\,\frac{1}{2}\,z$	$2I$	
Rectangle	$0\,0\,z$	$222P$	$222P$
Rectangle	$\frac{1}{2}\,\frac{1}{2}\,z$	$222I$	
Rectangle	$0\,\frac{1}{2}\,z$	$222A$	
Diamond	$0\,0\,z$	$222C$	
Diamond	$\frac{1}{2}\,\frac{1}{2}\,z$	$222F$	
Square	$0\,0\,z$	$4P$	$4P$
Square	$\frac{1}{2}\,\frac{1}{2}\,z$	$4I$	
Square	$0\,0\,1$	$23P$	$23P$
Square	$\frac{1}{2}\,\frac{1}{2}\,\frac{1}{2}$	$23I$	
Square	$0\,\frac{1}{2}\,\frac{1}{2}$	$23F$	
Equilateral triangle	$0\,0\,z$	$3P$	$3P$
Equilateral triangle	$\frac{1}{3}\,\frac{2}{3}\,z$	$3R$	

| 5 plane lattice types | | 14 space lattices   6 primitive cells |

The interaction of mirrors with themselves and with axes and the interaction of an axis and an inversion center have previously been described. It remains to consider the interaction of intersecting axes.

COMBINED ROTATIONS

In general, rotation about two intersecting axes is equivalent to some other single rotation about a third axis passing through the common center. This may be seen by observing the motion of a point on the surface of a sphere in consequence of its rotation about an axis normal to the plane of the motion. In Figure 1–36, rotation around axis A through

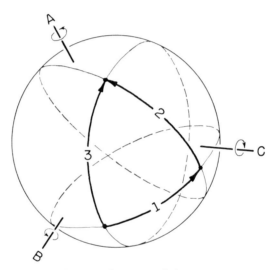

Fig. 1–36. Combination of three rotations.

some angle α causes an initial point to follow path 1; rotation about axis B through an angle β then causes the point to follow path 2. The same final point may be reached by a single rotary operation of γ around axis C, with the point following path 3.

The counterclockwise rotation A_α followed by the counterclockwise rotation B_β is thus equivalent to the single clockwise rotation C_γ, ie., $A_\alpha \cdot B_\beta = C_{-\gamma}$. This is an identical operation and may be rewritten in the form $A_\alpha \cdot B_\beta \cdot C_\gamma = 1$.

Three rotations related by such an identical operation are designated by a set of three numbers which give the symmetry axes of the successive operations. Thus, 432 signifies a set of three rotations corresponding to the four-fold operation, the three-fold operation, and the two-fold operation. Successive operation of these axes, when combined at appropriate angles, will reproduce an initial point.

In the general case, any pair of axes, A_α and B_β, can be combined at any angle of intersection, and such a combination requires the presence of a third rotation axis, C_γ. In crystals, however, the only permissible values of α, β, and γ are those of one-, two-, three-, four-, and six-fold rotary operations. A limited number of combinations can be anticipated which will repeat the initial motif after three successive rotary operations because the axial set must meet fixed requirements of angular displacement and interaxial angles in order that an initial motif be reproduced.

All of the possible axial combinations can be found by "cut and try" methods, but a more elegant proof may be obtained through the use of a construction credited to Euler.

Euler's Construction. Three axes are imagined to have their intersection at the center of a sphere, and the rotary operations of the axes are made symmetrical about great circles joining the axes, as shown in Fig. 1–37a. Thus the $\triangle ABC = \triangle A'BC = \triangle ABC'$. A point at A is unmoved by A_α, rotated to A' by B_β, and restored to A by C_γ; $A_\gamma \cdot B_\beta \cdot C_\gamma$ is therefore an identical operation.

A formula suitable for the determination of the permissible combinations of interaxial angles and rotary operations may be obtained by using half angles, as shown in Fig. 1–37b,* which reproduces the critical information of Fig. 1–37a. The law of cosines provides that

$$\cos x = \cos y \cos z + \sin y \sin z \cos X$$

where X, Y, and Z are three angles and x, y, and z the opposite sides. Thus

$$\cos AB = \cos BC \cos AC + \sin BC \sin AC \cos \gamma/2$$

This formula for a spherical triangle may now be transformed into its polar equivalent by setting $AB = 180° - \gamma/2$, $BC = 180° - \alpha/2$, $AC = 180° - \beta/2$, and $\gamma/2 = 180° - AB$. The formula for the polar triangle is then

$$\cos (180° - \gamma/2) = \cos (180° - \alpha/2) \cos (180° - \beta/2) \\ + \sin (180° - \alpha/2) \sin (180° - \beta/2) \cos (180° - AB)$$

which reduces to

$$\cos \gamma/2 = -\cos \alpha/2 \cos \beta/2 + \sin \alpha/2 \sin \beta/2 \cos AB$$

Thus the arc AB can be found by solving for $\cos AB$:

$$\cos AB = \frac{\cos \gamma/2 + \cos \alpha/2 \cos \beta/2}{\sin \alpha/2 \sin \beta/2}$$

* Figure 1–37b modified by permission from *Elementary Crystallography*, by M. J. Buerger. Copyright, 1956, by John Wiley & Sons, Inc., New York.

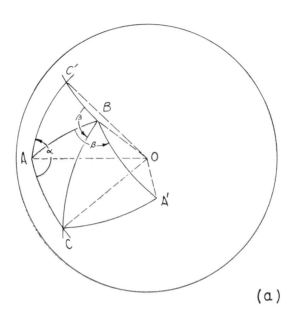

(a)

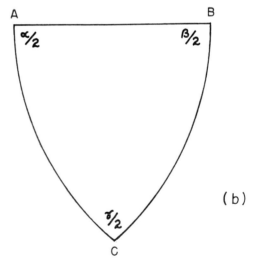

(b)

Fig. 1–37. Euler's construction for the possible combinations of three intersecting axes (after Buerger).

Table 1–8 presents the results for the solution of cos AB for all the permissible combinations for three intersecting axes. A few of the combinations are trivial, i.e., $AB = 0$. Most combinations are precluded because the results are impossible for a cosine. Only six axial combinations are found to be permissible.

TABLE 1–8

Permissible Crystallographic Solutions for Euler's Construction

Axial Combination	cos AB	AB
222	0	90°
322	1/2	60°
422	$1/\sqrt{2}$	45°
622	$\sqrt{3}/2$	30°
332	$1/\sqrt{3}$	54° 44′
432	$2/\sqrt{6}$	35° 16′

A permissible combination of rotation axes may be illustrated by a step-by-step discussion of the set 322. Figure 1–38 represents the top view of a sphere with a three-fold axis normal to the page. The three-fold operation moves a motif through 120° from position 1 to position 2. Any

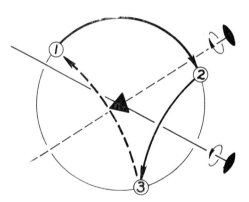

Fig. 1–38. Positions and operations of the axial set 322.

two-fold axis in the plane of the page and intersecting the three-fold axis then moves the motif through 180° to some position 3. If the sequence 322 is an identical operation, the other two-fold axis must be positioned in such a way as to move the motif from position 3 back to position 1 by a rotation through 180°. Such a position must be at 60° from the first two-fold axis, passing through the common intersection, and in the plane of the page.

All the permissible combinations for three intersecting axes are illustrated in Figure 1–39.* In each of the sets the successive operation of the axes symmetrically repeats the other axes. This repetition of axes results in the six sets of permissible combinations of axes shown in Figure 1–40.

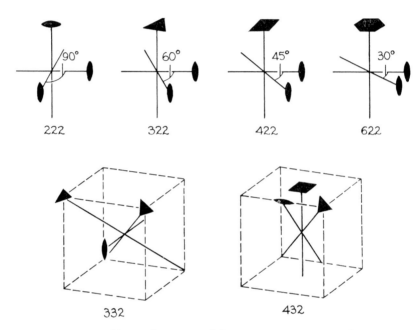

Fig. 1–39. Permissible combinations of three intersecting axes (after Buerger).

Combined axes may be proper or improper providing only that the initial motif is reproduced by successive operation of the three intersecting axes. It is apparent that this condition may be fulfilled by the successive operation of three proper axes or by a proper axis and two improper axes. The combinations of one improper and two proper or of three improper axes will produce an enantiomorph of the initial motif and cannot be combined in a consistent set.

The axial sets 222, 322, 422, and 622 each have a pair of two-fold axes perpendicular to the principal axis. When these two-fold axes are improper, the set becomes identical with $2mm$, $3m$, $4mm$, and $6mm$ because the operation of the rotoinversion axis, $\bar{2}$, is identical with that of a mirror parallel to the principal axis. This situation is illustrated in Figure 1–41 for the sets 222 and $2\bar{2}\bar{2}$.

* Figures 1–39 and 1–40 modified by permission from *Elementary Crystallography*, by M. J. Buerger. Copyright, 1956, by John Wiley & Sons, Inc., New York.

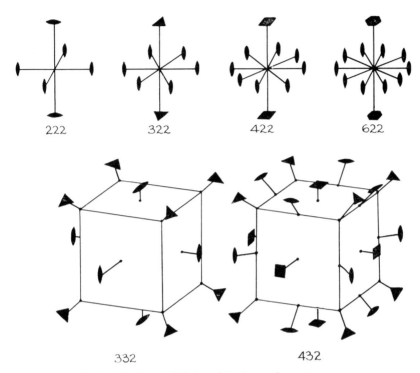

222   322   422   622

332   432

Fig. 1–40. Permissible combinations of rotation axes.

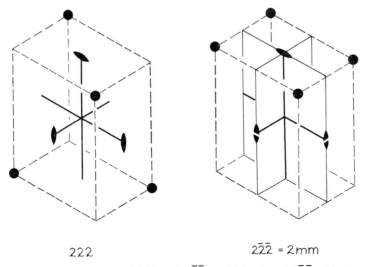

222                              $2\bar{2}\bar{2}$ = 2mm

Fig. 1–41. Comparison of 222 with $2\bar{2}\bar{2}$ and identity of $2\bar{2}\bar{2}$ with 2mm.

As in the case of single axes, a set of three proper axes may be simultaneously coincident with another set of three axes in permissible proper-improper combinations. The apparent combinations are:

$$\frac{n_1\ n_2\ n_3}{\bar{n}_1\ \bar{n}_2\ \bar{n}_3},\quad \frac{n_1\ n_2\ n_3}{\bar{n}_1\ \bar{n}_2\ \bar{n}_3},\quad \text{and}\quad \frac{n_1\ n_2\ n_3}{\bar{n}_1\ \bar{n}_2\ \bar{n}_3}$$

However, if the lattice is consistent simultaneously with these sets, it must also be consistent with any three sequential axes chosen from the complete group. In the case of the combination $\dfrac{n_1\ n_2\ n_3}{\bar{n}_1\ \bar{n}_2\ \bar{n}_3}$, such a selection is permissible for $n_1\ n_2\ n_3$ or $\dfrac{n_1}{\bar{n}_2\ \bar{n}_3}$ but not for $\dfrac{n_2}{(\ )\ \bar{n}_3}$ unless the axis in the parentheses is improper. This requires that the coincident sets are not complete unless each coincident pair contains both n and $\bar{n}$. Thus the only permissible combinations of sets of coincident axes have the form $\dfrac{n_1\ n_2\ n_3}{\bar{n}_1\ \bar{n}_2\ \bar{n}_3}$.

POINT GROUPS

All of the symmetry elements or their combinations which are consistent with lattice translations and which reproduce an initial motif have now been examined. No new sets may be found by new combinations, and it is now appropriate to summarize the symmetrical sets so far determined and to relate them to crystalline matter.

The symmetry sets which have been discussed were developed by examining the symmetrical distribution of lattice points about some particular lattice point. Since this distribution is the same for all lattice points in the same lattice, the symmetry sets describe the over-all symmetry of the particular lattice. In this view, a single point (at the intersection of axes, in a mirror, or at a center) will be unmoved by the operation of the symmetry elements. In consequence, these sets of symmetry elements are called *crystallographic point groups*.

The lattice provides a reference framework to which atoms of a structure are related. Crystals must, therefore, conform to point group symmetry. The symmetry of crystals is shown by the distribution of faces bounding the crystalline solid. A crystal face represents some particular rational plane which is symmetrically repeated by the point group. Other rational planes are also repeated, and the result is a polyhedral solid bounded by collections of symmetrically disposed faces. The mineralogical divisions based on these polyhedra and corresponding to point group symmetry are the *crystal classes*.

The external symmetry of crystals is a readily determined feature and constitutes an extremely useful criterion for mineral identification, classification, and understanding of the directional properties which minerals possess.

Several different kinds of notation are used for the designation of the symmetrically unique point groups or crystal classes. Two different summary tabulations follow which illustrate the commonly used international and Schoenflies notations.

International Notation. The permissible kinds and combinations of rotation axes can be used to tabulate all of the crystal classes since improper axes incorporate the operations of mirrors and centers. This tabulation is presented in Table 1–9. The considerations which apply are listed below:

1. Proper n-fold axes are consistent with the five plane lattice meshes when n is 1, 2, 3, 4, or 6. When n is greater than 1, the axis must be perpendicular to the lattice plane.
2. The combinations of n-fold axes with inversion centers result in the roto-inversion axes, $\bar{1}, \bar{2}, \bar{3}, \bar{4}$, and $\bar{6}$. (All lattices are centrosymmetrical and must be consistent with inversion centers.)
3. An n-fold axis may be coincident with an $\bar{n}$-fold improper axis of equal multiplicity. This combination is written $\dfrac{n}{n}$.
4. Certain sets of intersecting axes in permissible proper-improper combination are consistent with lattices. Such sets are written $n_1\, n_2\, n_3$.
5. Certain coincident sets of proper and improper axes are consistent with lattices. These sets have the form $\dfrac{n_1}{n_1}\ \dfrac{n_2}{n_2}\ \dfrac{n_3}{n_3}$.

Schoenflies Notation. The foregoing tabulation of the 32 crystal classes was accomplished by the use of axial symmetries only, using both proper and improper rotation. In the following tabulation, only proper rotations (1, 2, 3, 4, 6, 222, 322, 422, 622, 332, and 432) will be employed, and enantiomorphic repetition will be incorporated by the addition of mirrors and inversion centers to these axes. The Schoenflies symbols and their meanings are given in Table 1–10.

The tabulation of the 32 possible crystal classes may be begun by listing the 11 axial groups (C_n, D_n, T, and O) which include all of the operations not involving enantiomorphous repetition. This listing of the C_n and D_n groups in Table 1–11 is straightforward, as is the single S_4 class. In the next division of the table, planes and centers are added systematically to the C_n groups. First a horizontal plane is added to each of the C_n groups. An inversion center is then added to those C_n groups for which n is odd (when n is even, $C_{ni} = C_{nh}$). Finally, vertical planes are added to the cyclic groups. The permissible ways of combining reflection planes and inversions with C_n groups are then exhausted.

TABLE 1-9
The Thirty-Two Crystal Classes

Axial Type	Classes							Number of Classes
	1	2	3	4	6			
n	1	2	3	4	6			5
$\bar{n}$	$\left(\dfrac{1}{1}=\bar{1}\right)$	$\bar{2}=m$	$\bar{3}$	$\bar{4}$	$\bar{6}=\dfrac{3}{m}$			5
$\dfrac{n}{n}$		$\dfrac{2}{2}=\dfrac{2}{m}$	$\left(\dfrac{3}{3}=\bar{3}\right)$	$\dfrac{4}{4}=\dfrac{4}{m}$	$\dfrac{6}{6}=\dfrac{6}{m}$			3
$n_1 n_2 n_3$		222	322 called 32	422	622	332 called 23	432	6
$\bar{n}_1 \bar{n}_2 n_3$ $n_1 \bar{n}_2 \bar{n}_3$ $\bar{n}_1 n_2 \bar{n}_3$		$2\bar{2}\bar{2}=2mm$	$3\bar{2}\bar{2}=3mm$ called $3m$ $\left(3\bar{2}\bar{2}=\bar{3}m2=\bar{3}\dfrac{2}{m}\right)$	$4\bar{2}\bar{2}=4mm$ $\bar{4}2\bar{2}=\bar{4}2m$	$6\bar{2}\bar{2}=6mm$ $\bar{6}\bar{2}2=\bar{6}m2$		$\bar{4}\bar{3}2=\bar{4}3m$	7
$\dfrac{n_1 n_2 \bar{n}_3}{\bar{n}_1 \bar{n}_2 n_3}$		$\dfrac{222}{\bar{2}\bar{2}\bar{2}}=mmm$	$\dfrac{322}{\bar{3}22}=\bar{3}\dfrac{2}{m}mm$ called $\bar{3}\dfrac{2}{m}$	$\dfrac{422}{\bar{4}\bar{2}\bar{2}}=mmm$	$\dfrac{622}{\bar{6}\bar{2}\bar{2}}=mmm$	$\dfrac{332}{\bar{3}\bar{3}\bar{2}}=\bar{3}\dfrac{2}{m}$ called $\dfrac{2}{m}\bar{3}$	$\dfrac{432}{\bar{4}\bar{3}\bar{2}}=\dfrac{4}{m}\bar{3}\dfrac{2}{m}$	6

Total number of classes 32

TABLE 1–10

Schoenflies Notation

Symbol	Name	Definition	Example of Relation to International Notation
C_n	Cyclic group	Having a single n-fold axis	$4 = C_4$
S_4			$\bar{4} = S_4$
D_n	Dihedral group	Consisting of a set of two-fold axes perpendicular to an n-fold chief axis	$422 = D_4$
O	Octahedral group	A set of three axes along the rational directions of a cube	$432 = O$
T	Tetrahedral group	A set of three axes along the rational directions of a cube	$332 = T$

Subscripts to basic symbols:

i	Inversion center	$\bar{3} = C_{3i}$
(i)	Inversion center arising in consequence of symmetry collection. Added as a superscript	$\dfrac{2}{m} = C_{2h}{}^{(i)}$
v	"Vertical" mirror. Reflection plane parallel to chief axis	$4mm = C_{4v}$
h	"Horizontal" mirror. Reflection plane perpendicular to chief axis. (When $n = 1$, the symbol s is used.)	$\dfrac{4}{m} = C_{4h}$
d	"Dihedral" mirror. Reflection plane midway between dihedral axes and parallel to chief axis	$\bar{4}2m = D_{2d}$

In the last division of Table 1–11, reflections and inversions are added to the D_n, T, and O groups resulting in D_{nh}, T_h, and O_h classes. In each of these classes the "horizontal" mirror plane and the "horizontal" two-fold axis combine to require another mirror, which is vertical. Therefore, no new classes would result if a "vertical" rather than a "horizontal" plane were added to the D_n, T, and O groups. The final possible way to add an operation producing an enantiomorphous figure to these groups is to introduce a vertical plane midway between pairs of similar two-fold axes in the dihedral and tetrahedral groups (such a plane already exists in the octahedral group). The addition of such a plane to D_4 and D_6 would require eight- and twelve-fold principal axes, respectively, and is therefore not permitted.

The distribution of symmetry elements in the 32 crystal classes, together with the international and Schoenflies notation, is shown in Figure 1–42.* The diagrams represent the top view of a sphere whose outline is dotted unless there is an equatorial (horizontal) mirror, in which case it

* Redrawn by permission from *Elementary Crystallography*, by M. J. Buerger. Copyright, 1956, John Wiley & Sons, Inc., New York.

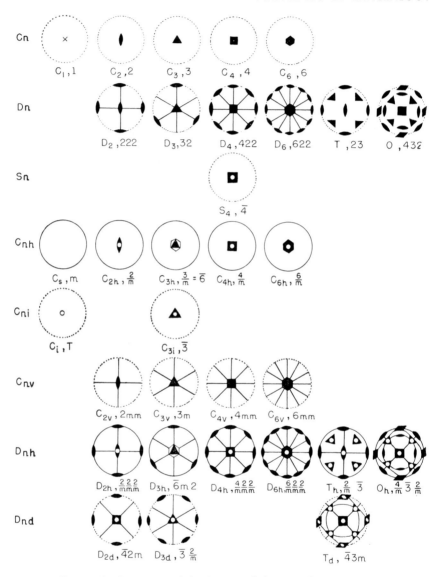

Fig. 1–42. Symmetry of the 32 crystal classes (after Buerger).

is shown as a solid line. The projections of other mirrors on the spherical surface are shown as solid lines. The symbols for vertical axes are centered, the symbols for horizontal axes are on the periphery of the circular projection, and those for inclined axes have intermediate positions. Improper axes, alone or in combination, are represented by a small open circle within the symbol for an axis.

TABLE 1–11

The Thirty-Two Crystal Classes

Type of Group	Classes					Number of Classes
C_n	C_1	C_2	C_3	C_4	C_6	5
D_n		D_2	D_3	D_4	D_6	4
Cubic			T	O		2
S_4				S_4		1
C_{nh}	C_s	$C_{2h}^{[t]}$	C_{3h}	$C_{4h}^{[t]}$	$C_{6h}^{[t]}$	5
C_{ni}	C_i		C_{3i}			2
C_{nv}		C_{2v}	C_{3v}	C_{4v}	C_{6v}	4
D_{nh}		$D_{2h}^{[t]}$	D_{3h}	$D_{4h}^{[t]}$	$D_{6h}^{[t]}$	4
Cubic			$T_h^{[t]}$	$O_h^{[t]}$		2
D_{nd}		D_{2d}	$D_{3d}^{[t]}$			2
Cubic			T_d			1
Total number of classes						32

Crystal Systems

It was earlier shown that the translations of a space lattice provide a natural coordinate system for crystallographic reference. Further, the distinctively different combinations of lattice translations are those which determine the six types of primitive cells. It follows, then, that the natural coordinate systems for crystals will be the edges of the primitive cells. These axes are called the *crystallographic axes*.

By reference to Table 1–7 it may be seen that each primitive cell has several related multiple cells. Mineral structures based on such a group of related cells are called a *crystal system*.

Several parallel sets of terminology for lattices and structures have now been defined. In summary these are:

Lattice Terms	Structure Terms
Conjugate translations of a primitive cell	Crystallographic axes
6 primitive cells	6 crystal systems
32 crystallographic point groups	32 crystal classes

Crystallographic axes are labeled and oriented according to accepted conventions, as illustrated in Figure 1–43. The translation directions of the unit cell chosen for the axes are labeled *a*, *b*, and *c* except when a particular symmetry causes two or more of them to be equal. In this case, the equivalent axes are labeled a_1, a_2, etc. It is customary to orient crystals and crystal drawings with the *c* axis vertical, the *b* axis left and right (*broadside*), and the *a* axis front and back (*at you*).

The interaxial angles are designated α, β, and γ. The angle between axial pairs can be readily remembered because it completes the "*abc*" group, i.e., *abc*, *aβc*, and *abγ*.

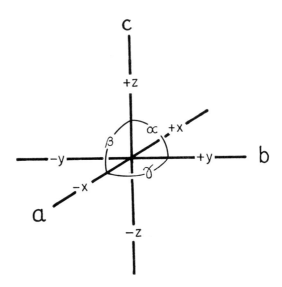

Fig. 1–43. Orientation and labeling of crystallographic axes.

Table 1–12 summarizes the essential features of the six crystal systems, and the following paragraphs provide detailed information as to the labeling and orientation of axes in each of the systems.

TRICLINIC SYSTEM (Classes 1 and $\bar{1}$)

This system is based upon a perfectly general parallelepiped cell, usually outlined by the three shortest translations of the lattice. The cell edges are conventionally taken as *a*, *b*, and *c* and the interaxial angles as α, β, and γ.

The coordinate origin of a triclinic cell may be chosen so that α, β, and γ are all acute, all obtuse, or some combination. The *c* axis may be taken as either the longest or shortest translation, but *b* is always greater than *a*. Some of these conventions for orientation and labeling are illustrated in Figure 1–44.

The Crystal Systems *

Name	Description	Coordinate System	Cell Types
Triclinic	$a \neq b \neq c$ $\alpha \neq \beta \neq \gamma$		
Monoclinic	$a \neq b \neq c$ $\alpha = \gamma = 90°$		
Orthorhombic	$a \neq b \neq c$ $\alpha = \beta = \gamma = 90°$		
Tetragonal	$a_1 = a_2 \neq c$ $\alpha = \beta = \gamma = 90°$		
Hexagonal	$a_1 = a_2 = a_3 \neq c$ $\beta_1 = \beta_2 = \beta_3 = 90°$ $\gamma = 120°$		
Isometric	$a_1 = a_2 = a_3$ $\alpha = \beta = \gamma = 90°$		

* Diagrams of cell types redrawn by permission from *Elementary Crystallography*, by M. J. Buerger. Copyright, 1956, by John Wiley & Sons, Inc., New York.

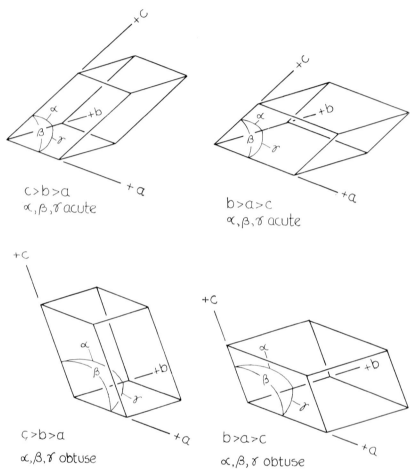

Fig. 1–44. Some orientations for the triclinic system.

MONOCLINIC SYSTEM $\left(\text{Classes } 2, m, \dfrac{2}{m}\right)$

The axes of this system coincide with the cell edges of a right prism having a parallelogram base, i.e., one axis is perpendicular to the plane of the other two which are inclined to one another.

Two conventional assignments of axes are used, as illustrated in Figure 1–45. Either *b* or *c* may be selected as the unique two-fold axis.

ORTHORHOMBIC SYSTEM $\left(\text{Classes } 222, 2mm, \dfrac{2\ 2\ 2}{mmm}\right)$

The three orthogonal axes of this system correspond to the edges of a brick-shaped cell. The axes are always labeled according to length so

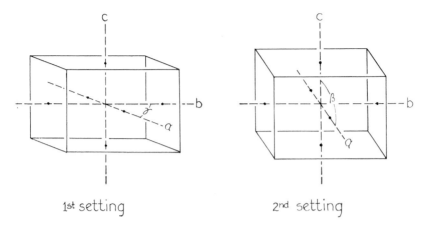

1st setting   2nd setting

Fig. 1–45. Conventional orientations for the monoclinic system.

that b is longer than a, but sometimes c is taken as the shortest and sometimes as the longest axis.

TETRAGONAL SYSTEM $\left(\text{Classes } 4, \bar{4}, \dfrac{4}{m}, 422, 4mm, \bar{4}2m, \dfrac{4\,2\,2}{mmm} \right)$

The axes of this system correspond to the edges of a right prism having a square base. The four-fold axis is always chosen as c, and the a and b axes are equivalent and become a_1 and a_2.

HEXAGONAL SYSTEM $\left(\text{Classes } 3, \bar{3}, 32, 3m, \bar{3}\dfrac{2}{m}, \right.$

$\left. 6, \bar{6}, 622, 6mm, \bar{6}m2, \dfrac{6}{m}, \dfrac{6\,2\,2}{mmm} \right)$

Hexagonal axes correspond to the edges of a right prism having a 120° rhombus as a base. The unique three- or six-fold axis is always chosen as c. The edges of a rhombus are equal and are repeated by the three-fold axis to three equivalent axes separated by 120°. Extension of these axes through the origin provides the same repetition sequence as required by the six-fold axis. All axes other than c are equivalent and are designated a_1, a_2, and a_3. The hexagonal system is thus referred to a set of four axes in which the c axis is perpendicular to the plane of three equal coplanar axes separated by 120°.

Structures which can be referred to the rhombohedral space lattice, $3R$, are sometimes related to a set of rhombohedral axes. These axes have the advantage of corresponding to a primitive cell; but since this cell is difficult to work with and the symmetry of a crystal does not distinguish it from a hexagonal cell, it is probably best to use hexagonal axes.

ISOMETRIC SYSTEM $\left(\text{Classes } 23, \frac{2}{m} \bar{3}, 432, \bar{4}3m, \frac{4}{m} \bar{3} \frac{2}{m}\right)$

The reference cell for this system is a cube which has equal orthogonal edges. Since all of the edges are the same, they are labeled a_1, a_2, and a_3.

Crystal Morphology

The symmetrical relations which exist between the atoms or molecules of a crystal cannot be observed without the use of X-ray or similar techniques, and then only indirectly. There is, however, a consequence of this symmetry which can often be seen and used by the mineralogist. This is the external shape or *morphology* of crystals.

When minerals crystallize in an environment where unhindered growth is possible, the exterior shape of the crystal reflects the symmetrical relations among its constituents. The external surfaces are then plane *faces*, each of which is parallel to a stack of rational planes of the lattice. The faces which actually develop are controlled by growth rate, environment, and the nature of the compound, but such faces always have simple indices.

The symmetry of crystals requires that parallel stacks of rational planes be chemically and physically, as well as geometrically, equivalent. Equivalent faces must, therefore, behave identically during growth, assuming that the external environment is also symmetrical. Under such conditions, faces corresponding to the symmetries of point groups arise.

CRYSTAL FORMS

Single Forms. Plane faces which have a like position with respect to the symmetry elements constitute a *form*. Some forms enclose space and are called *closed forms*. Other forms do not enclose space and are called *open forms*. A crystal may show only a single form, provided it is a closed form, but an open form can exist only in combination with other forms. Ordinarily, a crystal will display more than one form.

The same general names are used for the forms of all but those of the isometric system, which has a special terminology. The general open forms are described below and illustrated in Figure 1–46.

1. Pedion—an open form consisting of a single face.
2. Pinacoid—an open form consisting of two faces which are parallel to two of the three crystallographic axes. (In the hexagonal system this form is parallel to the three a axes and hence is normal to the six-fold axis).
3. Dome—an open form whose two faces intersect two axes and are parallel to a third.

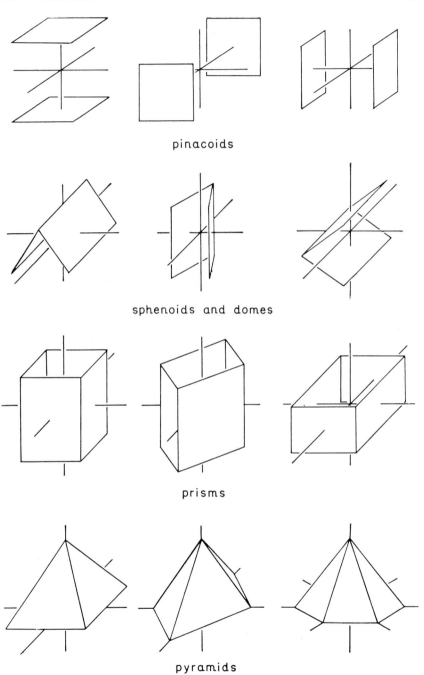

pinacoids

sphenoids and domes

prisms

pyramids

Fig. 1–46. Open forms.

4. Sphenoid—an open form which is geometrically indistinguishable from a dome, but whose faces are related by a two-fold rotation, whereas those of a dome are related by a reflection.
5. Prism—an open form whose faces parallel the maximum-fold (vertical) axis and intersect one or both of the other axes.
6. Pyramid—an open form with three or more faces which intersect the maximum-fold axis and one or more of the other axes.

The general closed forms, exclusive of those for the isometric system, are described below and illustrated in Figure 1–47.

1. Bisphenoid—a closed form composed of two sphenoids.
2. Bipyramid—a closed form composed of two pyramids placed base to base.
3. Trapezohedron—a closed form whose faces are trapeziums (four-sided plane figures, no two sides of which are parallel).
4. Scalenohedron—a closed form whose faces are scalene triangles.
5. Rhombohedron—a closed form having six parallelogram faces.

The names of general closed forms are usually prefixed by a term which gives the symmetry of the form and provides a unique geometrical description of the solid. These terms are: *tetragonal,* symmetrical with respect to a four-fold axis and hence having a square cross-section normal to the axis; *trigonal,* symmetrical with respect to a three-fold axis and having an equilateral triangular cross-section; and *hexagonal,* symmetrical with respect to a six-fold axis and having a hexagonal cross-section.

The distributions of these forms among the various crystal systems and classes are given in Tables 1–13 and 1–14. Some of these forms are illustrated in Figure 1–48.

The crystal forms of the isometric system are all closed forms. These forms are closely related to those already described, but because of the high symmetry of this system and the consequent regularity of its forms, they are given distinctive names. As examples of the relations between isometric and nonisometric forms, consider a tetrahedron which is a specialized bisphenoid all of whose faces are equilateral triangles; further, compare an octahedron and a bipyramid or a cube and a trigonal trapezohedron or a rhombohedron.

The forms of the isometric system and their distribution among the isometric classes are shown in Table 1–14. Some of the forms of this system are illustrated in Figure 1–49.

Combined Forms. Combinations of two or more forms are often developed on the same crystal, but the forms which may occur in combination are restricted to those that are permissible for the particular crystal class. For example, a pinacoid, a tetragonal prism, and a tetragonal bisphenoid are possible forms of class $\bar{4}$ (see Table 1–13). These three

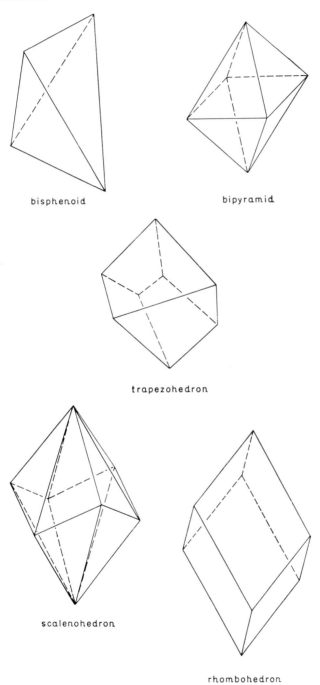

bisphenoid   bipyramid

trapezohedron

scalenohedron

rhombohedron

Fig. 1–47. Closed forms.

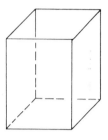

Tetragonal prism

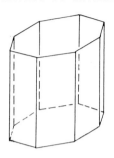

Ditetragonal prism

Tetragonal pyramid

Ditetragonal pyramid

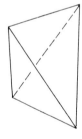

Tetragonal bisphenoid

Tetragonal scalenohedron

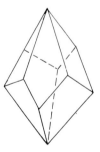

Tetragonal trapezohedron

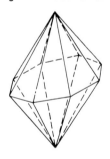

Ditetragonal bipyramid

Fig. 1–48. Hexagonal and tetragonal forms (after Buerger).

TABLE 1–13

The Distribution of Forms Among the Various Crystal Systems and Classes

Triclinic-Monoclinic-Orthorhombic Systems

Number of Faces	Form	Class							
		1	$\bar{1}$	2	m	$\frac{2}{m}$	222	$2mm$	$\frac{2\ 2\ 2}{mmm}$
1	Pedion	x		x	x			x	
2	Pinacoid		x	x	x	x	x	x	x
2	Dome				x			x	
2	Sphenoid			x					
4	Prism					x	x	x	x
4	Bisphenoid						x		
4	Pyramid							x	
8	Bipyramid								x

Tetragonal System

Number of Faces	Form	Class						
		4	$\bar{4}$	$\frac{4}{m}$	422	$4mm$	$\bar{4}2m$	$\frac{4\ 2\ 2}{mmm}$
1	Pedion	x			x			
2	Pinacoid		x	x	x		x	x
4	Tetragonal prism	x	x	x	x	x	x	x
4	Tetragonal pyramid	x				x		
4	Tetragonal bisphenoid		x			x		
8	Ditetragonal prism				x	x	x	x
8	Tetragonal bipyramid			x	x		x	x
8	Tetragonal trapezohedron				x			
8	Tetragonal scalenohedron						x	
8	Ditetragonal pyramid					x		
16	Ditetragonal bipyramid							x

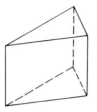

Trigonal prism

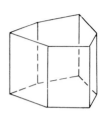

Ditrigonal prism

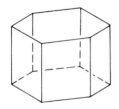

Hexagonal prism

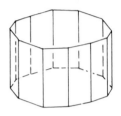

Dihexagonal prism

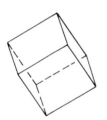

Rhombohedron

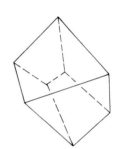

Trigonal trapezohedron

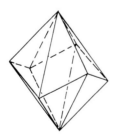

Hexagonal scalenohedron

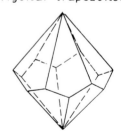

Hexagonal trapezohedron

Fig. 1–48. (Continued.)

TABLE 1–13 (Continued)

HEXAGONAL SYSTEM

Number of Faces	Form	Class											
		3	$\bar{3}$	32	$3m$	$\bar{3}\dfrac{2}{m}$	6	$\dfrac{3}{m}$	$\dfrac{6}{m}$	622	$6mm$	$\bar{6}m2$	$\dfrac{6\,2\,2}{mmm}$
1	Pedion	x			x		x				x		
2	Pinacoid		x	x		x		x	x	x		x	x
3	Trigonal prism	x		x	x			x				x	
3	Trigonal pyramid	x			x								
6	Ditrigonal prism			x	x							x	
6	Hexagonal prism		x	x	x	x	x	x	x	x	x	x	x
6	Trigonal bipyramid							x				x	
6	Rhombohedron		x	x		x							
6	Trigonal trapezohedron			x									
6	Ditrigonal pyramid				x								
6	Hexagonal pyramid				x		x				x		
12	Hexagonal bipyramid					x			x	x		x	x
12	Hexagonal scalenohedron					x							
12	Dihexagonal prism					x				x	x		x
12	Ditrigonal bipyramid											x	
12	Hexagonal trapezohedron									x			
12	Dihexagonal pyramid										x		
24	Dihexagonal bipyramid												x

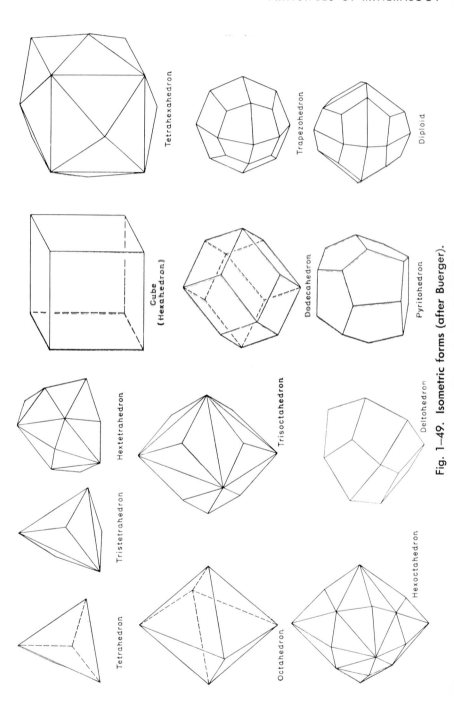

Fig. 1–49. Isometric forms (after Buerger).

TABLE 1–14

The Distribution of Forms in the Isometric System

Number of Faces	Form	Class				
		23	432	$\dfrac{2}{m}\bar{3}$	$\bar{4}3m$	$\dfrac{4}{m}\bar{3}\dfrac{2}{m}$
4	Tetrahedron	x			x	
6	Cube (hexahedron)	x	x	x	x	x
8	Octahedron		x	x		x
12	Dodecahedron	x	x	x	x	x
12	Pyritohedron	x		x		
12	Tristetrahedron	x			x	
12	Deltohedron	x			x	
12	Tetratoid	x				
24	Tetrahexahedron		x		x	x
24	Trapezohedron		x	x		x
24	Trisoctahedron		x	x		x
24	Hextetrahedron				x	
24	Diploid			x		
24	Gyroid		x			
48	Hexoctahedron					x

forms could be found in combination, but the combination of a tetragonal pyramid and a tetragonal bisphenoid is not possible from the symmetry of this class. If these two forms were found in combination, the crystal class would have to be 4mm.

Open forms cannot exist except when combined with other forms in such way as to enclose space with the combination. Some combinations of open forms are illustrated in Figure 1–50. A small face of one form which changes the principal form by beveling is called a *modification*. Forms which extend or modify the principal form in such a way as to enclose space are called *terminations*.

Closed forms and open forms may exist in combination. This feature is illustrated in Figure 1–51, which shows the shapes which arise as the result of the combination of various open forms with a bipyramid.

Finally, a closed form may be combined with another closed form, as illustrated in Figure 1–52, which shows the shapes resulting from the combination of a cube and an octahedron or tetrahedron.

The shapes of real crystals often deviate markedly from the ideal forms figured. Some specimens show no crystal form because of mutual interference between growing crystals in an aggregate. A nonuniform environment, for example, one in which the nutrient fluid is in motion, may cause misshapen crystals to develop. Impurities in the fluid from which a crystal grows may inhibit the development of certain faces.

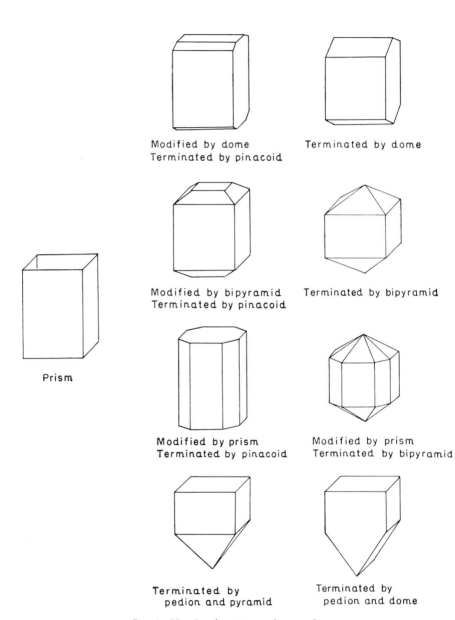

Prism

Modified by dome
Terminated by pinacoid

Terminated by dome

Modified by bipyramid
Terminated by pinacoid

Terminated by bipyramid

Modified by prism
Terminated by pinacoid

Modified by prism
Terminated by bipyramid

Terminated by
pedion and pyramid

Terminated by
pedion and dome

Fig. 1–50. Combinations of open forms.

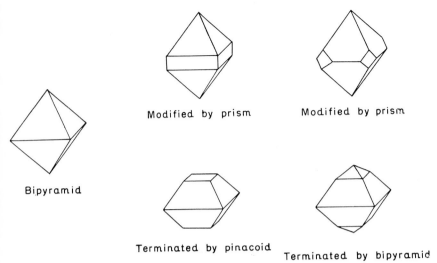

Modified by prism   Modified by prism

Bipyramid

Terminated by pinacoid

Terminated by bipyramid

Fig. 1–51. Combinations of open and closed forms.

Whatever their external shape, however, minerals exhibit an orderly and characteristic internal arrangement of their constituent atoms; this arrangement can be observed indirectly with X-ray equipment or a petrographic microscope.

The interfacial angles of a form remain constant even though the form may be distorted or incomplete. The ideal form may therefore be deduced from measurement of the nonideal form. Figure 1–53 shows a dis-

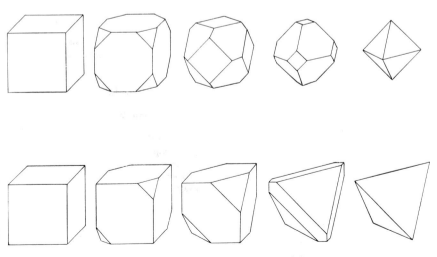

Fig. 1–52. Combinations of closed forms.

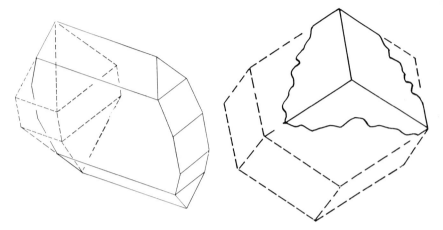

Fig. 1–53. Crystal distortion.   Fig. 1–54. Crystal reconstruction.

torted crystal in solid lines and the ideal form in dashed lines, and Figure 1–54 illustrates the reconstruction of a complete form from a partial crystal.

References

BUERGER, M. J. 1956. *Elementary Crystallography.* John Wiley & Sons, Inc., New York. A detailed and closely reasoned presentation of the geometrical interplay which controls the crystalline state together with morphological results are given in Chapters 1 to 9. This work is closely followed in the preceding chapter.

GROTH, P. 1921. *Elemente der physikalischen und chemischen Krystallographie.* Druck und Verlag von R. Oldenbourg. A classic book on mineralogy with very complete mineral listing. Obsolete nomenclature.

GUDE, A. J. Cut-out construction kit for three-dimensional models of the basic crystallographic forms. Ward's Natural Science Establishment. Useful for visualization of crystal forms.

HURLBUT, C. S. 1952. *Dana's Manual of Mineralogy.* 16th ed. John Wiley & Sons, Inc., New York.

KRAUS, E. H., W. F. HUNT, and L. S. RAMSDELL. 1951. *Mineralogy.* 4th ed. McGraw-Hill Book Co., Inc., New York. Morphological crystallography is adequately covered in most mineralogy books such as the two books above.

PHILLIPS, F. C. 1956. *Introduction to Crystallography.* 2nd ed. Longmans, Green & Co., London. A helpful text which presents crystallography in the classical manner. International notation is used.

2

FUNDAMENTALS
OF CRYSTAL CHEMISTRY

The distinctive properties of the different kinds of atoms together with their arrangement in space determine whether a mineral species will form and, once formed, what its chemical and physical properties will be. A rational approach to the study of minerals is thus through study of the laws which control the orderly arrangements of atoms into crystals and the kinds of atoms which can take part in given arrangements.

The Architecture of Atoms

ATOMS

All atoms appear to be aggregates which contain three constituents—protons, neutrons, and electrons. The exact nature of these fundamental units of matter is unknown, but, following conventional ideas, protons and neutrons may be considered to be very small, very dense spheres, whereas electrons are rather diffuse units of matter. Each of these fundamental units has associated with it a distinctive mass and electrical charge as follows:

	Mass Units	Electronic Unit of Charge
Proton	1.00758	+1
Electron	0.00055	−1
Neutron	1.00896	0

The mass discrepancy between a neutron and a proton plus electron is accounted for as energy, according to the Einstein equation $e = mc^2$.

As a first approximation, an atom consists of a nucleus about which a planetary array of electrons revolves, the balance of electrical forces being such that the atom is externally neutral. The nucleus is a compact aggregate composed of protons and neutrons and is held together by powerful binding forces. The electrical charge of a nucleus is neutralized by the presence of an appropriate number of orbital electrons.

NUCLEAR PROGRESSION

Every atom contains an integral number of protons in its nucleus, and the number of protons determines the particular atomic species or *element*. Naturally occurring elements have nuclei with a regular progression from 1 proton (in hydrogen) to 92 protons (in uranium). The number of protons in a nucleus is given by the atomic number, z, of the element. The nucleus of every element with the exception of hydrogen [*] also contains neutrons in numbers about equal to the protons. The number of neutrons plus protons largely determines the mass of the atom, since the mass of an electron is relatively small. The atomic weight of an element is its weight relative to that of oxygen, which is taken as 16.000.

The number of neutrons, unlike the number of protons, is not rigidly fixed for each element, and two atoms of a given element may have different numbers of neutrons in their respective nuclei. This variation in neutron content is shown by variations in the atomic weight of elements. The different, although related, atoms are called *isotopes*. As an example of isotopes, the nucleus of lithium contains three protons ($z = 3$) and either three or four neutrons. Two isotopes of lithium exist, with atomic weights of approximately six and seven, respectively. Naturally occurring lithium is a mixture of these two isotopes and has an atomic weight (6.940) between the two extremes.

ELECTRONIC CLOUD

The conventional laws of mechanics, which are concerned with the interaction of mass and energy at the gross scale of daily living, do not completely hold at the minuscule scales which must be considered in atomic studies. The following adjustments in mental scale must be made: (1) The wave properties associated with all matter are very important at atomic scales. The wave properties of electrons are as important as their mass, and only by considering electrons as waves may some phenomena be understood. Electrons may be described only in very general terms as elementary units of matter with both particular and wave properties. (2) Relativity assumes an important role, and (3) indeterminacy of electron speed for a given position or position for a given speed arises. Electron space-time coordinates can therefore be given only in terms of probability. (4) Energy is not continuous, but is composed of discrete and indivisible energy packets or *quanta*, one quantum of energy being

---

[*] Small amounts of deuterium (heavy hydrogen) exist, but most hydrogen atoms have only a proton as their nucleus.

the smallest energy change which may occur. Energy changes within and between atoms are of the order of magnitude of quanta, and the energy changes of whole-number multiples of quanta prescribe the manner in which electrons may neutralize the electrical field surrounding a nucleus. This neutralization is a simple electrostatic balance, but the location and motions of the electrons within the field are governed by quantum considerations.

QUANTUM STATES

The "bookkeeping" system which is used to specify the particular energy status of electrons is known as *quantum mechanics.*

The quantum state of an electron may be specified by a consideration of the kinds of energy which it possesses, both kinetic and potential. The energy of an electron is conveniently described in terms of the size of its orbit, its total angular momentum, the magnetic contribution due to the motion of a charged electron in an electric field, and the spin of an electron on its own axis.

The energy of an electron in an orbit depends upon the *size* of the orbit. Electrons can only occupy orbits (elliptical in the general case) whose energy differences are regulated by quantum changes proportional to $\frac{1}{n^2}$, where n is called the *principal* or *total quantum number* and may have values of 1, 2, 3, ...

The angular momentum of an electron depends upon the *shape* of its orbit, and changes in the eccentricity of the orbit may take place only in whole quantum steps designated by the *serial* or *azimuthal quantum number l*, which takes values of 0, 1, 2, 3 . . . $n - 1$, there being n values of l possible. For example, if n is 3, l may be 0, 1, or 2. These quantum values of l are usually expressed in a different way because spectral line production related to changes of l was early used to investigate the electronic envelope of atoms. Spectral lines arising from electrons in $l = 0$, 1, 2, and 3 were termed *s, p, d,* and *f,*[*] and this nomenclature has been preserved. Hence if $l = 0$, 1, 2, or 3, atoms are said to be in an *s, p, d,* or *f* state.

The *magnetic quantum number, m_l,* describes the energy levels into which the preceding states are split under the influence of a magnetic field. Moving electrons have a magnetic field associated with them just as does electrical current flowing in a wire. The interaction of these fields is responsible for the small changes in electron energy.

The values of m_l are dependent on the azimuthal quantum number, l, which, in turn, is dependent upon the principal quantum number, n. A

---

[*] Sharp, principal, diffuse, and fundamental.

total of $2l + 1$ values of m_l are possible for each value of l, and these m_l quantum numbers may be obtained from the series

$$l, l - 1, l - 2 \ldots 0 \ldots -l$$

which reduces to the numerical sequence

$$\ldots +5, +4, +3, +2, +1, 0, -1, -2, -3, -4, -5 \ldots$$

If $l = 2$, there will be $2(2) + 1 = 5$ possible values of m_l, and these are $+2, +1, 0, -1, -2$. If $l = 4$, the nine possible m_l values are $+4, +3, +2, +1, 0, -1, -2, -3, -4$. If $l = 0$, the only possible value of m_l is 0.

The *spin quantum number*, s, is required because an electron may be considered to have an extension in space and to be spinning with a constant angular momentum. This spin may have either of two directions with reference to an arbitrary coordinate system, and s is assigned values of $+\frac{1}{2}$ or $-\frac{1}{2}$. Note that the spin quantum number is independent of the preceding quantum numbers.

Atoms are electrically neutral groupings of fundamental particles. A nucleus is surrounded by a continuous electrical field which must be neutralized by an appropriate number of electrons embedded within it. In order for neutrality to be attained, both the number of electrons and their positions are determined by quantum mechanical considerations in such a way that only electrons in equal numbers to the nuclear protons and having specific associated energies comprise the electronic envelope. The energy of electrons is described by quantum numbers. The use of quantum numbers in the classification of the elements is described in a later portion of this chapter.

Quantum mechanical studies have provided a powerful means for investigating and understanding atomic systems. However, certain phenomena cannot be clearly described in this manner, and a further development known as *wave mechanics* is also used to describe atomic systems. The two viewpoints of quantum and wave mechanics are analogous to the treatment of light as either waves or particles. The two approaches are not mutually exclusive, but are only different approaches to the same fundamental problems. A useful analogy is to picture a boat and its wake and consider the mathematical and mensurative techniques which would best describe this system.

The wave mechanical approach has been especially fruitful in studies of the more complex atomic systems and in the understanding of the quantum conditions themselves. In essence, the motion of any corpuscle (i.e., an electron) has an associated wave motion and wavelength.[*] Only

---

[*] Wavelength, $\lambda, = \dfrac{h}{mv}$, where h = Planck's constant, m = mass, and v = velocity.

such wave paths can occur as will provide standing waves because only such stationary vibration modes can occur as are not destroyed by interference. The frequencies which do occur are those whose energy values are separated by integral quantum differences. Electron orbits of a planetary model are thus replaced by vibrating surfaces having an integral number of nodes.

The actual position of an electron on this surface is not strictly definable. However, the distance of an electron from the nucleus may be given in terms of probability. Figure 2–1 is a plot showing radial electron den-

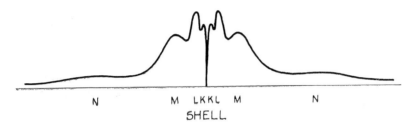

Fig. 2–1. Electron distribution in a rubidium atom (from calculations by Hartree).

sity in a rubidium atom. The highest densities (most-probable electron locations) define the electron shells.

The vibratory surfaces have the nucleus as a center only for electrons in the s state ($l = 0$). For all other values of l, the nodal surfaces are tangent to the center of the atom and may conveniently be thought of as probability volumes occupying different positions with respect to a set of orthogonal axes. s electrons occupy a probability volume whose center is the origin of coordinates, p electrons occupy volumes on the orthogonal axes, and d electrons are along the diagonal directions.

PAULI EXCLUSION PRINCIPLE

The amount of energy available per atom at ordinary temperatures is small compared with the difference in energy between two quantum states, and it would be natural to expect that all the electrons in an atom would go to the quantum state of lowest energy. This is not the case, however, and the situation is summed up by the Pauli exclusion principle, which seems to be of universal validity: *"In any atomic system, no two electrons can have all four quantum numbers the same."* This principal applies not only to single atoms, but also to systems in which two or more atoms share the same electron(s).

Periodic Classification of Elements

PRINCIPLES

The principles in the preceding section can be used to arrange the different elements in an orderly manner according to their electronic configurations. Each proton in the nucleus must be balanced by an extranuclear electron of equal and opposite charge in order to attain neutrality for the atom. The number of protons, which is given by the atomic number (z), thus establishes the number of electrons which are required.

The arrangement of these electrons around the nucleus is that arrangement which has the lowest energy and is consistent with the Pauli principle. The maximum number of electrons for any orbit may be therefore determined by finding all the possible combinations of quantum numbers without violation of Pauli's exclusion principle. As an example, in the $3p$ state $(n = 3,\ l = 1,\ m_l = 1,\ 0,\ -1,$ and $s = +\frac{1}{2}$ and $-\frac{1}{2})$ the possible combinations of quantum numbers, as shown in Table 2–1, is 6, and therefore 6 electrons completely fill the $3p$ state.

TABLE 2–1

Quantum Number Combinations for 3p

n	3	3	3	3	3	3
l	1	1	1	1	1	1
m_l	1	1	0	0	-1	-1
s	$+\frac{1}{2}$	$-\frac{1}{2}$	$+\frac{1}{2}$	$-\frac{1}{2}$	$+\frac{1}{2}$	$-\frac{1}{2}$

An extension of this simple analysis to other possible values of n and l shows that the maximum number of electrons in any group or subgroup is as shown in Table 2–2.

TABLE 2–2

Distribution of Electrons According to Quantum States

n (number of orbits or shells)	1	2	3	4	etc.
l (eccentricity, subshells, orbitals) .	0	0 1	0 1 2	0 1 2 3	
Symbolic representation of n and l combinations	$1s$	$2s\ 2p$	$3s\ 3p\ 3d$	$4s\ 4p\ 4d\ 4f$	
Number of m_l quanta ($= 2l + 1$) . .	1	1 3	1 3 5	1 3 5 7	
Number of spin quanta $(+\frac{1}{2},\ -\frac{1}{2})$	2	2	2	2	
Number of electrons in subgroup . .	2	2 6	2 6 10	2 6 10 14	
Number of electrons in principal group $(= 2n^2)$	2	8	18	32	
Shell designation	K	L	M	N	etc.

The principal groups enumerated are related to groups of orbits which are usually referred to as shells, and from the nucleus outward are designated K, L, M, N, etc. The subgroups, which are related to orbital eccentricity, are usually referred to as subshells.

The addition of electrons around a nucleus in order to neutralize its field begins with those quantum states for which the energy is at a minimum and proceeds to higher states as the lower states become filled. The K shell is filled first with two electrons in the $1s$ state, then the L shell is filled by two electrons in $2s$ followed by six electrons in $2p$.

The $3s$ and $3p$ states of the M shell are filled in sequence; they are, however, not followed directly by $3d$ electrons, but rather by $4s$ electrons. The reason for this is that the energy of the $4s$ state is actually lower than that of $3d$ owing to the high eccentricity of the former orbit. This same situation arises in all succeeding shells, the d state always following the next larger s state. A similar argument obtains for the $4f$ state, which is not filled until after $5p$ and $6s$. The sequence in which the shells are filled is shown diagrammatically in Figure 2–2.

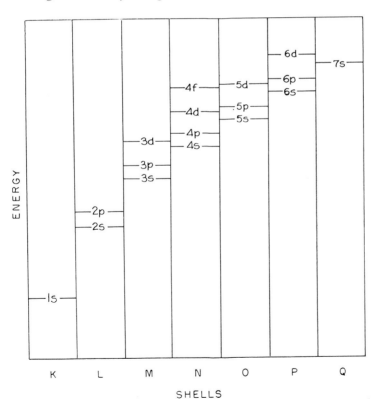

Fig. 2–2. Shell filling sequence.

The outermost shell of any atom can never contain more than eight electrons (two in the s state and six in the p state). The s and p subshells of a given shell are always filled before any increment to shells of higher n is made. Such an eight-electron shell is developed periodically as electrons are added to balance the progressive increase of protons in the nucleus. It is energetically a very stable electron configuration and will be used as a reference shell in future discussion. When an eight-electron shell is completed, the next two electrons always go into the s subshell of the next larger shell, and, following the filling of this s subshell, electrons may enter the higher energy subshells of either the same or smaller shells.

The orderly addition of electrons to satisfy the energy requirements of the atomic system is presented in a simplified tabulation in Table 2–3.

TABLE 2–3

Electronic Build-up of Elements

Atomic Number	K	L	M	N	O	P	Q	Remarks
1–2	1–2							
3–10	2	1–8						Short periods
11–18	2	8	1–8					
19–28	2	8	8–16	1–2				
29–36	2	8	18	1–8				
37–46	2	8	18	8–18	1–2			Periods
47–54	2	8	18	18	1–8			
55–57	2	8	18	18	8–9	1–2		
58–71	2	8	18	19–32	9	2		Rare earths
72–78	2	8	18	32	10–17	1–2		
79–86	2	8	18	32	18	1–8		Long
87–92	2	8	18	32	18	8–12	1–2	

Completed shells   Shells being filled

THE PERIODIC TABLE

The 92 naturally occurring elements have nuclei which contain from 1 to 92 protons. Each proton must be electrically balanced by an extranuclear electron, and it is the arrangement of these electrons, especially in the outermost (valence) shells, which largely establishes the chemical properties of the elements.

Addition of electrons in successive shells repeats configurations which were present in previous shells, and a periodicity of chemical behavior results. The periodic classification of elements, Figure 2–3, epitomizes the chemical relationships which arise. Successive addition of electrons outside an eight-electron shell begins in Column I or IA (alkali metals) and ends in Column VIII in the short periods, e.g., Li to Ne,* and Column VIIIB in the long periods, e.g., Rb to Xe. Elements in the same column have the same number of outer electrons and have similar chemical properties, while a sequence of elements in a row will exhibit a continuous change of properties.

Eight-electron outer shells are completed at atomic numbers 10 and 18, which represent completions of the short periods, and at atomic numbers 36, 54, and 86, which represent completions of the long periods. Elements of these atomic numbers are called *noble gases*. All the long periods begin, as usual, with the addition of the two s electrons, but are then backfilled with d electrons after this outer shell is started. The elements of the A subgroup, which contain d electrons, may be called *transition elements*. A related term is *transition metals*, which includes the central elements of the long periods. The addition of s and then p electrons characterizes the A subgroup of the long periods, whereas elements of the B subgroup are built up of s followed by d electrons. Three complete and one partial transitional series exist in the long periods, respectively, from atomic numbers 21 to 29, 39 to 47, 57 to 79, and one beginning at atomic number 89. Backfilling into a deep inner shell occurs once in the process of electron addition. In this instance, the $4f$ state (14 electrons) is backfilled after the completion of shell 5 and beginning of shell 6. The 14 elements (atomic numbers 58 to 71) made in this manner are called *rare earths*.

Some Intrinsic Properties of Atoms

VALENCE

The state of lowest free energy for an atom is attained when it has a completed outer shell rather than when it is electrically neutral. As a consequence, atoms tend to exchange or share electrons in such a way as to gain completed outer shells even at the expense of electrical neutrality. Whenever several kinds of atoms are brought together, a brisk trading in electrons and development of new atomic groupings occurs if such activity

---

* The names of elements, here abbreviated as the chemical symbol, are given in Appendix I.

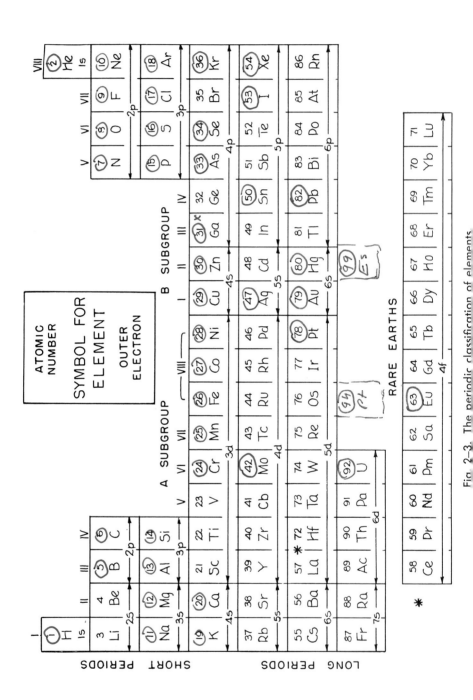

Fig. 2-3. The periodic classification of elements

favors the decreased free-energy status of the various atoms. Such activities are conveniently designated as chemical reactions.

The loss or gain of electrons by an atom is known as *ionization*. Electron loss results in a net positive charge on the atom which is numerically equal to the number of electrons lost, while the opposite is true for a gain in electrons. Such electrically charged atoms are called *ions* or, more specifically, *cations* (attracted to the cathode) if the net charge is positive and *anions* (attracted to the anode) if the net charge is negative. The numerical value of the residual charge is called *valence*.

The valences of elements which are usually found in natural materials may be found readily from the periodic table. The general rule is that the atom loses or gains electrons to attain the nearest noble gas configuration. Thus Li, in losing one electron, attains the electronic configuration of He; Sc loses three electrons to attain the Ar configuration; and I gains one electron to have the configuration of Xe.

Elements in column I have one electron outside a closed subshell; this electron is loosely bound, and its loss results in a valence of $+1$ for these elements. Similarly, elements in columns II, III, IV, and V have two to five chemically removable electrons and valences of $+2$, $+3$, $+4$, and $+5$. Elements in columns VI and VII in the short periods and VIB and VIIB in the long periods, on the other hand, tend to gain two and one electrons, respectively, to become -2 and -1 anions. Elements in columns VIA, VIIA, and VIIIA have many removable electrons as a result of their transitional nature, but $+2$ and $+3$ valences are the most common.

The generalizations given for the valence of various elements must not be followed blindly. Many elements have two or more common valence states as a result of partial rather than complete loss of electrons outside of their eight-electron shell. In this instance, a number of valences may be possible, such as, for example, manganese, which has valences of $+2$, $+3$, $+4$, and $+7$.

Changes in valence are usually described by the terms *oxidation* and *reduction*. Oxidation is that process whereby electrons are lost, as, for example, in the change from Na^0 to Na^{+1} or Fe^{+2} to Fe^{+3}, and reduction is that process whereby electrons are gained, as, for example, in the change from Cl^0 to Cl^{-1} or Mn^{+4} to Mn^{+2}.

SCREENING

The presence of a number of moving electrons in an atom, which are attracted to the nucleus by coulombic forces * and which repel each other with similar forces, results in a complex and continuously varying electri-

---

* The force of coulombic attraction is directly proportional to the product of the charges and inversely to the square of their separation, $F = \dfrac{qq'}{r^2}$.

cal field intensity in and beyond the outer shells. The problem of the distribution of energy in such a system cannot be solved without drastic approximations, but a measure of the magnitude of the field affecting an outer electron may be obtained experimentally. The ionization potential of an atom is a measure of the work required to remove an electron from the atom and hence is equal to the forces which hold it to the atomic system. Elements with high ionization potentials must have a large proportion of nuclear charge "leaking through" to and beyond the outer electrons in order that the electron be strongly held. The situation may be described as one of poor screening of the nuclear charge from outer electrons and extra-atomic points by intermediate electronic shells. The opposite situation of lightly bound electrons and consequent low ionization potential is found when screening is efficient. Ionization potential may thus be taken as a direct measure of the tightness with which an outer electron is bound to the atom. Figure 2–4 illustrates the manner in which the potential required to remove the first electron from a neutral atom varies from element to element across the periodic table.

The different screening efficiencies of the elements allow differences in the the magnitude of the electrical field in their immediate vicinity with important consequences to their neighbors. Each atom will prey on its neighbor's electrons to the extent of which it is capable, and atoms with the strongest external fields (poorest screening) will be the most successful hunters. As an atom is exposed to a stronger and stronger pull from a neighboring atom, it first is distorted from its normally spherical form—is polarized—and eventually may lose one or more of its valence electrons to its neighbor—is ionized. (The changes in the energy status of the electrons concerned is, of course, by quantized increments.) Both polarization, with the consequent possibility of the overlapping of the outer shells of the reacting atoms, and the transfer of electrons from one atom to another have important consequences in the mechanism of chemical bonding.

Bonds and Bonding

The electrical fields associated with atoms are capable of interacting with other atoms at distances of many atomic diameters. The existence of these long-range forces can be readily shown, since they are the cause of friction between smooth surfaces. Such forces are important in bringing atoms closely enough together that interaction between their respective outer shells may occur, resulting in a chemical bond. Many factors contribute to this close interatomic linkage, and the usual bond combines several mechanisms in its formation. In the following section, the principal mechanisms contributing to a chemical bond are discussed as pure cases, but it must be borne in mind that a real bond is a mixture of types.

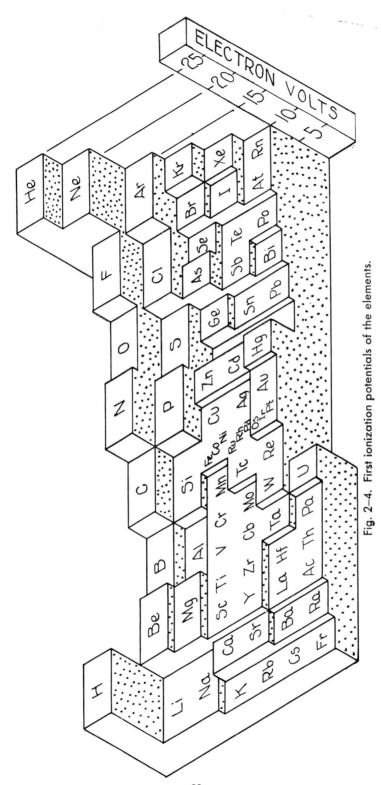

Fig. 2–4. First ionization potentials of the elements.

When atoms or ions are brought closely together, they gain stability by mutually attaining noble gas configurations (eight-electron outer shells). For ions, these shells may be formed in the process of ionization, and the ions bond by the coulombic attraction of the spherical ions—this is called *ionic bonding*. For neutral atoms, bonding may be accomplished by a sharing of the electrons in the respective incomplete shells to form a single eight-electron shell surrounding the reacting atoms—this is called *covalent* or *homopolar bonding*. Bonding of atoms may also be accomplished by the sharing of electrons from incomplete shells between a number of atoms. In this case, the electrons may be compared to a gas filling the interstices in a pile of marbles—this is called *metallic bonding*. These three bonding mechanisms are contrasted in Figure 2–5, which shows diagrammatically the different paths of valence electrons in the different bond types. In ionic bonding the valence electrons have paths around only a single nucleus. The extension of this path to include adjacent nuclei which mutually share the electrons illustrates the covalent bond. Complex and nonrepeating paths characterize the metallic bond.

These three bonding mechanisms are not mutually exclusive, and most solids are bonded by some combination of the pure types. Since these are dynamic systems, any particular electron may be envisioned as changing from one path to another with resulting hybridization of the chemical bond. If the change from path to path is accomplished in a regular manner, the bond resonates between two pure types. For example, an electron may generally follow a covalent path but occasionally circulate among a number of atoms or orbit around a single nucleus. The covalent bond in this instance would then exhibit some metallic or ionic characteristics. The view that a bond must be either of one type or another is incorrect, and a sharp distinction is not implied when bonds are described as ionic, covalent, or metallic, although it is convenient to describe mineral bonding in terms of a predominant bond type. An illustration of the gradational nature of chemical bonds is presented in Figure 2–6. Corners of the triangle represent "pure" bond types, and typical minerals or mineral groups are located on the edges in positions representing the mixture of bond types present in them.

IONIC BONDING

The ionic bond is usually developed between elements in the flank columns of the periodic table. Elements in columns I to IV in the short periods and IA to IVA in the long periods have screening efficiencies such that electrons may be readily removed from the atom, causing it to become a positive ion (cation). On the other hand, elements of columns VI and VII of the short periods and VIB and VIIB of the long periods have a high affinity for electrons which, when added to a neutral atom, produce

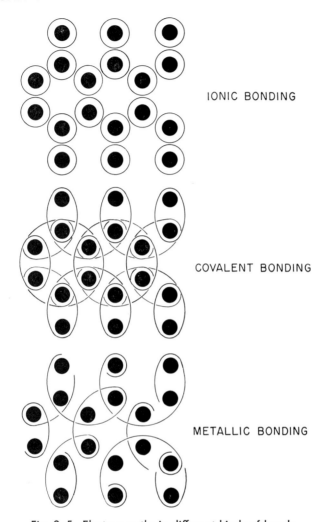

IONIC BONDING

COVALENT BONDING

METALLIC BONDING

Fig. 2–5. Electron paths in different kinds of bonds.

a negative ion or anion. In effect, electrons are transferred from the well to poorly screened atoms in the process of ionization.

Ions of opposite sign, once formed, are mutually attracted by coulombic forces until their respective noble gas shells are in contact. The ions in the aggregates thus formed are so disposed that the ionic charges of the individual ions are neutralized and the whole aggregate is electrically neutral. The proportion of $+$ and $-$ ions present in such an aggregate is controlled by the valences of the participating ions. There will be equal numbers of cationic and anionic elements if their $+$ and $-$ valences are numerically equal, e.g., $Na^+ + Cl^- \rightarrow NaCl$ or $Ca^{+2} + O^{-2} \rightarrow CaO$,

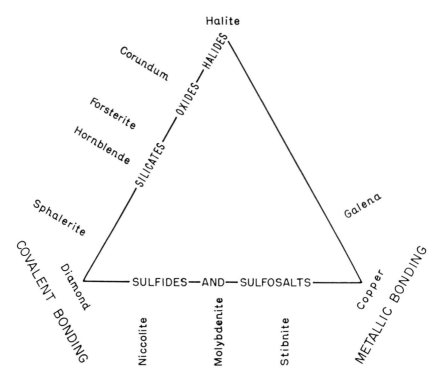

Fig. 2–6. The gradational nature of the chemical bond.

and the proportions of elements of different valences will be reciprocal to their neighbors' valences, e.g., $Fe^{+3} + O^{-2} \rightarrow Fe_2O_3$; $Ca^{+2} + F^{-1} \rightarrow CaF_2$; and $V^{+5} + O^{-2} \rightarrow V_2O_5$.

COVALENT BONDING

The covalent bond predominates in the formation of chemical compounds from elements in columns IV to VII in the short periods and the B subgroup of the long periods. In terms of screening efficiency this bond forms when poorly screened atoms react—each such atom has a strong affinity for electrons, but neither will relinquish its own. A compromise to this stalemate is effected by the mutual deformation of outer electron shells and the interpenetration of these shells in such a way as to make the electrons competed for common to the reacting atoms. A single eight-electron outer shell is developed by this pooling or sharing of electrons between the reacting atoms, and the participation of the various atoms in this mutual stable shell gives rise to a very strong bond.

Participation of atoms in a common stable shell implies, of course, that the shared electrons do not violate the Pauli exclusion principle. This is ordinarily accomplished by restricting the bond formed to that in which electrons of opposed spin participate. Thus two hydrogen atoms, each having a single $1s$ electron, may bond covalently into a diatomic hydrogen molecule, H_2, if the electrons have opposed spins.

The restriction of the Pauli principle may also be met by transferring a few electrons to orbits of different eccentricity only slightly higher energetically than their normal orbits. Thus in carbon where there are two electrons with unpaired spins (in $2p$), a very small energy increment will transfer one of the $2s$ electrons to $2p$, and four electrons with unpaired spins (one in $2s$ and three in $2p$) become available for bonding. The small increase in energy required for the formation of covalent bonds by this mechanism may be likened to making a small investment for a large guaranteed return.

The strength of a covalent bond is a direct function of the energy which is localized in the bond. In certain situations the energy of the bond may be increased by resonance of the electron between two or more bonding combinations. For reacting atoms with unpaired spins of both s and p electrons, s—s and p—p bonds could form, but a stronger bond is produced by resonance of electrons between s and p states. Diagrammatically this may be shown as follows:

The two s—p bonds formed by resonating electrons are stronger than the sum of the s—s and p—p bonds formed by nonresonating electrons.

METALLIC BONDING

The external fields of very poorly shielded atoms affect not only the outer electrons of their neighbors, but also electrons in deeper shells. The interaction of such atoms raises the electrons of neighboring atoms to levels of higher energy, and bonding reactions following the principles of covalent sharing occur. It can be expected that this will be a very complex interaction, since each atom in common metal structures is surrounded by a number of similar neighbors. An individual electron which is participating in the bond will circulate through the structure in a manner analogous to a Virginia reel and cannot be considered as having a fixed relation to any given nucleus. The Pauli restrictions must be fulfilled for numerous reacting atoms, however, and the discrete quantum states which characterize the interaction in covalent bonding must be split up into a number of slightly differing energy levels in order that all the reacting atoms may participate in the bonding. The energy "zones" so developed may vary from those of negligible width (covalent bonds) through discontinuous zones (metallocovalent or metalloidal bonds) to continuous zones (metallic bonds).

The individual electron in an aggregate of atoms so bonded is in continual transition from one quantum state to another and as such is essentially free of alliances to any one atom. The application of an electrical potential to the aggregate causes such "free" electrons to migrate readily through the structure, thus producing the electron flow which is familiar to us as electrical current. Metallic bonding is found principally in the long periods in the transition metals of group VIIIA and columns IB to IIB.

SPATIAL DISTRIBUTION OF BONDS

The nature of an ionic bond is such that it has no directional properties. The spatial distribution of the bonds formed around a given ion is only a function of the distribution of neighboring ions; the problem of bond direction reduces to a consideration of the ratio of radii of the ion and its neighbors in a close-packed array.

The distribution of bonds around a given ion is fixed in ionically bonded aggregates by the relative sizes of the positive and negative ions involved. For an anion of given size, it may be seen that many more may pack at uniform spacing around a large cation than around one of smaller radius. The geometry of this packing is thus fixed in terms of the ratio of the ionic radii and may readily be proved to conform to the values given in Table 2–4. The minimum radius ratio values in the table are those for which all ions are in contact. The same arrangement is retained with increasing size of the central ion until the radius-ratio for the next larger number of neighbors is reached. Figure 2–7 illustrates this situation for a hypothetical change from a triangular to a square arrangement.

The number of nearest neighbors (ions in contact) to any ion is called its *coordination*. Each ion is bonded to or coordinated by its nearest

Fig. 2–7. Change in coordination.

TABLE 2–4

Packing of Ions

Minimum Radius Ratio Cation/Anion	Number of Nearest Anion Neighbors	Geometrical Arrangement of Nearest Neighbors	
.155	3	Corners of an equilateral triangle	
.255	4	Corners of a tetrahedron 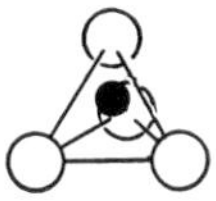 	
.414	6	Corners of an octahedron 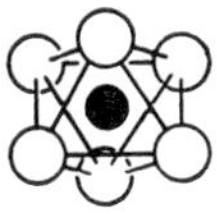 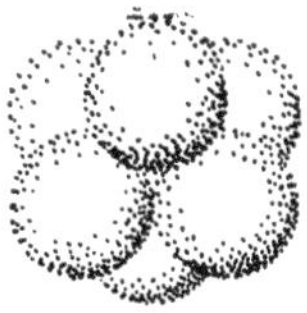	
.732	8	Corners of a cube 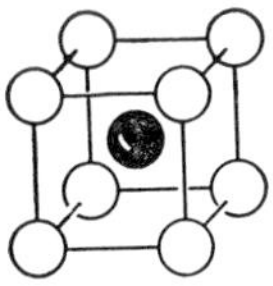 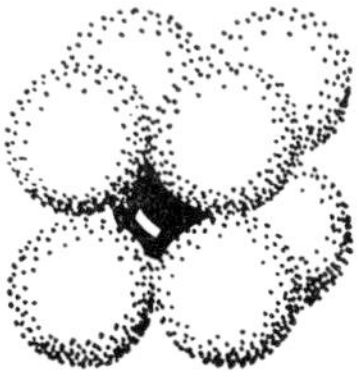	
1.0	12	Corners of a cubo-octahedron  	

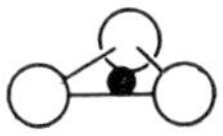

neighbors, and the coordination polyhedra are stacked to make up the crystal structure. Usually these coordination polyhedra share their corner ions, since this arrangement allows the greatest distance between ions of like sign, but sometimes edges or even faces are shared.

The relative strength of the ionic bond linking one ion to another is a function of both the valence of the ion and of the number of neighboring ions to which it is bonded. If, for example, Na^+ is surrounded by six Cl^- neighbors, the Na^+—Cl^- bond strength is $\dfrac{\text{valence of Na}}{\text{number of neighbors}}$ or $\frac{1}{6}$. In this structure the number of Na^+ ions around each Cl^- ion must also be 6, and the Cl^-—Na^+ bond strength is also $\frac{1}{6}$. Similarly for SiF_4, the Si^{+4}—F^{-1} bond is $\frac{4}{4}$ and the F^{-1}—Si^{+4} bond is $\frac{1}{1}$.

In cation-oxygen compounds, which comprise the majority of ionically bonded minerals, those structures in which the bond strengths throughout the crystal are essentially equal are termed *isodesmic*, whereas those in which some bond strengths are markedly different are called *anisodesmic*. A necessary part of an anisodesmic structure is the presence of more tightly bonded groups which are linked together by means of less-strong bonds. For example, in $CaCO_3$ the C—O bonds are stronger than the Ca—O bonds,* and discrete CO_3^{-2} groups present in the structure even retain their identity when the mineral is dissolved. These tightly bound groups are always composed of a cation coordinated by anions and are called *radicals* or *complex ions*. Typical radicals are $(CO_3)^{-2}$, $(SiO_4)^{-4}$, $(SO_4)^{-2}$, and $(PO_4)^{-3}$.

The shapes of these radicals reflect the screening efficiency of the positive element in that radicals containing a cation with efficient screening have regular geometric shapes, whereas radicals containing cations with a poor screening efficiency and consequent high external field may be considerably deformed, as, for example, in the sequence $(SiO_4)^{-4}$, $(MoO_4)^{-2}$, $(PtO_4)^{-4}$ where the screening efficiency decreases from silicon to platinum and the radicals are, respectively, tetrahedral, distorted tetrahedral, and square. This sequence is illustrated in Figure 2–8.

The spatial distribution of covalent bonds is related to the spatial distribution of the probability volumes of electrons in the various states within an atom. The probability of finding an electron at some particular distance from the nucleus has been illustrated in Figure 2–1. The separation of electrons in any particular shell may also be expected to be governed by probability, with the electrons distributed in such a way as to be at maximum separation. For the two electrons in the *s* state such positions can be on opposite sides of the nucleus, while the six electrons

---

* The valences of C and Ca are +4 and +2, and they can surround themselves with three and six oxygen neighbors, respectively. The relative strength of the C—O bond is thus $\frac{4}{3}$ and the Ca—O bond is $\frac{2}{6}$

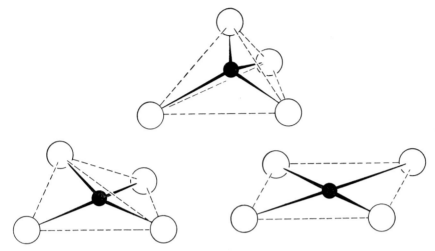

Fig. 2–8. Distortion of a coordination polyhedron by polarization.

in the p state would be spaced at equal distances and their statistical positions would correspond to the corners of an octahedron. Bonds arising because of the overlap of shells and sharing of electrons might thus be expected to be strongest in the direction of the concentration of these probability volumes.

The s state is spherically symmetrical, and atoms bonded by paired electron spins between s electrons have no directional preference for the bond. Since, however, only a single s state is present in the valence shell of a given atom, the s—s bond is restricted to the formation of diatomic molecules.

The probability volumes of p electrons lie along mutually perpendicular axes (p_x, p_y, and p_z), each of which may accommodate two electrons. p—p bonds tend, therefore, to be at right angles to one another. For example, the water molecule, H_2O, is held together by p bonds (the $1s$ electron of the hydrogen atom being elevated to the p state), and the angle H—O—H is $104° 31'$. The deviation of this angle from $90°$ may be accounted for by a partial ionic character of the bond and a consequent repulsion between the hydrogen atoms.

The combination of s and p states provides the possibility of four bonds—one s electron and three p electrons being available for bonding.[*] These bonds are oriented in such a way as to obtain the maximum interbond angle, and are thus directed towards the corners of a tetrahedron. As an example, the free energy of a system of carbon atoms is minimized by making the bond energies as large as possible, which in turn is accom-

[*] Only half the electrons needed to fill a quantum state are available for bonding because of the necessity of having opposed spins.

plished by s—p hybridization. The resulting structure is a network of carbon atoms on tetrahedral corners with bonds directed along tetrahedral edges.

Hybridization of d, s, and p states occurs when the energies of the d state are close to that of the s and p states, as in the transitional elements. Theoretically, nine bonds could be formed by such hybridization—one from s, three from p, and five from d—but in reality the d state is always at least partly filled, and a maximum of two d electrons are available for bonding. The maximum number of d—s—p bonds is thus six, and such bonds are found to be directed toward the corners of an octahedron.

The spatial distribution of metallic bonds cannot be readily determined by examination of the bonding mechanism, but the nature of the bond implies that it is nondirectional. Only three common arrangements of atoms in metal structures are known: cubic close-packed, hexagonal close-packed, and body-centered cubic. In the first two arrangements a given atom is surrounded by twelve neighbors and may be thought of as having twelve symmetrically disposed bonds. In the third arrangement a given atom has eight neighbors located on the corners of a cube, and the bonds thus lie along cube diagonals.

The Size and Shape of Atoms and Ions

The size of atoms or ions might at first glance be thought to be constant for each element, but this is far from the truth. The actual size of an atom or ion depends not only upon itself but also upon its environment. The degree of ionization of an atom, the kind of neighbors which it has, and the number and arrangement of these neighbors, as well as the manner in which the atoms are bonded, all affect the size of the atom of a particular element.

The size of an atom or ion is then a variable and is controlled by factors intrinsic to the element in balance with environmental factors beyond the control of the atom. Radii of atoms or ions can strictly be used only when the atoms exactly correspond to the situation in which the radius was determined, since the radius of ion A in situation X is not the same as the radius of ion A in situation Y. However, the factors which affect the radius difference of ion A in situations X and Y are reasonably well known, and it is possible to estimate an atomic or ionic radius in a new situation with good accuracy by appropriate corrections to the measured value. The principal factors which determine the radius of atoms and ions are described in the following paragraphs.

An atom may be thought of as a positive nucleus imbedded in a ball of negative electricity which represents the distribution of electrons through space. The electron density of this ball is greatest near the nucleus and decreases rapidly as distance from the nucleus increases, so that the greater part of the atom is within a few Ångstroms * of the nucleus.

The density of electrons around the nucleus is not uniform, however, but appears as a series of shells of decreasing density. Also, the distance of the outer shell from the nucleus does not vary linearly as new shells are added, since inner shells are compressed to such an extent that the overall atomic radii are not greatly different. This drawing-in of electronic shells is due to the increasing strength of the nuclear field as a result of increasing numbers of nuclear protons. In crystals of the elements the range of atomic radii is only from about 0.8 to 2.6 Å, and lithium, atomic number 3, is about the same size as uranium, atomic number 92.

The equilibrium position of the outer electronic shell controls the size of the atom, and, in turn, this equilibrium distance is related to the strength of attraction of the nucleus for outer electrons less the screening effects of intermediate electron shells.

Ionization of atoms as a result of the loss or gain of electrons markedly changes the effective radius of the atom. Should an electron be lost, the radius of the resulting cation is less than that of the atom from which it is formed because of the proportionately greater attractive power of the nuclear field per electron. The opposite is true when anions are formed by addition of electrons to the electronic envelope of an atom. The change in atomic radius as a result of ionization is illustrated by Table 2–5.

TABLE 2–5

Radius Changes with Ionization

Atom or Ion	Nuclear Charge	Electrons in Shell				Radius Å
		K	L	M	N	
K	19	2	8	8	1	2.31
K$^+$	19	2	8	8		1.33
Cl	17	2	8	7		0.97
Cl$^-$	17	2	8	8		1.81

If a radius change occurs when a neutral atom is ionized, it follows that further valence changes will result in different ionic radii, and the smaller radii will be associated with higher positive valences. The change of ionic radius with valence is especially well illustrated by the various ions of manganese whose radii for $+2$, $+3$, $+4$, and $+7$ cations are, respectively, 0.80, 0.66, 0.60, and 0.46 Å.

* An Ångstrom unit (Å) is 10^{-8} cm.

The mechanism of the chemical bond implies that the size of a given atom must be different when it bonds in different ways because of electron transfer and electronic shell overlap. In the case of a cation participating in an ionic bond, the loss of its electrons diminishes its effective size more than when it links by the covalent mechanism in which its outer electrons are retained. The opposite is of course true in the case of an anion. The effect of bond type on the radius of an atom or ion may be illustrated by considering aluminum, whose radius in ionically bonded structures is 0.50 Å, in covalent structures is 1.30 Å, and as metallic aluminum is 1.37 Å.

The radius of an atom or ion is affected slightly by the number of neighbors which surround it as well as the manner by which it is bonded to them. The effect is a small but systematic decrease of radius with decrease in coordination in the order of 2 to 3 per cent for the usual changes in the number of nearest neighbors. As an illustration of this point again consider aluminum which has radii of 1.37 and 1.43 Å, respectively, with 6 and 12 neighbors in metallic structures. In ionic structures the radii of Al^{+3} are 0.50 Å in six-fold coordination and 0.49 Å in four-fold coordination.

One of the more important parameters to be considered in mineralogical studies is the size of ions in their more usual valence states. Figure 2–9 presents this basic information in graphical form as a periodic property. Ionic radii are listed also in Appendix I.

In a general way, two ions undergoing reaction are attracted by their respective electrostatic charges inversely as the square of the distance separating them to some finite distance at which the like charges of their respective nuclei limit their approach. The force of repulsion at close approach appears to follow an inverse 6 to 8 power law, and, in consequence, reacting atoms to the first approximation are rigid spheres. The

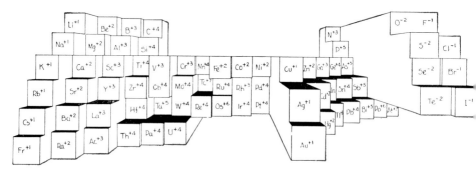

Fig. 2–9. Ionic radii.

effect of one ion upon another, however, is such that deforming forces are at work. Should an ion be small, highly charged, and poorly screened, it will suffer very little distortion if it is brought into the electrical influence of another ion; but if such an ion is juxtaposed to a large ion of low charge, it will tend to deform the larger ion (and incidentally change its radius) in such a way as to most effectively neutralize its own charge. The ability of one ion to deform another is called its *polarizing power*, and the reaction of an ion to such deforming forces is called *polarizability*. Most cations have low polarizability, and most anions, with the exception of fluorine, are polarizible. The amount of polarization present in a structure is essentially the resultant of the polarizing power of the cations and the polarizibility of the anions. As the degree of polarization increases the tendency to form self-limiting units increases because the anion field is distorted in such a way that its attraction for another cation is lessened. Eventually layer structures and finally discrete molecules result.

References

AHRENS, L. H. 1952. The use of ionization potentials—1. *Geochimica et Cosmochimica Acta* 2: 155–169. Published ionic radii are reviewed and new and revised radii are given.

GOLDSCHMIDT, V. M. 1929. Crystal structure and chemical constitution. *Transactions of the Faraday Society* 25: 253–283. A summary of papers appearing in the Norske Videnskaps-Akad. Skrifter dealing with crystal structures. These studies enabled ionic radii to be attributed to almost all of the common ions.

HERZBERG, G. 1944. *Atomic Spectra and Atomic Structure.* Dover Publications, Inc., New York. Translated by J. W. T. Spinks. Introductory formulation of quantum and wave mechanics, discussion of the Pauli principle, and description of the periodic system of the elements.

MORRIS, D. F. C., and L. H. AHRENS. 1956. Ionization potentials and the chemical binding of simple inorganic crystalline compounds—1. *Journal of Inorganic Chemistry* 3: 263–269.

PAULING, L. 1948. *The Nature of the Chemical Bond.* Cornell University Press, Ithaca. The types of bonding in elements and compounds are discussed in detail. The covalent mechanism is emphasized.

THORNE, P. C. L., and E. R. ROBERTS. 1948. *Fritz Ephraim, Inorganic Chemistry.* Interscience Publishers, Ltd., London. The structure of matter, molecules and crystal structures, periodic properties, and some physical properties of crystals are treated in the early part of this book.

3

MINERALOGICAL RELATIONS

Determinative mineralogy is often unduly complicated by the emphasis placed on the minor differences between individual mineral species. Familial characteristics of large groups of minerals are thereby obscured in the extensive detail that is required for species classification. A more fruitful approach should be through a study of the mineral groups whose characteristics are rather similar, combined with an understanding of why species within these groups differ. This chapter is concerned with descriptions of common mineralogical relations. It is these relationships which provide the connective tissue joining the individual mineral species into family groups and which provide a rational basis for understanding many mineralogical differences.

In general, mineralogical relations may be subdivided into chemical and physical types. The former are represented by variations of the chemical constituents without essential change of the mineral structure and the latter by geometric variations of the structure with the chemical composition constant. The possible variations are analogous to the possibilities confronting a mason supplied with bricks of various sizes and colors when he starts to build a wall.

Chemical Variations

ISOMORPHISM

A growing crystal has certain definite specifications for size, charge, and screening efficiency which must be met before an ion can find a permanent place in its structure. However, the crystal may not exercise much or any selectivity when confronted by two different ions with similar properties, and both may be accepted indiscriminately.

Minerals always contain small amounts of "foreign" ions, even when such ions are quite dissimilar to the formulary constituents. As the similarities increase, the substitutional ability of the foreign atoms increases accordingly. A significant amount of substitution can occur in ionic crystals when: (1) the radius difference of the formulary and foreign ions is within 20 to 40 per cent; (2) their valences are within one unit of each other; and (3) their ionization potentials do not differ by more than about 25 per cent (about 40 per cent for fluorides, 20 per cent for silicates, and 10 per cent for sulfides). Complete substitution can often occur when the radius difference is less than 15 per cent of the smaller ion, the valences are equal, and the ionization potentials do not differ by more than 10 per cent.

Some substitution also takes place when ions substitute by pairs whose total size, valence, and screening is equivalent to the pair being replaced. Such paired substitution is exemplified by the series of plagioclase feldspars in which $(Ca + Al)$ substitutes for $(Na + Si)$. The formulae for the end-members of the plagioclase series are $Na(AlSi_3O_8)$ and $Ca(Al_2Si_2O_8)$ and all intermediate ratios of $(Na + Si)$ and $(Ca + Al)$ may occur.

For example, a compound midway between the two end-members would have the formula $Na_{0.5}Ca_{0.5}(Al_{1.5}Si_{2.5}O_8)$ or $NaCa(Al_3Si_5O_{16})$. The percentage change in the valence, radius, and ionization potential sums for the substituting pairs which indicate that such paired substitution is easy in this mineral series are listed in Table 3–1.

TABLE 3–1

Comparison of the Pairs (Na + Si) and (Ca + Al)

	Valence Sum	Radius Sum	Ionization Potential Sum
(Na + Si)	+ 5	1.39 Å	13.24 ev
(Ca + Al)	+ 5	1.40 Å	12.05 ev
Per cent difference	0	0.7	9.8

The substitution of one atomic species for another, because the size of the proxy atom must be nearly that of the formulary atom, can have little effect upon the geometry of the structure and hence upon the crystal form. Mineral series showing a continuous change in composition without change in form are said to be *isomorphous*—having the same form—and isomorphs may be defined as minerals with the same crystal structure and similar, but not identical, formulae.

When extensive substitution is possible, the resulting continuous isomorphous series are often arbitrarily divided into several different species of minerals, a procedure which tends to obscure the intimate relationship within such a series and adds unnecessary mineral names. A more exact approach to the designation of the intermediate compounds in an isomorphous series may be made by describing them in terms of the proportions of the end-members present. For example, olivine, $(Mg, Fe)_2$ (SiO_4), is an intermediate member of an isomorphous series from forsterite, $Mg_2(SiO_4)$, to fayalite, $Fe_2(SiO_4)$, but no indication of the relative proportions of magnesium to iron is given in the olivine formula other than that the Mg, being written first, predominates over Fe. A precise notation for the composition of an olivine is given by the notation $Fo_{63}Fa_{37}$ (forsterite 63 per cent, fayalite 37 per cent) which indicates a ratio of Mg to Fe atoms of 63:37.* Diagrammatically this olivine may be represented as a point on a line or two-component diagram (Figure 3–1).

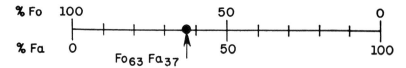

Fig. 3–1. Two-component diagram for the olivine series.

The substitution for magnesium in olivine is not restricted to iron. Manganese commonly competes successfully for this site, thus forming minerals with the general formula $(Mg, Fe, Mn)_2 (SiO_4)$. Perhaps the best way to visualize the isomorphous relations in such a three-component system is to make a triangular diagram in which each corner represents 100 per cent of the constituent. In Figure 3–2 such a diagram is drawn, representing various ratios of Mg, Fe, and Mn in the olivine family of minerals. Points 1, 2, and 3 represent forsterite, fayalite, and olivine as discussed above. Point 4 is a magnesium-iron-manganese olivine, the mineral hortonolite; point 5 represents a manganiferous fayalite, the mineral knebelite; and point 6 the manganese end-member, tephroite. All the individual minerals mentioned are isomorphs, and intermediate mineral types must be expected to occur.

In many instances isomorphism, although present, is incomplete because of the inability of the structure to accept more than some fixed proportion of substituting ions without exceeding a limit imposed by energy considerations. The substitution of nonidentical atoms always causes a local increase in strain, and accumulation of such local strains may eventually surpass the strength of the bonds. Obviously, crystals cannot form if the tendency for forming bonds is opposed by greater forces, and sharp limits to the amount of isomorphous replacement may be imposed by dissimilarities of atoms. An example of incomplete isomorphism is the clinopyroxene series shown in Figure 3–3, in which no

---

* It will be noted that the number of atoms (mole per cent) rather than the weight of atoms (weight per cent) is being used. This provides a clearer picture of the replacement process and allows a direct conversion to the formula.

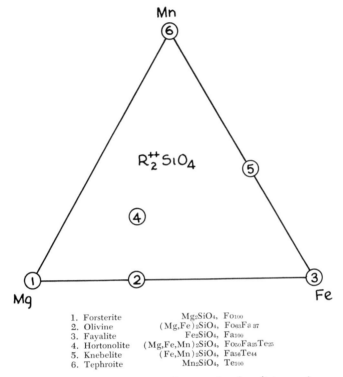

1. Forsterite Mg_2SiO_4, Fo_{100}
2. Olivine $(Mg,Fe)_2SiO_4$, $Fo_{63}Fa_{37}$
3. Fayalite Fe_2SiO_4, Fa_{100}
4. Hortonolite $(Mg,Fe,Mn)_2SiO_4$, $Fo_{50}Fa_{25}Te_{25}$
5. Knebelite $(Fe,Mn)_2SiO_4$, $Fa_{56}Te_{44}$
6. Tephroite Mn_2SiO_4, Te_{100}

Fig. 3–2. Three-component diagram for the olivine series.

natural members having either Ca or Fe in excess of Mg exist. Complete isomorphism is, however, found within the area bounded by solid lines in the diagram.

Isomorphism is not restricted to the interchange of cations although this is its most common expression. Anions also may substitute for one another, especially $(OH)^-$ and F^-, and occasionally an unoccupied structure site (a "hole") may interchange with an atom.

An interesting effect resulting from isomorphous replacements is the "camouflage" of certain of the rarer elements, which do not form mineral compounds of their own because of their ready substitution for more common ions. Examples of such elements are rubidium, which is camouflaged in potassium-containing minerals; gallium, which is completely absorbed in the formation of aluminous minerals; and hafnium, whose association with zirconium is so close that hafnium minerals are unknown.

Generalizations concerning the ability of one element to substitute for another may be made by reference to the periodic table, Figure 2–3, page 80. Since valence is constant within a column, and size increases while ionization potential decreases rather slowly down a column, re-

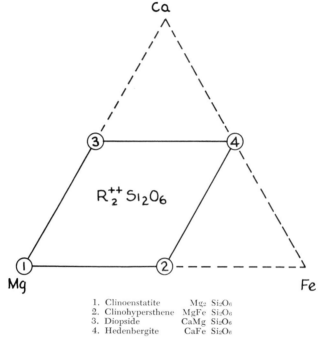

1. Clinoenstatite Mg_2 Si_2O_6
2. Clinohypersthene $MgFe$ Si_2O_6
3. Diopside $CaMg$ Si_2O_6
4. Hedenbergite $CaFe$ Si_2O_6

Fig. 3–3. Limited isomorphism in the clino-pyroxene series.

placing ions will tend to have adjacent positions in the table. Replacement pairs such as Sr-Ba, Cb-Ta, S-Se, and Ag-Au will thus arise.

Transition within the A subgroup of the periodic table limits the higher valences of these elements, and such geochemically cohesive groups as V-Cr-Mn-Fe-Co-Ni or Os-Ir-Pt are found. Occasionally the position of an A subgroup element, being farther down the table, brings its size in line with that of a short period element in a numerically earlier column. The pair Fe-Mg is thus explained.

Replacements between the B subgroup and early columns in the short periods or the A subgroup, although possible on size and charge considerations, do not generally occur. The barrier is the difference in ionization potential. Thus copper and sodium ions may have the same charge and very similar radii, but their respective ionization potentials of 7.7 and 5.1 electron volts preclude significant substitution.

It should be emphasized at this point that the foregoing discussion of isomorphism is concerned only with those minerals whose bonding is sufficiently ionic that the electrical charge of the reacting constituents is an important consideration. For covalently and metallically bonded compounds the criterion for replacement is not controlled by charge and ionization potential, but by size and the ability of the proxy element to form similarly quantized bonds as those of the formulary element. Mineralogically, the compounds of sulfur (the sulfides and sulfosalts) are the most important compounds in this category. Since these minerals are metal-sulfur compounds, isomorphism will be found whenever two metals of similar covalent radius can satisfy the electronic requirements of the metal-sulfur bond. Sulfur is poorly shielded and lacks two electrons (in $3p$) for completion of an eight-electron outer shell. It will, therefore, bond covalently with any poorly shielded element which will supply this deficiency. Such elements are found in the central portions of the long periods in the periodic table—columns VIA to VB. As an example of the amount of isomorphism which is possible, consider the fact that Cu, Fe, Mo, Sn, Ag, Hg, and Cd all may replace Zn in sphalerite, ZnS.

The phenomenon of isomorphism among the sulfides has considerable practical meaning to the mining man or metallurgist, since camouflaged elements may represent considerable value. Cases in point are the silver content of galena, gold values of pyrite, cadmium in sphalerite, and nickel in pyrrhotite.

Isomorphous relations in metallo-covalent structures are not limited to metal for metal replacements. Replacements of metals for "holes" are common, and replacements of selenium or tellurium for sulfur should be expected.

EXSOLUTION

Isomorphism may occur at elevated temperatures when a mineral's tolerance for foreign ions is greatly increased by the additional free energy of the structure resulting from the thermal agitation of the atoms about their structural sites. The number of foreign ions accepted under such circumstances is often greater than can be tolerated in the structure at some lower temperature, and in this situation the crystal structure must either be disrupted or cast out the excess of foreign atoms on cooling. The latter phenomenon is called *exsolution* or *unmixing* and is the separation of a single homogeneous mineral into two distinct minerals in the solid state. This is analogous to the formation of two immiscible liquids on cooling from some homogeneous liquid mixtures, e.g., the separation of fat from soup. Separation into two (or more) solid phases without physical disruption is necessarily controlled by the structures of the resultant phases. These structures must have at least partial registry at their mutual boundary, and the energy localized in the boundary layer must be less than that required for rupture.

A very common mineralogical example of exsolution is perthite, a mixture of potassium feldspar and albite, which at high temperatures is a homogeneous single mineral of the composition $(K, Na)(AlSi_3O_8)$ and which exsolves $Na(AlSi_3O_8)$ on cooling. This process is reversible, and heating of perthite to about 800°C will regenerate the homogeneous solid mixture.

The general phenomenon of exsolution may be described graphically by use of a three-component diagram such as was used in the section on isomorphism. Assume that the region of complete isomorphism of A, B, and C at some elevated temperature is represented by field 1 ($A_{0-50} B_{0-100} C_{0-50}$) in Figure 3–4. Further, assume that at some lower

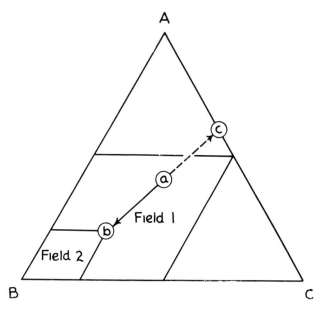

Fig. 3–4. Exsolution in a three-component system.

temperature the complete isomorphism of these components is restricted to field 2 ($A_{0-20} B_{60-100} C_{0-20}$). A compound, $A_{40}B_{30}C_{30}$ (point a), can exist as a single phase at the elevated temperature but is unstable at the lower temperature and exsolution occurs. Assume the stable composition of the host is $A_{20}B_{60}C_{20}$ (point b). In order to reach point b from point a, the content of both A and C must be decreased, and, therefore, A and C or $A + C$ will be the exsolved product(s). Should an AC compound be a stable product, its composition is readily determined by extrapolating the line ba to the edge AC (point c). The composition of $A + C$ is thus determined to be $A_{60}C_{40}$. The entire exsolution reaction may now be written:

Exsolves

$$A_{40}B_{30}C_{30} \longrightarrow A_{20}B_{60}C_{20} + A_{60}C_{40}$$

This use of a three-component diagram is in many ways applicable to the study of phase diagrams which represent the equilibrium relations between solids and liquids rather than between solids only. With reference to a typical phase diagram between three components represented by Figure 3–5, it may be seen that at elevated temperature the liquid

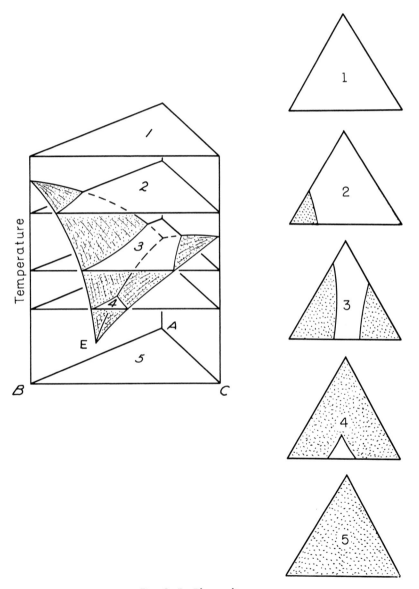

Fig. 3–5. Phase diagram.

phase (field 1) can accommodate components A, B, and C in all proportions. With falling temperature, the liquid cannot retain all of component
B (field 2), and some of B is removed by crystallization. Further temperature decreases require the elimination of some of component C and
then of A (fields 3 and 4) with consequent decrease in the size of the
liquid field. The liquid field is finally completely eliminated at the temperature of the BC eutectic point, (point E).

ISOSTRUCTURE AND ISOTYPE

Isostructural minerals are those which have an identical arrangement
of atoms but which have totally dissimilar formulae; for example, the
cubic crystals galena, PbS, and halite, NaCl. The idea of isostructure is
especially useful in describing a mineral by reference to a well-known
structure. This practice reduces to a minimum the number of geometric
configurations which must be learned.

Isotypic minerals are those with both isostructural characteristics and
chemical similarity. No rigid requirements for crystallographic identity
or for formula are implied by the term. An example of an isotypic pair is
tridymite, SiO_2, and nepheline, $Na(AlSiO_4)$. These minerals are based
on the same silicon-oxygen structural framework and hence have structural
similarity. The Al of nepheline occupies the same kind of structure site as
does the Si of both tridymite and nepheline. Therefore Al = Si except for
a charge discrepancy. The presence of Na balances the charge, and Na
occupies holes in the framework and does not disturb it. Another such
pair is quartz, SiO_2, and eucryptite, $Li(AlSiO_2)$. The story is here the
same, but since the holes are smaller, a smaller ion (Li) is utilized.
Another isotypic pair is soda-niter, $NaNO_3$, and calcite, $CaCO_3$, in both
of which triangular radicals alternate with cations to make up the structure, and paired substitution of radical and cation may take place. It
should be emphasized that the members of an isomorphous series are
isotypic, but that isotypic minerals are not necessarily isomorphous.

In review, the terms *isomorph, isostructure,* and *isotype* are concerned
with the idea of similar or identical geometry and variable composition:

Isomorph—very similar geometry; continuous variation of composition
Isostructure—identical geometry; no necessary relation of composition
Isotype—similar geometry; similar composition

DERIVATIVE STRUCTURE

The successive suppression of symmetry elements will produce a related series of crystal structures. The structures of lower symmetry are
thus "derived" from those of higher symmetry and are termed *derivative*

structures. Diamond, C, to sphalerite, ZnS, to chalcopyrite, $CuFeS_2$, to stannite, Cu_2FeSnS_4, is such a sequence of derivatives. Zn and S atoms in sphalerite occupy comparable sites to the C atoms in diamond, and Cu and Fe atoms in chalcopyrite are found in sites equivalent to the Zn in sphalerite, etc. The suppression of symmetry in such a series may be seen in the increase in identity period as represented graphically below.

C	C	C	C	C	C	C	C	C	C	Diamond
Zn	S	Zn	S	Zn	S	Zn	S	Zn	S	Sphalerite
Cu	S	Fe	S	Cu	S	Fe	S	Cu	S	Chalcopyrite
Cu	S	Fe	S	Cu	S	Sn	S	Cu	S	Stannite

Geometrical Variations

POLYMORPHISM

Polymorphs, as implied by the name—many forms—are compounds with the same chemical makeup but capable of crystallizing in more than one structural arrangement. In certain cases these various forms are also capable of being readily transformed from one structural arrangement to another.

Fundamentally, polymorphism in ionic structures rests on (1) the possible existence of more than one distinct grouping of constituents with fixed radius ratios, and (2) on different groupings which may arise if the radius ratio varies. The possibility of combining a few constituents into several different structures may be likened to the possibilities which arise when a mason lays a brick wall; certain fundamentals of good bricklaying must be observed, but within such limits a number of patterns may be developed, and so in minerals.

Consider, for example, the polymorphs of SiO_2 wherein the "bricks" are tetrahedral units composed of a silicon ion surrounded by four oxygen neighbors. The oxygen ions on the corners of each tetrahedral "brick" are in all cases shared between (common to) two adjacent tetrahedra, and all SiO_2 structures are some arrangement of the resulting network of linked tetrahedra. Several of the various ways in which these linked tetrahedra may be arranged in space are shown in Figure 3–6. It may be readily seen that the various arrangements are quite different geometrically, and further examination will prove that one arrangement cannot be transformed into another without complete disruption of the structure. The situation is similar to that represented by the two stacks of lumber illustrated in Figure 3–7 wherein the transformation of one stack to the geometry of the other will require a complete rebuilding.

Because of the necessity of tearing down and rebuilding, a large energy barrier, represented by the energy required to break chemical bonds,

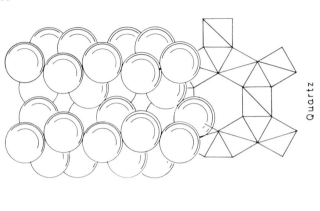

Quartz

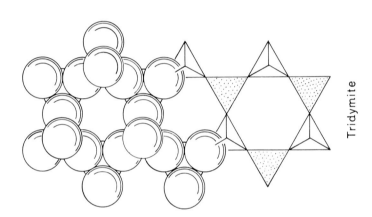

Tridymite

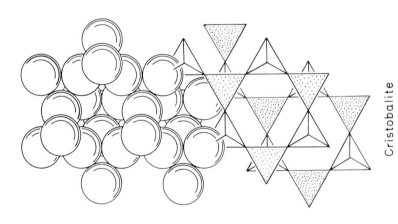

Cristobalite

Fig. 3–6. The principal polymorphous forms of SiO_2.

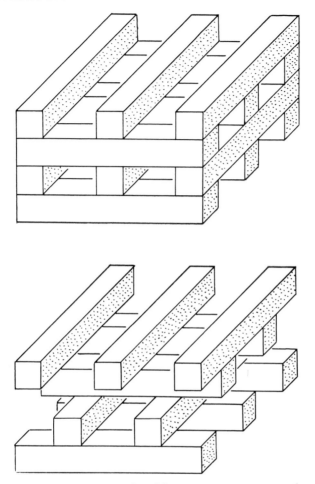

Fig. 3–7. Polymorphic forms related by a reconstructive transformation.

separates any such polymorphic forms. The rearrangements are necessarily sluggish, not uncommonly requiring the presence of a flux. Polymorphic transformations of this nature are termed *reconstructive*.

Another, and somewhat more subtle, kind of polymorphism may be seen in the existence of "mirror image structures" which are identical in all other respects. An analogy is the geometrical relationship between the left and right hands. Organic compounds related by this phenomenon have the prefixes "levo" (left) and "dextro" (right). A mineralogical example is quartz, in which rows of atoms in one plane may be succeeded in the next layer by rows displaced by 60° either clockwise or counterclockwise. The diagram of the quartz structure in Figure 3–6 shows a counterclockwise or left-handed arrangement. Figure 3–8 shows the

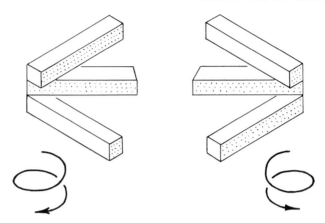

Fig. 3–8. Right- and left-handed structures.

essentials of right- and left-handed polymorphs with the rows of atoms being simplified to square rods.

Each of the polymorphic forms of a particular compound may be further modified by slight displacements of the structural units in such a fashion as to change the symmetry but not to disrupt any chemical bonds. This type of polymorphic modification is illustrated in Figure 3–9 which shows how square rods, here representing rows of tetrahedra, may themselves be modified. The energy difference between two such forms is very small since no bonds are broken, and transformation will occur very readily at an appropriate temperature. This kind of polymorphic transformation is termed *displacive* and is characterized by its rapid accomplishment and reversibility.

The various polymorphic forms connected by displacive transformation are called *high* and *low* (*temperature*) *forms*. These are often termed α and β forms, but there is no consistent usage as to which is high and which is low.

In the silica group of minerals which has been used to illustrate reconstructive polymorphic transformations, there also occur displacive transformations of each of the mineral species characterized by different basic structures. Quartz has a high and low form with a transformation temperature at about 573°C; cristobalite has high and low forms which transform between 198°C and 273°C; and tridymite has high, middle, and low forms transforming at 117°C to 163°C.

The interrelationships between the various polymorphic forms of silica are epitomized in Figure 3–10.* Solid horizontal lines represent the stable forms. Horizontal dashed lines represent the metastable forms

---

* Redrawn by permission from *The Properties of Silica*, by Robert B. Sosman. Copyright, 1927, by Reinhold Publishing Corp., New York.

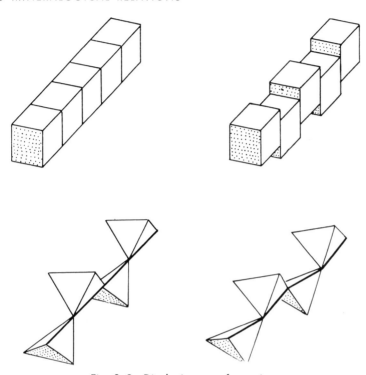

Fig. 3–9. Displacive transformation.

which are found because of the sluggish nature of the reconstructive transformation. Several "bypass" routes exist because of the sluggish transformations, such as, for example, the formation of vitreous silica rather than tridymite from high quartz at 1410°C or the crystallization of high tridymite from vitreous silica held at 1670°C.

Combinations of ions whose radius ratio is close to the critical coordination values (Table 2–5) provide still another source of polymorphs, in that a very small change in the energy of the structure, either from thermal or chemical sources such as contamination by substitution, may affect the average size or shape of the ions enough to dictate the assumption of a new coordination and hence a new structural arrangement. An example of polymorphic forms arising because the radius ratio of the components is close to a critical value may be seen in the forms of $CaCO_3$. The radii of Ca^{+2} and O^{-2} are, respectively, 1.02 Å and 1.40 Å and the radius ratio is thus 0.73. This is almost exactly the critical value separating structures in which the coordination polyhedron contains six and eight ions, and $CaCO_3$ may thus be expected to occur in two forms. If calcium is in six-fold coordination with oxygen, the mineral is calcite, whereas calcium in higher coordination is found in aragonite.

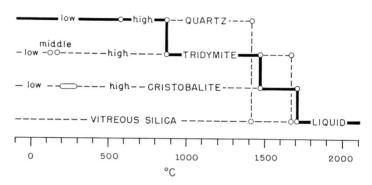

Fig. 3–10. Principal polymorphs of silica (after Sosman).

ORDER-DISORDER

The mason who must build a wall and finds that his bricks are of two different colors is confronted with the choice of using the bricks at random or laying them in a regular pattern. Growing crystals, also, must make a similar choice in many of their structures.

Reacting ions tend to seek the structure sites in which their presence causes the greatest reduction of free energy. These sites are necessarily positions of regular pattern and spacing. On the other hand, thermal agitation and rapid growth promote random occupation of all of the possible sites with consequent irregular patterning. As an example of the interaction of these factors, assume some number of sites to be available on a crystal surface and that some lesser number of ions are to occupy those sites. When reaction is complete, the occupied and vacant sites will have a regular pattern if the choice is entirely up to the individual ions which seek to minimize the free energy or they will have some random arrangement if thermal agitation predominates and/or the rain of atoms on the surface has been rapid. The former instance is known mineralogically as an *ordered arrangement* or *order* and is the preferred arrangement since it provides the lowest free energy for this structure. In contradistinction, the situation of random or irregular arrangement is one of *disorder*. A completely random arrangement is one of complete disorder, and all intermediate degrees between complete order and complete disorder are possible. The general form of these intermediate stages as a function of temperature is shown in Figure 3–11.

Disorder may occur between any of the structural components—ions and ions, ions and holes, or between radicals. Should a mineral be heated, disorder sets in slowly, but once begun it increases rapidly to some critical temperature at which all trace of order is lost. Disorder is more common at elevated temperatures where thermal energy provides for the energy difference between the ordered and disordered states.

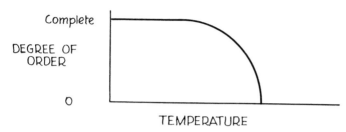

Fig. 3–11. Order-disorder.

Disorder may be "frozen in" by rapid cooling. Such statically disordered structures may be ordered by raising them to intermediate temperatures (annealing). The relation between the various kinds of disorder and the common ways in which they are produced is shown in the cycle, Figure 3–12. Continued heating will, of course, eventually cause the solid to melt or dissociate. In this sense melting is an extreme case of dynamic disorder in which an atom is no longer restricted to a definite region.

Order-disorder phenomena in minerals are common, but only in rather rare instances are their effects sufficiently profound to warrant the designation of distinct polymorphic species. One instance in which polymorphic forms do appear to be connected by order-disorder relationships is the potassium feldspar group. This group consists of four minerals (orthoclase, mirocline, sanidine, and adularia) of identical formula, $K(AlSi_3O_8)$, which apparently differ fundamentally because of various order-disorder combinations between aluminum and silicon and between potassium and possible potassium sites.

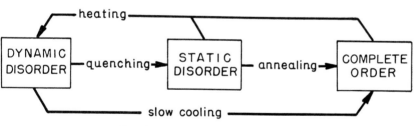

Fig. 3–12. Order-disorder cycle.

TWINNING

Mechanics of Twinning. A *twin* is the term applied to a rational, symmetrical intergrowth of two individual crystals of the same species— rational because the two portions of the twin have a point, line, or plane in common, and symmetrical because they are related by some crystallographic symmetry operation such as reflection, translation, or rotation.

Twins may arise in several different ways, and may be classified according to their origin as *growth twins, transformation twins,* or *gliding twins.*

Growth twins are always the result of an accident during the earlier stages of crystal growth. They are perpetuated in the growing crystal as distinct individuals with a mutual boundary or composition plane. A common accident which results in a twin configuration rather than a continuation of the normal structure may be visualized by considering the possibilities confronting the first ion to arrive in the situation illustrated in Figure 3–13. This ion, the first to arrive to start the third layer,

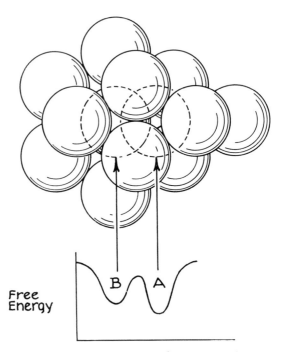

Free Energy

Fig. 3–13. Choice of site for twinned or continuation structure.

has a choice of two kinds of sites, *A* or *B*, respectively, over a first layer hole and a first layer ion. Site *A* is preferred since its occupation provides the larger decrease in free energy. However, the energy difference between sites *A* and *B* is very slight, and it is possible that thermal agitation may be insufficient to move an ion initially arriving at site *B* over the energy barrier to site *A*. In this case, the position of all future atoms in this layer is fixed, and the structure is continued as a twin of the earlier structure with a twin boundary between layers two and three. A similar accident may be visualized should the rain of reacting ions be so heavy that the first atom to arrive does not have time to adjust from the twin to the continuation position before it is hemmed in by new arrivals. Contrarily, it may be seen that if crystallization is sufficiently slow and there is competition for the lower energy state, growth twins will not occur.

Growth twins are usually restricted by energy considerations to a single twinning episode. This is because a very small crystal has a very high free energy, and additions of more ions in either twin or continuation positions cause significant diminution of this free energy. On the other hand, additions of ions in twin positions at a later stage of crystal growth will increase the free energy of the crystal and will hence not be tolerated. This situation is illustrated diagrammatically in Figure 3–14.

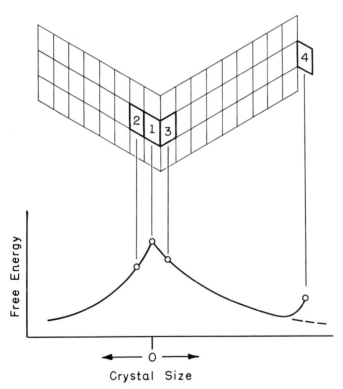

Fig. 3–14. Restriction of growth twinning to a single episode.

The decrease in free energy of a crystal nucleus (1) is rapid for either continuation (2) or for twin (3) increments. However, later twin configurations (4) are unlikely since their presence requires an increase in free energy.

Growth twins, because of their manner of formation, may usually be recognized in mineral specimens by the single often sinuous, boundary separating twin components with slightly different orientations or by the interpenetration of the two individuals composing the twin. Nonparallel twin boundaries are also evidence for growth twinning.

The mechanism of displacive polymorphic transformation may also be a mechanism for the formation of twins. The transformation is based on a displacement of adjacent structural units, and, if these are not congruent, transformation may bring them into a twin relationship. In the high form of a crystal, the atoms may be vibrating rapidly between two possible sites which gives the atoms an average position of high symmetry, Figure 3–15a. Should thermal vibration cease, the atoms cannot occupy the average position but must assume one of the less symmetrical terminal arrangements, Figure 3–15b.

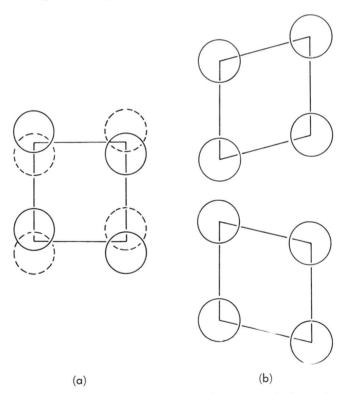

(a)   (b)

Fig. 3–15. Possible mechanism for transformation twin formation.

When crystals are taken through a displacive transformation, all regions of the crystal may not arrive simultaneously at the transformation temperature because of various crystal imperfections and consequent differences in thermal conductivity. Two different areas may thus arrive independently at the transformation temperature and transform with different

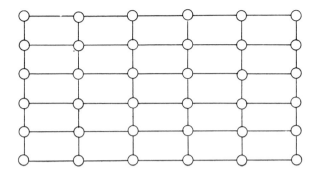

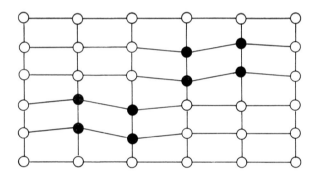

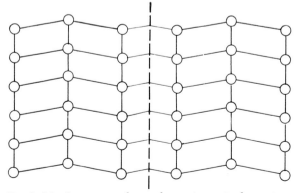

Fig. 3–16. Sequence of transformation twin formation.

orientations. As transformation continues, the orientation of the original patch is continued by adjacent areas. Eventually the two transformed regions grow to a mutual boundary which is a composition plane separating the two parts of the twin. This sequence is illustrated in Figure 3–16. Structural transformations with different orientations may thus spread out from different nuclei; and when transformation is complete, adjacent areas of the mineral may be in twin configuration. In minerals, a large number of transformation centers may develop, and the end result of transformation twinning is a mosaic of twins. Transformation twins may also arise in a similar way as a result of the ordering of structures with a fall in temperature.

Crystals may sometimes be deformed by the application of mechanical stress. Assume that the aggregate of atoms, Figure 3–17a, is stressed and yields by a slipping along the plane separating rows 2 and 3. If the amount of slippage is less than an identity period (as shown), row 2 will bear a twin relationship to row 3, Figure 3–17b. On the other hand, *slip*

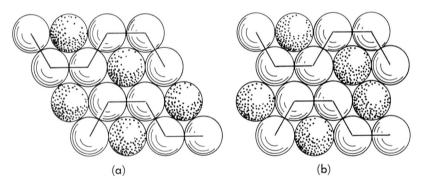

(a)   (b)

Fig. 3–17. Twin formation by glide deformation.

or *gliding* for any identity periods deforms, but does not twin, the structure. The situation illustrated is only one of a number of possible ways to produce twins or deform crystals by mechanically induced translational movements. The student should draw a few layouts similar to Figure 3–17 and see the results of gliding in monatomic aggregates, different geometric arrangements of binary compounds, and a ternary compound.

Glide twins may form if adjacent sites of the continuation and twin configuration are separated by a low-energy barrier. This situation is illustrated in Figure 3–18. The energy barrier separating the sites for continuation and twin development in Figure 3–18a is low and would readily allow the displacement of an ion from the normal to the twin location, whereas the energy barrier in Figure 3–18b would prohibit

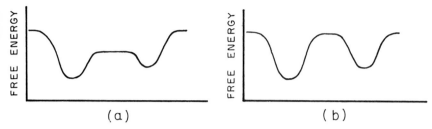

Fig. 3–18. Energy profiles for gliding.

displacement because the energy required for slip equals the energy for rupture.

The direction of gliding movement may be dictated by the presence of low-energy troughs leading away from the normal site. For example, an ion in position A, Figure 3–19, may migrate readily to position B but may not continue to position C. The "topography" of the energy surface with its barrier hills and valley troughs is, of course, directly related to the mineral structure.

Twin gliding in a uniformly stressed crystal begins by the localization of movement due to fortuitous circumstances such as a flaw, foreign atom, or heat motion. The twin lamellae grow laterally because of the high energy associated with their boundary until blocked by fortuitous circumstances which favor the start of a new twin lamella in preference

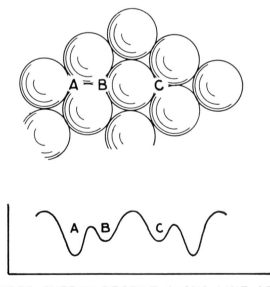

FREE ENERGY PROFILE ALONG LINE ABC

Fig. 3–19. Restrictions to direction and amount of glide.

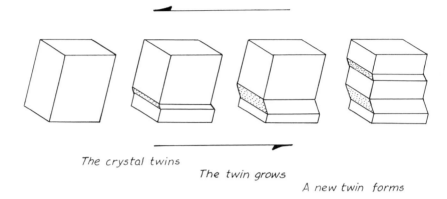

The crystal twins

The twin grows

A new twin forms

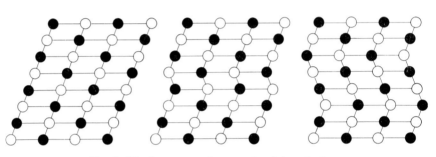

Fig. 3–20. Sequence of events in glide twinning.

to continuing the earlier twin. Figure 3–20 illustrates a series of episodes in the formation of glide twins. Crystals which have undergone twinning of this nature are characterized by the presence of numerous parallel twin lamellae or bands with linear boundaries. Twin gliding is readily induced in calcite (on $(01\bar{1}2)$) and in many metals.

It should be remembered that mechanical deformation of crystals may also take place by translation gliding or slip without inducing twins. In this case the ions or atoms are moved from one site to an equivalent structural site which is a continuation rather than a twin position. The crystal is thus deformed but not twinned. Figure 3–21 illustrates this phenomenon.

Symmetry of Twinning. Twins have been previously defined as being rational, symmetrical intergrowths of two individual crystals of the same species.* The component parts of a twin crystal are symmetrically related to each other by either a reflection plane (*twin plane*), a proper

---

* Intergrowths which do not conform to this definition can and do occur both between crystals of the same species and between crystals of different species. Such intergrowths, however, are not twins.

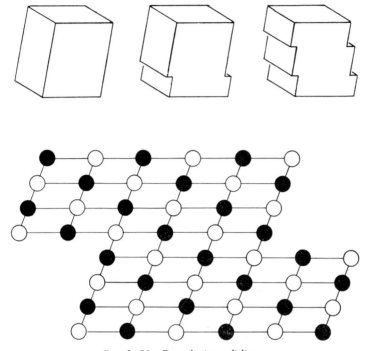

Fig. 3–21. Translation gliding.

rotation axis (*twin axis*), or simultaneously by both. Twinning planes and axes have simple and rational relations to the crystallographic axes. Twin planes are parallel to possible crystal faces.

Certain twin planes and axes are forbidden for twinning simply because they are already elements of symmetry of the individual crystal, and no operation of these elements can produce a new geometrical arrangement of the parts. No plane of symmetry in the individual crystal can be a twin plane in its compound crystal, and no two-, four-, or six-fold axis can become a twin axis in the compound crystal.

Combined twin planes and axes are present in all twin crystals in crystal classes having a center of symmetry ($m \cdot i \cdot A_{-180°} = 1$, see p. 13). Either a twin plane or a twin axis may be present when the crystal class lacks a center of symmetry. The plane on which twinned crystals are united is termed the *composition plane*. This plane often coincides with the twin plane.

The operation of these elements of symmetry in the development of twinned crystals is illustrated in Figures 3–22, 23, and 24.* An octa-

* Figures 3–22a, 3–22b, Figure 3–23, and Figure 3–24 redrawn by permission from *A Textbook of Mineralogy*, 4th Ed., by E. S. Dana and William E. Ford. Copyright, 1932, by John Wiley & Sons, Inc., New York.

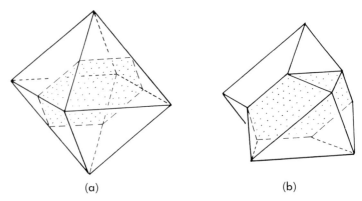

(a)   (b)

Fig. 3–22. Twins related by reflection or rotation (after Dana and Ford).

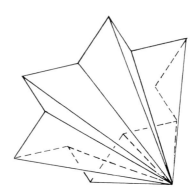

Fig. 3–23. Twins related by rotation (after Dana and Ford).

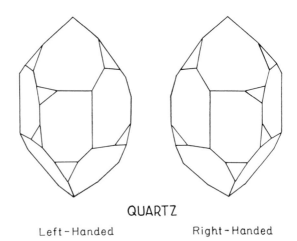

QUARTZ

Left–Handed   Right–Handed

Fig. 3–24. Twins related by reflection (after Dana and Ford).

hedron, Figure 3–22a, which contains a center of symmetry may be twinned by reflection across the plane outlined by dashed lines or by 180° rotation to produce the twinned octahedron, Figure 3–22b. The twin and composition planes are identical. Twinning of a tetrahedron as the result of the operation of a twin axis only is shown in Figure 3–23. Enantiomorphous individuals possess neither a plane nor center of symmetry. Enantiomorphs can, therefore, twin only by reflection across a twin plane. A left- and a right-handed individual of quartz are shown in Figure 3–24 and could be combined into a single crystal.

The mechanisms of twin formation treated previously do not always allow twins to be readily classified, since a given mechanism may give rise to different symmetrical relationships. It is often more useful to employ a descriptive rather than genetic terminology in describing twins in mineral identification studies.

Twins may be descriptively classified into *contact, penetration,* and *repeated* twins. Contact twins are united to each other by the composition plane. Penetration twins are those in which two or more crystals seem to cross through each other. Repeated twins may have the individuals in parallel orientation (*lamellar* or *polysynthetic* twins) or in nonparallel orientation (*cyclic* twins). Cyclic twinning tends to produce circular forms. Examples of the different kinds of twins are shown in Figure 3–25.

CRYSTAL IMPERFECTION

A perfect organization of atoms or ions into a crystal structure is an exception rather than a rule of crystal growth. Minor deviations from the ideal case may be seen in the most cursory examination of a crystal, and as investigation is pursued further more and more evidence of imperfection may usually be found. Illustrative examples of such deviations from the ideal are the slight nonparallelism of paired faces, the presence of inclusions and color centers of various kinds, zoning, lineage structure, internal flaws, ionic conduction, and discrepancies between the measured and the computed strength. Such deviations from perfection should not, however, cause dismay; rather, one should be surprised that crystal structures are so homogeneous when it is realized that a crystal face 0.1 inch across when magnified until the constituent atoms have diameters of about 1 inch would require almost 200 miles of travel over its monotonous, pebbly surface in order to reach the opposite side.

Departures from ideal crystallinity (defect structures) are of two types and are of different magnitudes. A coarse-grained imperfection may result from slight nonregistry of adjacent parts of the structure. The structure is continuous from any point on the surface to the center of the crystal, but accidents during growth have resulted in imperfect registry between adjacent parts. This is called *lineage structure*. The situation may be compared to that of a tree in which continuity from leaves to trunk is present, but disorientation of the leaves is found. Figure 3–26 is a diagrammatic representation of lineage structure. A common example may be seen in the zinc crystals on zinc-plated ware.

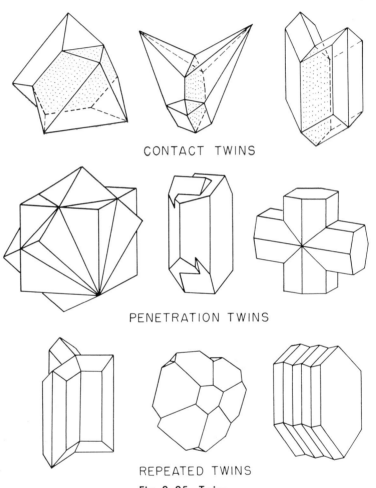

CONTACT TWINS

PENETRATION TWINS

REPEATED TWINS

Fig. 3–25. Twins.

Defect structures may also depart from the requirements of ideal crystals by defects present within lineage blocks. These are postulated to be either (1) an interstitial atom and its vacant site, or (2) a vacant site, the ion from which has migrated to the surface of the crystal. When structures containing such defects are under the influence of an external electric field, migration of interstitial ions and vacant sites (the latter

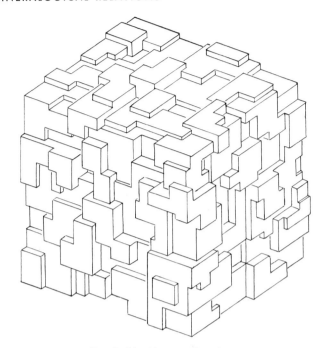

Fig. 3–26. Lineage structure.

equivalent to ionic movement in the opposite direction) takes place, accounting for the conductivity often observed in ionic crystals.

Minerals containing color centers or phosphors or which are semiconductors owe their respective phenomena to nonstoichiometric proportions of their constituent atoms and hence to structural defect. It is interesting to note that many of the useful properties of crystals are the result of defect structure and are not properties of ideal crystals.

References

BUERGER, M. J. 1945. The genesis of twin crystals. *American Mineralogist* 30: 469–482.

BUERGER, M. J. 1948. The role of temperature in mineralogy. *American Mineralogist* 33: 101–121. The thermodynamic basis for mineralogical relations is developed in terms of the energy of crystal structures.

EVANS, R. C. 1952. *An Introduction to Crystal Chemistry.* Cambridge University Press, London. A systematic treatment of crystal chemistry.

WELLS, A. F. 1945. *Structural Inorganic Chemistry.* Clarendon Press, London. A thorough treatment of crystal chemistry followed by a systematic description of the structures of the more important classes of inorganic substances.

4

PHYSICAL CHARACTERISTICS OF MINERALS

Introduction

The beginning student of mineralogy may easily become bewildered with the mass of descriptive information covering all phases of the subject, and it is probably of value to set forth here some of the philosophy and practice which underlie the identification of minerals.

Given a single property it is possible to divide all minerals into at least two large groups, with two properties each of these groups may be further subdivided, and with a half-dozen or so properties minerals may be assigned to very small groups or individual species. It is, therefore, important to know thoroughly the more distinctive properties and imperative that no error be made in the use of these properties for the identification of minerals. Experience has shown, however, that the mineralogist soon develops an ability to summate the physical characteristics of a mineral and thus short-cut a laborious tabulation of properties and winnowing of the possibilities until a match is obtained. Snap identification of specimens should therefore be respected.

Many kinds of determinative tables, which classify minerals into groups according to various sets of properties, have been designed and such tables have considerable value in developing a facility for mineral identification. Tables utilizing the properties of luster, cleavage, color, and hardness are included as Appendix II. Students who find identification difficult may gain confidence and ability by designing their own tables.

The tentative identification of a mineral should always be followed by a confirmatory test. Such a test may be found by reading over the description of the mineral and checking those physical or chemical properties which were not used in the original identification against the specimen.

The practice, here recommended, of mineral identification by "inspiration" may seem unscientific, especially to one trained in a scheme of analysis where the investigation always follows the same plan of attack, but the proof of its usefulness lies in the speed with which an accomplished mineralogist correctly names the specimens brought before him.

124

Physical Properties of Minerals

A number of physical properties of minerals which are applicable to the hand-specimen identification of a wide variety of minerals are described below. The relationship of these properties to the internal structure of the mineral is also discussed.

MANNER OF BREAKING

The kind of surface which is produced when minerals are subjected to sufficient stress to cause their rupture and the orientation of these surfaces with respect to crystallographic directions are characteristics of primary importance in mineral identification. The direction and ease with which the mineral may be broken are two of the best clues to its internal structure.

Fracture. Substances which are equally strong in all directions are those in which the density and strength of the interatomic or interionic bonds is similar in all directions. Rupture of such material may occur in any crystallographic direction, the break being localized by some flaw in the crystal. The irregular surfaces produced are called *fracture surfaces,* and the quality of such surface is often further described as:

Even: nearly flat fracture surfaces. Example, lithographic limestone.
Uneven or irregular: rough and irregular fracture surfaces. Example, rhodonite.
Hackly: ragged fracture surface with sharp edges and points. Example, copper.
Splintery: fibers and splinters are produced by fracture. Example, pectolite.
Conchoidal (shell-like): smoothly curving, ribbed fracture surface. Example, glass.

Cleavage. In many minerals planes exist across which there are fewer or weaker bonds than in other parts of the crystal. This condition might arise, for example, if the mineral were composed of sheets of atoms held together by strong bonds within the sheets and weaker bonds between the sheets or by a framework made up of an alternation of strongly bound radicals held together by weaker cation bonds. Two possibilities are shown in Figure 4–1, and others will be described under the appropriate minerals. In general, such weak planes arise as a natural consequence of the atomic packing or because of strongly developed polarization. Whatever the cause, planes of low bond density occur periodically at small separations within the crystal structure and provide the natural locus for rupture. When a mineral breaks along this locus, the observable result is a planar surface, and the mineralogic property of breaking with

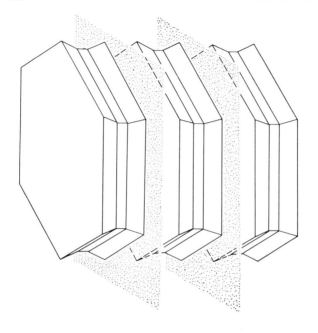
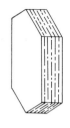
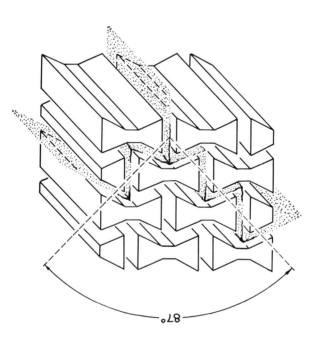
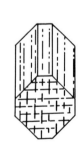

Fig. 4–1. Cleavage of pyroxene (left), cleavage of mica (right).

such a surface is called *cleavage*. The cleavage "planes" are not necessarily true planes on an atomic scale (see Figure 4–1) but are macroscopically so.

Four factors should be noted when the property of cleavage is being considered—ease of production, perfection of surface, number of cleavage directions, and crystallographic directions (indices of the planes). Mineral cleavage seldom yields a single perfect plane, more generally the surface is composed of many parallel planes connected stepwise by other cleavages or by fracture.

The number of potential cleavage planes in a given direction is theoretically limited only by atomic spacing and hence is essentially infinite. The number of possible directions of cleavage through a given mineral is restricted to planes parallel to actual or potential crystal faces and is thus always consistent with symmetry. The intersections of cleavage planes produce characteristic cleavage fragments, examples of which are shown in Table 4–1.

Parting. Under certain conditions a mineral may break with a cleavage-like rupture which, on close examination, is found to be related to weak planes having a macroscopic spacing. *Parting* is the name given to this phenomenon. Parting and cleavage are superficially similar, and the distinction in hand specimens must usually be based on the fact that the solid bounded by two adjacent planes of parting cannot be broken by further parting.

Parting, like cleavage, is related to weak bond planes within the mineral structure but, unlike cleavage, is not a necessary result of a given packing. Parting is usually related to weak planes arising from twinning or crystal deformation and is thus not necessarily present in all specimens of the same mineral. Planes of parting may occur in several different directions and circumscribe polygonal solids as do planes of cleavage.

Some difficulty may be experienced by the beginner in the distinction between plane surfaces arising from cleavage or parting and plane faces resulting from crystal growth. Careful examination of such surfaces will, however, usually show the delicate markings which serve to distinguish one from the other. Crystal faces commonly show the results of accidents in crystal growth in such observable features as lineage structure and striation, whereas cleavage tends to produce geometrically plane surfaces with a high reflectivity.

HARDNESS AND TENACITY

Hardness. The hardness of solids is measurable in numerous ways by a variety of ingenious devices. The technique of hardness testing which utilizes the simplest equipment and is the most satisfactory for general mineralogical work is that of relative resistance to scratching.

TABLE 4–1

Shapes of Typical Cleavage Fragments

Number of Cleavage Directions	Characteristic Fragment	Example
0		Quartz
1		Muscovite
		Augite
2		Orthoclase
		Hornblende
		Halite
3		Anhydrite
		Calcite
4		Fluorite
6		Sphalerite

The accepted scale of relative mineral hardness (scratchability) is given in Table 4–2 along with some readily available tools and materials for testing. This mineral scale is known as Mohs scale of hardness, and minerals are referred to it in terms of hardness numbers. For example, the hardness of chromite is $5\frac{1}{2}$ ($H = 5\frac{1}{2}$) and chromite will, therefore, scratch apatite and be scratched by orthoclase. Minerals of the same hardness may either scratch each other or not affect each other.

TABLE 4–2

Mohs Scale of Hardness

1 Talc
2 Gypsum
$2\frac{1}{4}$ Fingernail
3 Calcite
3 Copper coin
4 Fluorite
5 Apatite
$5\frac{1}{4}$ Knife blade
$5\frac{1}{2}$ Window glass
6 Orthoclase
$6\frac{1}{2}$ Steel file
7 Quartz
7 Streak plate
8 Topaz
9 Corundum
10 Diamond

The absolute spacing between the relative hardness values on Mohs scale is very unequal, and individual mineral hardnesses cannot be determined with any great precision. Attempts to place hardness on a truly quantitative basis have, however, been only partially successful. The relationship of hardness to crystal structure, difficult in itself, is thus hampered by the lack of an absolute reference scale.

All of the intrinsic properties of atoms as well as the variations possible in crystal structures must be called upon in order to obtain a full appreciation of mineral hardness. Some measure of bond strength is necessary, and this requires considerations of charge, radius, and screening efficiency. Bond density—a function of charge, coordination, and structure—must also be taken into account, and the distribution of bond density with respect to crystallographic directions is important. In addition, the presence of weak planes (e.g., cleavage) which intersect the test surface may markedly affect hardness determinations.

Some success in predicting the relative hardness of simple ionically bonded binary compounds of the same structure type has been attained on the assumption that hardness varies inversely with interionic distance and directly with valence. Thus MgO should be, and is, harder than NaCl, and the hardness of the isostructural oxides BaO, SrO, CaO, and MgO increases from BaO to MgO as the cation radius decreases. The extension of these simple rules to more complex substances is, however, not valid. As an example, the radii of cations and the hardness of the rhombohedral carbonates, as given in Table 4–3, show no such progression.

TABLE 4–3

Cation Size—Hardness Data for the Rhombohedral Carbonates

Mineral	Formula	Cation Radii (Å)	Hardness
Calcite	$CaCO_3$	1.02	$2\frac{1}{2}$–3
Rhodochrosite	$MnCO_3$	.80	$3\frac{1}{2}$–$4\frac{1}{2}$
Sphaerocobaltite	$CoCO_3$	.72	3–4
Smithsonite	$ZnCO_3$	.69	$5\frac{1}{2}$
Magnesite	$MgCO_3$	.64	$3\frac{1}{2}$–$4\frac{1}{2}$
Siderite	$FeCO_3$	.61	$3\frac{1}{2}$–4

A somewhat more general approach to the problem of the relationship of hardness to crystal structure in ionic minerals has been made by correlating hardness with the number of bonds per unit volume in the structure. The "bonding index" so obtained obviates the difficulty of variable interionic distances and valences when more than two cations are present, but does not account for the effect on hardness resulting from the uneven distribution of bonds in certain crystals. For many minerals, however, the uneven distribution of bonds is not the principal factor which controls hardness, and the bonding index may be readily correlated with mean hardness.

The unevenness of bond distribution may occasionally be of sufficient magnitude to be detected even by such a relatively insensitive standard as Mohs scale, as, for example, in calcite which has a hardness of 3 on its (1011) cleavage faces and 2.5 on its (0001) base or in kyanite with a hardness of 4.5 parallel to the c axis and 7 perpendicular to the c axis. These differences are readily explained in view of the crystal structure, since the soft and hard directions in kyanite are, respectively, parallel and perpendicular to chains, while in calcite the least hardness is on the plane of the CO_3 groups.

Hardness is very structure-sensitive, and the same atoms in two different arrays may have quite different hardnesses. This feature may be readily seen by inspection of Table 4–4, which gives the hardness of a few polymorphic pairs.

Hardness determinations should always be made on a fresh surface because of the possibility of soft surface alterations, and care should be

TABLE 4–4

Hardness of Some Polymorphic Pairs

Mineral	Formula	Hardness
Calcite	$CaCO_3$	$2\frac{1}{2}$–3
Aragonite	$CaCO_3$	$3\frac{1}{2}$–4
Arsenolite	As_2O_3	$1\frac{1}{2}$
Claudetite	As_2O_3	$2\frac{1}{2}$
Graphite	C	1–2
Diamond	C	10

taken that an apparently positive test is not the result of powdering one specimen against the other or the disruption of granules or cleavage fragments from the surface.

Tenacity. Tenacity is the manner in which a mineral ruptures or deforms under stress and is described as:

Brittle: The mineral breaks or powders. Example, quartz.

Sectile, ductile, malleable: The mineral deforms plastically under the stress of cutting, drawing, and hammering, respectively. Examples, copper, gypsum.

Flexible: The mineral may be bent, but does not return to its original form. Examples, talc, chlorite.

Elastic: The mineral, after bending, assumes its original form. Example, muscovite.

The degree of brittleness or sectility may usually be observed when scratch hardness tests are performed. Brittle minerals, when scratched with a sharp point, have small particles cast out beside the scratch. The scratching of sectile materials, on the other hand, causes material to flow from the deformed area, but not to be detached.

SPECIFIC GRAVITY

Specific gravity is the ratio of the weight of the mineral to the weight of an equal volume of water at 4°C. This property may be accurately determined by finding the ratio of a mineral's weight in air to its weight when immersed in water using an appropriately designed balance, or it may be estimated within reasonable limits without recourse to special equipment by handling the mineral.

The effect on specific gravity of a change in constituent atoms may be seen by reference to Table 4–5, in which the specific gravities and cation weights of the isotypic aragonite group minerals are listed.

TABLE 4–5

Relationship of Cation Weight to Specific Gravity

Mineral	Formula	Atomic Weight of Cation	Specific Gravity
Aragonite	$CaCO_3$	40.1	2.9–3.0
Strontianite	$SrCO_3$	87.6	3.6–3.8
Witherite	$BaCO_3$	137.4	4.2–4.35
Cerussite	$PbCO_3$	207.4	6.4–6.6

Specific gravity must also be a function of the packing of atoms or ions with higher specific gravities associated with closer packing. The specific gravities of some polymorphic pairs are given in Table 4–6 to illustrate this effect.

TABLE 4–6

Relationship of Specific Gravity to Packing

Mineral	Specific Gravity
Diamond	3.5
Graphite	2.1–2.2
Calcite	2.7
Aragonite	2.9–3.0
Quartz	2.65
Tridymite	2.3
Pyrite	4.9–5.1
Marcasite	4.8–4.9

PROPERTIES DEPENDENT UPON LIGHT

Luster. Luster is the general appearance of a fresh surface of a mineral in reflected light. The two major classes of luster are metallic and non-metallic, and these may be readily distinguished by the beginner. On the other hand, the delicate differences in luster so useful in mineral identification will usually pass unnoticed to any but the trained eye. One of the best ways to develop a sense for luster is to observe crystal faces or cleavage planes which are not symmetrically equivalent and which will usually display slightly different lusters.

Color. Mineral colors are the combined effect of a mineral's formulary constituents and their arrangement, chemical impurities, and crystal imperfections. As a rule, minerals whose colors are normally dark will not suffer color changes as the result of the presence of impurities or imperfections. On the other hand, impurities or imperfections in a mineral may interact strongly with light and markedly modify the colors of normally light-colored minerals. The amount of an impurity need not be large to produce a strongly colored substance; indeed, the amount of coloring agent is often measured in small fractions of a per cent.

Color should always be determined from the examination of a fresh surface since surface alterations and tarnishes can obscure the normal color.

Streak. Streak is the color of the powdered mineral and has a much more constant color than does the bulk mineral. For example, a series of colored glasses, when powdered, all show a very similar white streak.

Streak tests are usually made by rubbing the mineral across a piece of unglazed porcelain (streak plate) and examining the resultant powder smear against the white background of the plate. If no streak plate is available, the color of the mineral powder may be conveniently observed on a white paper background.

Miscellaneous Features Depending upon Light. An extensive group of mineral properties which depend upon light are sometimes observed, but because of their limited applicability to mineral determination no extensive description of them will be made. Such properties are:

Diaphaneity: the property of transmitting light. Described as transparent, translucent, or opaque.

Play of colors: different radiant colors observed as the mineral is turned. Example, precious opal, labradorite.

Iridescence: a play of colors due to thin coating on the mineral surface or because of partially opened cleavages. Example, goethite.

Opalescence: milky or pearly reflections from the interior of the specimen. Example, moonstone.

Chatoyancy: silky sheen resulting from a fibrous structure. Example, satin-spar variety of gypsum.

Tarnish: chemical reactions between the mineral and the air often produce thin coatings of the reaction products. Usually these coatings dull the surface, but occasionally they are brilliantly colored. Examples, copper, bornite.

Asterism: a six-pointed star of light seen in reflected or transmitted light. Examples, star sapphire, phlogopite.

Pleochroism: the specimen appears variously colored when viewed in different directions as a result of selective absorption of light along different crystallographic directions. Example, tourmaline.

Luminescence: emission of light from a nonincandescent material.

Triboluminescence: material becomes luminous when scratched, rubbed, or crushed. Examples, fluorite, sphalerite.

Thermoluminescence: material becomes luminous when heated.
Fluorescence: material becomes luminous during exposure to X rays or ultraviolet light. Example, scheelite.
Phosphorescence: luminescence continues after exposure to X rays or ultraviolet light.

THE INTERACTION OF LIGHT AND MATTER

Light is electromagnetic radiation whose wave motion is transverse to its direction of propagation. The passage of light causes an electrical disturbance which varies sinusoidally with time; as a consequence, any point in space over which light passes is subjected to a fluctuating electrical field in which any charged particle is set into forced vibrations. Since atoms consist of positive nuclei surrounded by negatively charged clouds of electrons, these differently charged parts will tend to be displaced slightly as a light wave passes. The electrons cannot leave the atom because of the intense internal electrical field, but they do tend to pile up at one part of the atom surface. The nucleus, being relatively heavy and thus having a large inertia, will not be moved very much, but the lighter electrons will be forced back and forth across the atom. The result is a rapidly oscillating atomic dipole as shown diagrammatically in Figure 4–2.

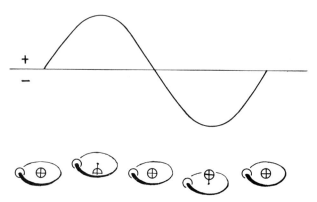

Fig. 4–2. Oscillating atomic dipole.

The periodic separation of an atom's nucleus and electron cloud sets up a small fluctuating electrical field of its own that opposes the field of the light wave at all times. This constitutes a load on the light wave and slows it down. An oscillating atomic dipole is only one of the many combinations of electrified units which may be set into forced vibration by the passage of light. Each positive and negative pair (e.g., a cation-anion pair) resonates with a characteristic frequency and, in general, the load on a light wave is the sum of all loads from the different oscillators.

A mechanical analogy for the slowing of a light wave by its interaction with other fields is a coiled spring hanging vertically. This spring will execute simple harmonic motion if it is displaced and released, and the frequency of this motion may be decreased by adding a weight to the end of the spring whose inertia must be overcome.

The loading of a light wave by electrical oscillators decreases the velocity of light in a material medium below that of its velocity in free space. The constant of proportionality between these two velocities is known as the *index of refraction, n,* which equals $\dfrac{\text{velocity in free space}}{\text{velocity in material medium}}$ and is hence always greater than unity. (The refractive index of air is only 1.00029 and is usually used as a reference.)

In general, the greater the contrast between light velocities within and outside a substance (the larger is n), the more flash and brilliance the substance shows. The variations in n are often qualitatively described under the loose term "luster," which includes this and other phenomena. For examples of the variations in refractive index, compare the appearance of the minerals in Table 4–7.

TABLE 4–7

Refractive Index of Some Isotropic Minerals

Mineral	Refractive Index
Fluorite	1.43
Analcite	1.49
Halite	1.54
Spinel	1.75
Andradite	1.87
Sphalerite	2.37
Diamond	2.42
Cuprite	2.85

The refractive index of a substance depends upon many things, among the more important of which are the nature of the constituent atoms or ions and their arrangement. As a rule, the heavier the atoms and the more tightly they are packed, the more they will slow passing light and the higher will be the index of refraction.

In some substances the kind and arrangement of atoms is such that every direction in the crystal presents the same aspect to passing light. Such substances are *isotropic*. In other crystals the arrangement of atoms is such that the electrical load on a ray of light is different in different directions. Light traveling through such materials must then move with different velocities along different crystallographic directions. Such substances are *anisotropic*. Amorphous substances and minerals crystallizing in the isometric system are isotropic, while minerals crystallizing in all of the other systems are anisotropic.

Light usually vibrates in all directions in a plane normal to its direction of propagation, but when reflected or refracted the vibration tends to be constrained to a single direction. When the vibration direction of light is thus restricted, it is *polarized*. When incident light strikes a crystal, part is reflected and part refracted, and both portions of the beam are polarized. In anisotropic crystals, the refracted light is further divided into two rays polarized at right angles to one another, and these two rays travel with different velocities along different paths. This separation of refracted light into two rays is called *double refraction*. The amount of double refraction is usually not sufficient to be detected without a properly equipped microscope, but in the case of calcite a doubling of images may be seen when viewed through a cleavage rhomb.

The charged components of matter which oscillate under the influence of a passing light wave have mass and, consequently, inertia. For this reason they do not react instantaneously to the electromagnetic field of light, but lag to some extent behind it. The amount of lag depends upon the frequency of the light, and as this frequency increases the amount of lag increases. As a consequence, there is a variation of the index of refraction with frequency as shown in Figure 4–3. This curve is only a

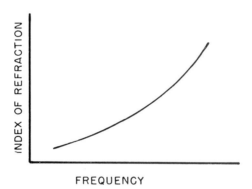

FREQUENCY

Fig. 4–3. Dispersion of light.

portion of a more extended curve which is shown in Figure 4–4. The strong change in the shape of the curve represents a resonant frequency at which light is strongly absorbed by the material because of energy transfer from the light to some resonant oscillator.

The frequency of light is an intangible property, and it is customary to use the readily measured parameter of wavelength when dealing with ordinary light. Light velocity equals frequency $\times$ wavelength, and hence frequency is 1/wavelength.

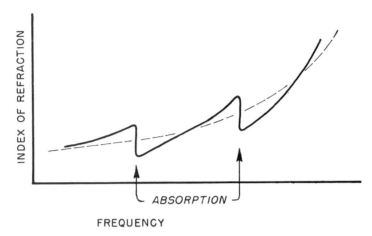

Fig. 4–4. Absorption of light.

Different wavelengths of light are perceived as different colors ranging through the visible spectrum from short wavelength violet light to long wavelength red light. When all wavelengths are present the light appears white, but removal of some wavelengths by absorption gives a substance the color of the other wavelengths. Thus, red-colored minerals result from the absorption of the shorter wavelengths, and blue minerals are those which absorb red light. Should all the light be absorbed, a mineral will be opaque, and if none is absorbed in the visible region the mineral is transparent.

Minute traces of foreign atoms are often responsible for the coloration of normally transparent minerals. Only a few hundredths or thousandths of a percent of foreign atoms will be required as coloring agents if they are such strongly absorbing atoms as carbon, titanium, manganese, or iron. No rigid laws restrict the possible substitution of such minute quantities of foreign atoms in a mineral structure, and the color of normally transparent minerals must be viewed with considerable suspicion as a determinative feature. For example, normally transparent quartz may be colored red, pink, green, yellow, blue, brown, and black. On the other hand, the color of dark-colored minerals is much more constant because the light-absorbing atoms are principal constituents of the structure.

The absorption of radiant energy from electromagnetic radiation is not restricted to wavelengths in the visible region. Most materials have several regions of anomalous dispersion in which absorption appears, e.g., quartz is opaque to certain infrared wavelengths to which stibnite is perfectly transparent.

For the preceding discussions as well as those in Chapter 2 it was tacitly assumed that atoms were built up of electrons disposed in a configuration which would place the electrons in the lowest possible energy state. Such an electronic configuration constitutes the *ground state* of an atom, but atoms whose electrons are in states of higher energy can and do exist. Additions of energy to the atom from an external source may cause its electrons to go to states of higher energy much as warming a balloon increases the potential energy of the enclosed air. Atoms in which electrons have been raised to higher levels of energy are in an *excited state*. Such electron states are not stable and an excited electron will return to its ground state a short but finite time after excitation, and at this time will re-emit the same amount of energy as was previously absorbed. The effect is as if the balloon had a delayed-action safety valve.

When an atom is under the action of an external electromagnetic field such as light, the various transitions which are allowed act as a series of oscillators with different resonant frequencies. Free atoms have only a discrete set of excited energy levels and can absorb only a discrete set of frequencies. Atoms bonded into various crystalline aggregates have a greater number of resonating frequencies, and in metals a continuum of excited levels exists.

The energy differences between the ground state and possible excited states of an atom are controlled by quantized energy differences according to the relation $E_2 - E_1 = h\nu$ where E_2 and E_1 are the energies of the higher and lower states, respectively, h is Planck's constant, and ν is the frequency. When the energy flow associated with an electromagnetic field provides an energy increment to an atom such that the energy difference between a lower and higher state is exactly matched, such energy is absorbed by the atom, held for a short time, and re-radiated.

In general, the re-radiated light has the same frequency as the absorbed light, but in certain situations the light re-radiated from an atom does not have the same frequency as it had when it was absorbed. Consider the situation shown diagrammatically in Figure 4–5 in which the energy of the ground state of an electron and two possible excited states are represented by horizontal lines. Absorption of energy sufficient to

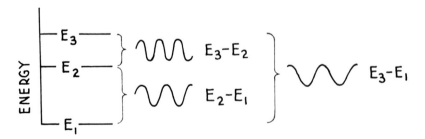

Fig. 4–5. Electron transition and radiation in an excited atom.

raise the energy level of the electron to level E_2 can only be re-radiated in a single frequency, $E_2 - E_1$. Absorption of energy sufficient to reach level E_3 can, however, be re-radiated as a single frequency ($E_3 - E_1$) or as two frequencies ($E_3 - E_2$ and $E_2 - E_1$) by a stepwise return of the electron to its ground state. If the frequencies at which re-radiation occurs are both in the visible region, the quality of the light is not affected. If, however, one or more of the re-radiated frequencies are outside the limits of visible light, then some portion of the visible light is removed, and colors arise by absorption as previously described.

The change of electromagnetic frequencies through the mechanism of electron transitions is not required for an understanding of the general phenomena associated with the interaction of light and matter, but is very useful in understanding certain associated phenomena. Many transitions between electron energy states, especially for outer electrons, cause energy to be radiated as light. Light itself may be the source of energy which starts the process, but is not necessarily so. Certain substances will absorb higher frequencies of radiant energy (shorter wavelengths) than visible light and will re-radiate some portion of that energy in the visible region. Fluorescence of substances irradiated with X rays or ultraviolet light may be laid to this cause. Electrons will radiate energy whenever they go through a transition by which they lose energy. There is no need, however, that the energy which raised the electron to an excited state initially be electromagnetic in nature. Thermal luminescence and flame coloration of substances occur as a result of the input of thermal energy, and chemiluminescence results from chemical energy inputs, as does phosphorescence.

Electrical, Magnetic, and Thermal Properties

The differing electrical and magnetic properties of minerals find limited use in the laboratory determination of species, since these properties are generally difficult to measure, and the values themselves overlap from species to species. Electrical and magnetic properties are, however, widely exploited in the search for ore deposits and in large-scale separation of valuable minerals from waste (gangue) material.

The magnetism of a material is an atomic property which depends upon the summation of the magnetic moments of constituent electrons. Electrons possess magnetic moments because they are spinning and orbiting in an electric field. When the spins of two electrons are opposed the net magnetic moment is zero, but parallel spins are additive. Atoms which have a symmetrical electronic structure and most ionic and covalent compounds in which electrons are paired tend to have small total magnetic moments and are repelled by a strong magnetic field. Such substances are called *diamagnetic*. Atoms or structures in which asymmetry of electron spins exists are attracted to a magnet, and such substances are called *paramagnetic*. If interatomic forces are present which maintain the magnetic moments of many atoms parallel to each other, the magnetic moment of this "domain" is correspondingly large, and the substance exhibits *ferromagnetism*.

The electrical properties of minerals may be separated into conductive, static charge, and thermoelectric phenomena.

The ability of a substance to conduct electricity depends upon the presence within the material of charge carriers which are free to migrate. In perfect crystals such carriers can only be electrons which in turn are free to migrate only in structures with metallic or semimetallic bonds. Electronic conduction through such structures takes place readily whenever a potential gradient is established. Relatively small amounts of charge transference may be accomplished by the migration of ions or holes through an imperfect or defective structure.

Poor conductors may be charged by any of several means and will retain this charge for a period of time. If the mineral does not have some symmetry element relating faces on opposite sides of the crystal (e.g., lacks a center of symmetry, but has a two- or six-fold rotoreflection axis, see Figure 1–10), unlike charges appear on the opposed faces. The presence of these charges may be readily determined by dusting the electrified specimen with a mixture of powdered red lead and sulfur, which are attracted to negatively and positively charged surfaces, respectively. Electrification may be accomplished by friction, by heating or cooling (pyroelectricity), or by pressure (piezoelectricity).

Thermoelectricity is generated when two conductors are placed in intimate contact. The conductors become mutually electrified (one positive and the other negative), and a current flows when the temperature of the junction is changed. A thermocouple is a temperature-sensing device based on this phenomenon.

The thermal properties of minerals are not readily utilized in the identification of minerals but are of the greatest importance in the theoretical aspects of mineralogical reactions. Thermal properties fall naturally into two groups with aspects of the transfer of heat or temperature constituting one group and changes in heat content with mineralogical changes constituting the second.

Heat passes through matter both by conduction resulting from thermal vibration of the constituent atoms and by transmission through interatomic space. The former mechanism is termed *thermal conduction* and the latter *thermal transmissibility*. Thermal conduction through matter differs with both the material and the crystallographic direction. The different conductivity in different directions may be studied by coating a crystal or cleavage face with paraffin and observing the shape of the melted area when the end of a hot wire is placed against the surface. Isometric crystals conduct heat equally well in all directions, i.e., are thermally isotropic. Minerals crystallizing in other systems are thermally anisotropic in exact analogy to optical character.

Thermal transmissibility is analogous to optical diaphaneity. Materials which are transparent to heat waves are termed *diathermanous* while those which are opaque are *athermanous*. This property, like thermal conduction, is symmetry controlled.

Changes in the heat content of substances undergoing chemical or physical reactions are as important to the theoretical understanding of the process as are the products themselves. Different terms have been applied to different kinds of reactions, but all have the common end of measuring the gain or loss of heat in the process. The amount of heat, which is usually expressed in calories (or kilocalories) per gram, is an intrinsic property of a substance. Changes whereby heat is liberated are called *exothermic reactions*, and those whereby heat is taken up are called *endothermic reactions*.

Reactions involving changes of state between gases, liquids, and solids absorb or liberate heat during the change while the temperature of the system remains constant. The term *latent heat* is given to the quantity of heat absorbed in producing a change in state without a rise in temperature. Latent heat is roughly a measure of the thermal energy given up when chemical bonds are formed or absorbed when the bonds are broken. Some particular latent heats of mineralogical interest are:

Heat of formation—the quantity of heat absorbed during the formation of a compound from its elements.

Heat of crystallization—the quantity of heat absorbed when a mineral crystallizes from a melt.

Heat of fusion—the quantity of heat absorbed, at the fusion temperature, to destroy the crystallinity.

Heat of solution—the quantity of heat absorbed when a substance is dissolved.

The sign of the heat absorbed may be either positive or negative, that is, the reactions may be either endothermic or exothermic. All measures of heats of reaction must take cognizance of temperature, pressure, and volume.

The *specific heat* of a substance is its heat capacity at constant pressure and known temperature with respect to that of water at 4°C, which is taken as unity.

The increased thermal agitation of atoms which occurs when minerals are heated causes each atom to effectively occupy a larger volume of space, and *thermal expansion* of the whole crystal follows. This expansion is not uniform in all directions for most structures, but is controlled by the symmetry of the mineral and may be divided into isotropic and anisotropic classes. Thermal expansion is usually expressed as the coefficient of expansion which is taken as the change in volume per unit volume for a temperature change of $1°C$.

Temperature, as distinguished from heat, provides one very useful marker in mineral identification. This is the temperature at which the crystallinity of the structure is destroyed and the mineral decomposes, vaporizes, or fuses. A useful scale of fusibility is given in Table 5–1, page 152.

Crystal Growth and Habit

CRYSTAL GROWTH

Crystals grow by the accretion of appropriate units of matter to a crystal surface, which is an interface between organized crystalline material on one hand and a source of growth units on the other. The growth units themselves may be atoms, ions, free radicals, or molecules, and they may be derived from a solid, liquid, or gaseous nutrient source. Some potential is obviously required to bring growth units to an accreting surface, and some mechanism must be active at the surface to cause the units to be attached in a regular manner. Despite the long study of crystals and crystallization, however, no unanimity exists as to the exact nature of either process. The details of the growth mechanism have, for example, been variously ascribed to functions of interface energy and face area, coordination of an accreting unit, degree of satisfaction of surface bonds, and interplanar spacing within the crystal. The present knowledge in this field makes it preferable not to attempt any detailed description of the growth mechanism. All in all, the mechanism of crystal growth and its logical extension to the interpretation of the endform (habit) constitutes one of the most provocative areas in mineralogical studies.

One of the principal phenomena to be explained by any mechanism of crystal growth is the development of plane, parallel faces having simple rational indices. The mechanism of secondary nucleation assumes these results to be the tendency of growth units to seek positions where the greatest energy drop will be produced by their presence. Such a position is the site at which the unit receives maximum coordination on a partially formed layer, Figure 4–6. If no partially formed layers are present, the face on which the largest unit cell area is exposed is favored, Figure 4–7.

Another crystal growth mechanism is ascribed to the presence of a spiral dislocation in the seed crystal. Local stress in crystalline structures

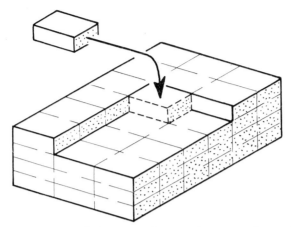

Fig. 4–6. Crystal growth by secondary nucleation with partially formed layers present.

due either to mechanical deformation or to the presence of impurity atoms may result in the dislocation of adjacent atoms. For example, differential compression of a crystal may dislocate atoms across a glide plane, as shown in Figure 4–8, where the same number of atoms are present over the distances d and d', and some discontinuity of the structure must exist across the glide plane g. Such an edge dislocation in a growing crystal could provide a locus for growth by secondary nucleation.

Dislocations may also develop with a rotary component as shown in Figure 4–9. Such dislocations then become the locus for accretion of growth units, and continuous spiral sheets form as indicated by the arrow on the figure. Several differently oriented spiral dislocations may

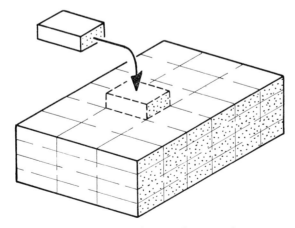

Fig. 4–7. Crystal growth by secondary nucleation when no partially formed layers are present.

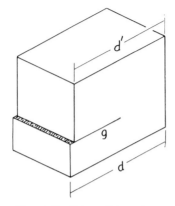 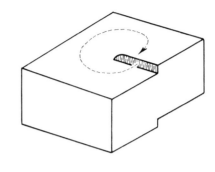

Fig. 4–8. Edge dislocation.   Fig. 4–9. Spiral dislocation.

be simultaneously present in a structure, and each may provide a step against which growth units find maximum coordination. Figure 4–10 shows three mutually perpendicular spiral dislocations on a cube.

Certain observable features of crystal growth always arise regardless of the actual mechanism of crystal growth. So long as there is a contrast in composition across the interface and the face may develop without interference, *the face will be planar.* Rounded crystal faces grow only when minerals crystallize or recrystallize in environments compositionally similar to themselves. Some rounded crystal faces are only apparent in that they are made up of minute planar elements. The direction of crystal growth is normal to the accreting surface, i.e., *new faces parallel the old.* This may sometimes be directly observed because the entrapment of impurities on early faces produces phantom crystals within a specimen.

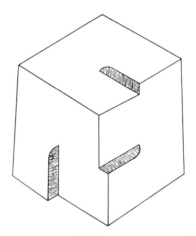

Fig. 4–10. Spiral dislocations on a cube.

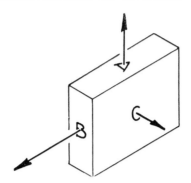

Fig. 4–11. Loss of rapidly growing face.

Rapidly accreting faces tend to disappear. In Figure 4–11 it may be readily seen that if the various faces grow at the rates indicated by the arrows the slowly accreting face (*C*) will soon predominate and faces *A* and *B* will become relatively less prominent. Appropriately oriented faces may be eliminated by rapid growth, whereas slow accretion may cause faces to appear. Figure 4–12 illustrates these phenomena. The successive faces are drawn for equal elapsed times. In Figure 4–12a the face 2–3 is accreting much more rapidly than either face 1–2 or face 3–4, and eventually this face is lost at 0. In Figure 4–12b a possible face, 2–3, begins to show at 0 when its growth rate falls below that of the adjacent faces, 1–2 and 3–4.

The actual number of faces displayed by a crystal may be sharply limited by the interrelationship of the growth rates of adjacent faces.

Not uncommonly it occurs that an accreting surface oscillates between the orientations of two adjacent faces or of itself and an adjacent face. The result is that such a face incorporates minute repetitions of the intersections of the adjacent faces into its own surface. Such a face ap-

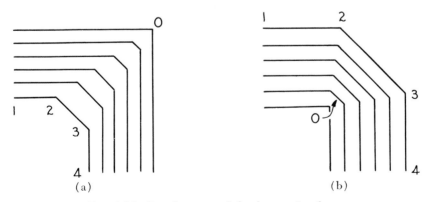

Fig. 4–12. Development of slowly growing face.

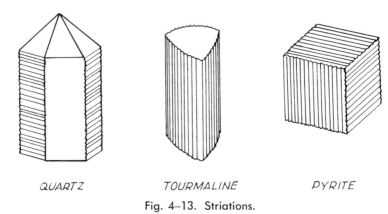

QUARTZ   TOURMALINE   PYRITE

Fig. 4–13. Striations.

pears to have been ruled or scratched in grooves or *striations* which are always parallel to a crystal edge. Some examples of striated crystals are shown in Figure 4–13.

CRYSTAL HABIT

The external form of a mineral results from the interaction of its internal structure with the environment in which the mineral forms. The direct and essentially unmodified effect of a mineral's internal structure may often be observed in the external form or habit. A small sampling of mineral habits which persist in the face of wide variations in the environment of growth is given in Table 4–8.

TABLE 4–8

Relation of Structure to Habit

Structural type	Habit	Example
Sheets of linked Si-O tetrahedra	Platy	Micas
Mo-S sheets	Platy	Molybdenite
Sb-S chains	Bladed	Stibnite
Si-O tetrahedral chains	Rodlike	Tremolite
Si-O tetrahedral network	Blocky	Orthoclase
Si-O isolated tetrahedral units	Equidimensional	Garnet

Structure also impresses characteristic planes of weakness upon the mineral, and the ready breaking or cleavage on these planes generates fragments with characteristic shapes, e.g., cubes of galena or halite, oblongs of feldspar, rhombs of calcite, and sheets of mica.

The effect of the environment in which a crystal grows on the habit of the mineral is very incompletely understood. Temperature and its rate of change, pressure (both uniform and directed), and the composition and nature of the nutrient material are all effective in habit modification. Pressure may vary from surface values of one atmosphere to pressures of many thousands of atmospheres deep within the earth's crust. Temperature ranges from 0°C to about 1000°C in the usual geological environments. Impurities are known to modify seriously the habit of a crystal and are often necessary for the development of a given habit or even for the crystal to attain its highest perfection.

Obviously, each environment impresses its own characteristics on the growing crystal; reciprocally, each mineral specimen, when fully interpreted, should provide a key for unlocking the history of the mineral. The difficulty of such interpretations lies in the incompleteness of our present knowledge.

A large number of adjectives are in common use to describe the appearance of an individual mineral or of a crystalline aggregate. A habitually assumed form or habit is, of course, not a constant mineral attribute, but is so often associated with particular mineral species that it is one of the most powerful means of mineral identification. Most practicing mineralogists tend to make tentative identifications based on habit and color, two inconstant mineral properties!

A glossary of the terms used in describing habit together with some sketches of these habits are given below.

Terms Used To Describe Single Crystals

Capillary, filiform, acicular—hairlike, threadlike, or needlelike crystals.

Bladed—crystals in elongate, flattened blades.

Tabular, lamellar—booklike in shape.

Stout or stubby—usually applied to pyramidally terminated crystals whose c axis is short compared with its other axes.

Blocky—brick-shaped.

Columnar—columnlike crystals.

TERMS USED TO DESCRIBE SINGLE CRYSTALS

Foliated, micaceous—easily separated into sheets or leaves, micalike.

Plumose—featherlike arrangement of fine scales.

Geometrical terms—various geometrical terms are used as applicable, e.g., cubic, tetrahedral, octahedral, prismatic, dodecahedral, scalenohedral, etc.

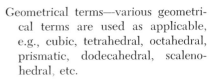

TERMS USED TO DESCRIBE CRYSTAL GROUPS
AND MINERAL AGGREGATES

Columnar—an aggregate of column-like individuals.

Bladed—an aggregate of bladed individuals.

Fibrous—an aggregate of capillary or filiform individuals.

Divergent, radiated, stellated—individuals arranged in fan-shaped groups or rosettes.

Colloform (botryoidal, reniform, mammillary, globular)—radiating individuals forming spherical or hemispherical groups. The various terms have been used to designate the extent and radius of the hemispherical surfaces developed. Colloform includes all other terms.

Reticulated—slender crystals arranged in a latticelike array.

Terms Used To Describe Crystal Groups and Mineral Aggregates

Dendritic—treelike or mosslike form.

Granular—an aggregate of mineral grains.

Massive—a compact aggregate without distinctive form.

Pisolitic, oölitic—composed of rounded masses respectively the size of peas or BB shot.

Banded—bands or layers of different color and/or texture.

Concentric—onion-like banding.

References

Dekeyser, W., and S. Amelinckx. 1955. Les Dislocations et la Croissance des Cristaux. Mason et Cie, Paris. The various mechanisms of crystal growth are reviewed.

Fairbairn, H. W. 1943. Packing in ionic minerals. *Bulletin Geological Society of America* 54: 1305-1374. Packing index (defined as volume of ions/volume of unit cell × 10) is correlated with hardness, specific gravity, density, and some mineralogical phenomena.

Hurlbut, C. S. 1952. *Dana's Manual of Mineralogy.* 16th ed. John Wiley & Sons, Inc., New York. Descriptions of the more useful physical properties of minerals are given in Chap. 2.

Kraus, E. H., W. F. Hunt, and L. S. Ramsdell. 1951. Mineralogy. 4th ed. McGraw-Hill Book Co., Inc., New York. Physical properties of minerals are described in Chap. 10.

5

CHEMICAL TESTING

Introduction

The physical appearance and properties of a mineral will usually relegate a specimen to a somewhat restricted group of similar minerals. Further careful examination of the specimen may then disclose a distinctive combination of physical properties which will allow the mineral to be uniquely classified. Another group of mineral properties which may be used for final classification or for confirmation are those concerned with the chemical properties of minerals. Chemical tests are especially useful in confirming an identification made by physical tests.

A number of chemical tests, which may be performed with a minimum of laboratory equipment, are described and tabulated in this chapter. These tests are simple, direct, qualitative operations for the detection of the various elements which compose minerals, but not directly for the mineral itself.

Dissolving a mineral in order to obtain a solution in which wet chemical reactions may be performed is not essential to chemical studies. Many chemical reactions occur through simple heating either of the mineral per se or in the presence of appropriate dry reagents. An extensive group of such tests may be performed, using a blowpipe as a source of heat.

The Blowpipe

The mineralogical blowpipe is a simple instrument for the production of intense local heating. The fuel source for the blowpipe is any hydrocarbon-rich flame such as that of a candle or a Bunsen burner with the air intake closed. Oxygen from the lungs is introduced into the flame through the blowpipe and a narrow, hot jet is produced, Figure 5–1. With practice, a steady supply of air may be kept available in the cheeks while breathing is continued through the nose. Too strong an air stream through the blowpipe will cause the jet to flutter and should be avoided. Care should be taken to keep the fingers out of the line of the jet as it is very hot.

The blowpipe is generally not used for *determinative testing* because the information obtained per test tends to be small whereas the number

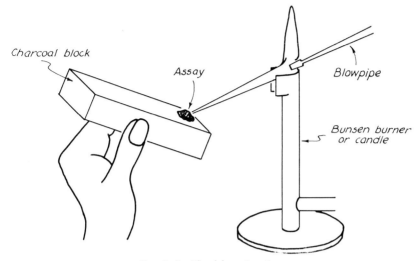

Fig. 5–1. The blowpipe jet.

of different tests is large. Identification of an unknown by the application of a series of blowpipe tests is hence a time-consuming, hit-or-miss procedure. The principal exception is the test series which use a charcoal block, described in a later section, when applied to sulfide minerals. On the other hand, the blowpipe may be used with great advantage for *confirmatory testing* because, if the presence of a given element is already suspected, a properly chosen blowpipe test may provide a clear-cut "yes" or "no" answer.

FUSION

The intense heat at the tip of a blowpipe jet is sufficient to cause fusion, transformation, or sublimation of many minerals. The absolute value of this temperature varies with the individual and his equipment, but is usually between 1200 and 1500°C. It is suggested that the student calibrate his blowpipe using the data in Table 5–1. This should be done by attempting to turn a sharp edge or point of a mineral fragment by a few minutes' application of the blowpipe jet. A mineral glass will be useful in examining the fragment before and after heating. A good estimate of relative fusibility can be obtained with very little practice, and this is a very useful property.

The manner in which a mineral fuses may also be distinctive and should be noted whenever minerals are fused. Characteristic manners of fusion are:

Simple melting—the assay fragment changes passively from a solid to a liquid. Example, stibnite.

Intumescence—the assay swells and bubbles because gases (steam, CO_2, etc.) are being liberated from the molten assay. Example, lepidolite.

Exfoliation—the assay protrudes small branches. Example, stilbite.

Decrepitation—the assay snaps or explodes due to the rapid evolution of gases such as steam, CO_2, SO_2, etc. Decrepitation of samples must be overcome before further blowpipe testing may be done. One of the following may serve: 1. Heat very slowly and uniformly in an oven or with a burner flame. 2. Heat in a tube until decrepitation ceases. 3. Grind fine and mix with water to a thin paste.

TABLE 5-1

Melting Points

Fusibility Number	Mineral	Degrees Centigrade	Metal
		3370	Tungsten
	Zircon	2500	
	Corundum	2050	
		1774	Platinum
7	Cristobalite	1710	
	Barite	1580	
	Anorthite	1551	
		1535	Iron
	WHITE HEAT		
6	Bronzite	1400	
	Fluorite	1360	
	Rhodonite	1323	
5	Orthoclase	1300	
	INCIPIENT WHITE HEAT		
	Cuprite	1235	
4	Actinolite	1200	
	Molybdenite	1185	
	Pyrite	1171	
	Covellite	1130	
	Chalcocite	1100	
	Albite	1100	
	YELLOWISH-RED HEAT		
		1083	Copper
		1063	Gold
3	Almandite	1050	
	Cryolite	1000	
	Niccolite	968	
		961	Silver
	BRIGHT RED HEAT		
	Argentite	835	
	Halite	801	
2	Chalcopyrite	800	

TABLE 5-1 (Continued)

Melting Points

Fusibility Number	Mineral	Degrees Centigrade	Metal
	DARK RED HEAT		
		660	Aluminum
		630	Antimony
1	Stibnite	550	
	DULL RED HEAT		
		419	Zinc
		327	Lead
	Realgar	307	
	Orpiment	300	
		271	Bismuth
	Carnallite	265	
		232	Tin
	Sulfur	120	
	Ice	0	

OXIDATION AND REDUCTION

The blue flame produced by the blowpipe represents an envelope on which intense burning (oxidation) is taking place. Mineral fragments held in this blue portion of the flame lose oxygen to this active burning and are themselves reduced. This blue portion of the flame, in consequence, is termed the *reducing flame*. The temperature of the air surrounding the reducing flame and for a considerable distance beyond it is greatly increased over normal, but no burning takes place. If a mineral fragment is placed in this invisible heat envelope, the increased temperature makes reactions with oxygen easier and oxidation of the sample often occurs. This invisible heat cone is called the *oxidizing flame*.

The most practical direct use of the oxidation-reduction capacity of the blowpipe flame is in the determination of iron, cobalt, and nickel. Other uses will be described in a later section, on bead tests.

Iron, with two valence states separated by only a moderate energy difference, is a very common constituent in minerals. The blowpipe is easily capable of transforming iron from the reduced (ferrous) form to the oxidized (ferric) form and vice versa. Since ferrous iron is magnetic and ferric iron is not, direct and simple testing for iron in a mineral may be accomplished with a blowpipe and a magnet. As an exercise, the student may reduce and oxidize hematite and distinguish between biotite (Mg, Fe mica) and phlogopite (Mg mica). A similar series of operations reduces nickel and cobalt compounds to a magnetic form. All samples should be allowed to cool before testing with a magnet.

USE OF CHARCOAL

The heating of mineral fragments on a charcoal block may provide a number of clues as to the elements present. Ease of fusion, formation of a globule or a sublimate, physical changes on heating, etc., may be simultaneously observed. The usual dimensions of the block are $\frac{1}{2} \times 1 \times 4$ inches. The blocks may be reused after scraping with a knife, but care should be taken that volatile products of a previous test have not saturated the charcoal. Tests are performed with the apparatus arranged as in Figure 5–2. Special care must be taken to have the blowpipe jet aligned with the charcoal block.

Fig. 5–2. Arrangement of equipment for blowpipe work.

The sequence of operations to be followed, and the observations to be made for a charcoal block test are outlined below and supported by Tables 5–2 and 5–3.

Operation	Observation
Place mineral fragment or powder near end of charcoal block	—
Heat fragment with reducing flame	1. Fusion—ease and manner 2. Gases—development, color(s), odor(s) 3. Sublimates—development, color both hot and cold, density, distance from fragment under assay, volatile or involatile
Continue heating until evolution of gases and/or sublimates ceases	Appearance of the fragment—consumed, globular, slaggy
Test remaining material when cool	Magnetism Globule—color and malleability Chemical reactivity

The particular elements characterized by these observation are detailed in the following tables.

The various sublimates which may be formed and observed by heating a mineral fragment (assay) on a charcoal block are tabulated in Table 5–2. The fluxes which may be mixed with mineral powders to produce distinctively colored sublimates are:

Iodide flux—grind together one part by weight of KI, one part of $KHSO_4$, and two parts of sulfur.
Bromide flux—substitute KBr for the KI of iodide flux.
Chromate flux—substitute K_2CrO_4 for the KI of iodide flux.

These fluxes are to be added in the proportions of three parts of flux to one part of ground mineral. Only those fluxes which produce distinctive sublimates are shown in Table 5–2.

Sublimates will often appear bluish on their thin edges because the black charcoal background shows through the coating. The volatility of the material originally driven off from the assay is indicated by the distance of the coating from the assay. The volatility of the sublimated material may be tested by touching the blowpipe flame to the coating. Care should be exercised not to confuse white charcoal ash with a sublimate.

In certain instances it may be preferable to observe the colors of sublimates against a white rather than a black background. For such observations it is common to cast small blocks from plaster of Paris and proceed in the same manner as with charcoal. Charcoal is generally preferred for blowpipe work, however, because it provides a strongly reducing environment which is very useful for other kinds of blowpipe testing.

Strong heating of a mineral fragment on charcoal removes those constituents which may be volatilized, and progressively refines the assay. Complete consumption of the assay implies that the mineral is composed entirely of volatile constituents, a slaggy product indicates infusible constituents, and a metallic globule results when a low melting point metal is present. The presence of iron, nickel, or cobalt may be ascertained because they are attracted by a magnet. The metallic globules which may form are given in Table 5–3.

BEAD TESTS

Certain elements, including some which are very difficult to determine by any other method, impart strong and distinctive colors to various fluxes. The colors are usually observed in a bead of flux held in a loop of platinum wire. An appropriate loop, about $\frac{1}{8}$ inch in diameter, may be formed by winding the wire around a pencil tip. Care must be taken to

TABLE 5–2

Sublimates on Charcoal

Element	Flux	Description	Characteristic Colors
Antimony, Sb	None	Dense white coating of Sb_2O_4 and Sb_2O_3 forms near the assay. Coat is less volatile than that of arsenic. No odor.	Dense white
Arsenic, As	None	Very volatile coating of As_2O_3. Sometimes tinted brown or yellow by sulfur. Often accompanied by garlic odor of arsine, AsH_3	Thin white
	Iodide	Thin white volatile coating with yellow inner border.	White and yellow
Bismuth, Bi	None	Coating of Bi_2O_3 forms near the assay. The color is orange-yellow when hot and lemon-yellow when cold. May have greenish-white outer border. Coating is volatile.	Yellow
	Iodide	Chocolate-brown coating with underlying scarlet which forms an outer border. Scarlet changed to yellow by NH_4OH fumes.	Brown and scarlet
Cadmium, Cd	None	Black to reddish-brown coating near assay with a yellow-green border. Coating is volatile. Often shows peacock colors.	Brown and yellow
	Chromate	Coating is reddish while hot and yellow when cold.	Red to yellow
Copper, Cu	None	No sublimate.	
Lead, Pb	None	Intense yellow coating of PbO near the assay which changes to light yellow or white on cooling. Volatile in the reducing flame. (A flux is required for lead phosphates.)	Yellow
	Iodide	Greenish-yellow coating with brown inner border.	Yellow
Mercury, Hg	None	Most mercury compounds yield a faint grayish coating of minute mercury globules.	Gray

TABLE 5–2 (Continued)

Sublimates on Charcoal

Element	Flux	Description	Characteristic Colors
Molybdenum, Mo ..	None	Copper-red coating of MoO_2 deposited under and around the assay and pale yellow MoO_3 farther away. The yellow fades to white on cooling. The reducing flame makes MoO_3 turn azure-blue and volatilize.	Red and yellow
	Bromide	A white coating near the assay is deposited after a yellowish-green coat at a distance.	Green and white
Selenium, Se	None	A volatile gray to white coating near the assay with a reddish outer border of metallic Se. Red fumes are given off which have a decayed horseradish odor.	Red and white
Silver, Ag	None	Faint reddish-brown coating of silver oxide formed after long heating with the oxidizing flame.	Brown
Sulfur, S	None	A thin coating of native sulfur, yellow when hot and white when cold, is formed. Accompanied by the pungent and irritating odor of SO_2.	Yellow to white
Tellurium, Te	None	Dense white volatile coating of TeO_2 near assay grading outwards into brownish-black metallic Te.	White and Brown
Tin, Sn	None	Faint yellow luminous coating of SnO_2 near assay fading to white on cooling. Coating becomes bluish-green if moistened with $Co(NO_3)_2$ solution and heated strongly. Coating is not volatile in the oxidizing flame.	Yellow to white
Zinc, Zn	None	A canary-yellow coating of ZnO is formed near the assay. The coating fades to white on cooling. Coating becomes grass green when moistened with $Co(NO_3)_2$ solution and then heated strongly. Coating is not volatile in the oxidizing flame.	Yellow to white

TABLE 5–3

Metallic Globules Formed by Heating on Charcoal

Metal	Description
Bismuth, Bi	Black brittle globule.
Copper, Cu	Reddish malleable globule. Surface blackens on cooling. Copper minerals should first be roasted to eliminate S, As, and Sb and then heated with a reducing mixture.*
Gold, Au	Soft, yellow, malleable globule. Remains bright on cooling and does not tarnish.
Lead, Pb	Soft, gray, malleable globule.
Silver, Ag	Soft, white, malleable globule. Remains bright on cooling. Usually necessary to use reducing mixture.
Tin, Sn	Soft, white, malleable globule. Becomes dull on cooling with white coating of oxide film. Globules formed with difficulty even with reducing mixture.

* Reducing mixture—equal parts of sodium carbonate and charcoal. Mix two parts to one part of powdered mineral.

have the loop just closed without crossing. The wire should be inserted in a handle of wood or glass tubing for convenience in handling.

The same element may generate distinctively different colors with different fluxes, depending on the temperature of the bead and whether the heating is accomplished in an oxidizing or reducing flame.

To perform a test, heat the loop strongly to remove any contamination and while still hot plunge the loop into the selected flux. Some of the powdered flux will stick to the loop and may then be melted into a bead. Repeat this operation until the loop is filled with flux. Continue heating until all gases have evolved and the bead is clear. Touch the hot bead to a very small amount of the ground mineral under study and heat the bead strongly in the appropriate flame. Observe the bead against a white background while still hot (but not red hot) and when cooled. If no coloration is observed, pick up more of the test powder, but be careful not to overload the bead with test powder. Any minerals which contain S, As, Sb, or Se must be roasted before incorporation into the bead in order to obtain true colors and also because these elements will cause the platinum wire to break. Tables 5–4 and 5–5 provide test details.

The materials which are used as fluxes in making bead tests are:

Borax (sodium tetraborate, borax glass), $Na_2B_4O_7 \cdot 10H_2O$
Salt of phosphorus (microcosmic salt), $HNaNH_4PO_4 \cdot 4H_2O$
Sodium carbonate, Na_2CO_3
Sodium thiosulfate, $Na_2S_2O_3 \cdot 5H_2O$

TABLE 5–4

Bead Tests

Element	Oxidizing Flame		Reducing Flame	
	Color Hot	Color Cold	Color Hot	Color Cold

BORAX BEAD TESTS				
Antimony, Sb	Pale yellow	Colorless	Pale yellow	Colorless
Bismuth, Bi	Pale yellow	Colorless	Gray	Gray
Cadmium, Cd	Pale yellow	Colorless	Pale yellow	Colorless
Chromium, Cr	Yellow	Green	Green	Green
Cobalt, Co	Blue	Blue	Blue	Blue
Copper, Cu	Green	Blue-green	Colorless to green	Opaque red with much oxide
Iron, Fe	Yellow to orange	Greenish to yellow brown	Bottle green	Pale bottle green
Lead, Pb	Pale yellow	Colorless	Pale yellow	Colorless
Manganese, Mn	Violet	Reddish-violet	Colorless	Colorless
Molybdenum, Mo	Pale yellow	Colorless	Brown	Brown to black
Nickel, Ni	Violet	Reddish-brown	Opaque gray	Opaque gray
Titanium, Ti	Pale yellow	Colorless	Grayish or yellowish	Brownish or brownish-violet
Tungsten, W .... (Wolfram)	Pale yellow	Colorless	Yellow	Yellow to yellow-brown
Uranium, U	Yellow to orange-red	Yellow to brown	Pale green	Pale green to colorless
Vanadium, V	Yellow	Yellow-green	Brownish to dirty green	Yellow to green
SALT OF PHOSPHORUS BEAD TESTS				
Antimony, Sb	Pale yellow	Colorless	Gray	Gray
Bismuth, Bi	Pale yellow	Colorless	Gray	Gray
Cadmium, Cd	Pale yellow	Colorless	Pale yellow	Colorless
Chromium, Cr	Reddish to dirty green	Yellowish-green to green	Red to dirty green	Green (brown to red if incompletely reduced)
Cobalt, Co	Blue	Blue	Blue	Blue
Columbium, Cb ..... (Niobium)	Pale yellow	Colorless	Brown	Red-brown
Copper, Cu	Dark green	Greenish-blue	Brownish-green	Opaque red
Iron, Fe	Yellow to brownish-red	Brownish-yellow to colorless	Reddish-yellow to greenish-yellow	Pale violet to colorless
Lead, Pb	Pale yellow	Colorless	Gray	Gray
Manganese, Mn	Grayish-violet	Violet	Colorless	Colorless

TABLE 5–4 (Continued)

Bead Tests

Element	Oxidizing Flame		Reducing Flame	
	Color Hot	Color Cold	Color Hot	Color Cold
SALT OF PHOSPHORUS BEAD TESTS				
Molybdenum, Mo	Yellowish-green	Colorless	Dirty green	Green
Nickel, Ni	Reddish to brownish-red	Yellow to brownish	Reddish to brownish-red	Yellow to brownish
Silica, Si	–	Insoluble skeleton	–	Insoluble skeleton
Tantalum, Ta	Pale yellow	Colorless	Pale yellow	Colorless
Titanium, Ti	Pale yellow	Colorless	Pale yellow	Violet
Tungsten, W .... (Wolfram)	Pale yellow	Colorless	Greenish to dirty blue	Greenish-blue to blue
Uranium, U	Yellow	Pale green to colorless	Pale dirty green	Green
Vanadium, V	Yellow	Greenish-yellow	Brown to dirty green	Green
SODIUM CARBONATE BEAD TESTS				
Chromium, Cr	–	Opaque yellow	–	–
Manganese, Mn ..... (addition of KNO₃ may be necessary)	–	Opaque bluish-green	–	–
Silica, Si	–	Insoluble skeleton	–	–

Sodium Thiosulfate Bead Tests. Borax beads are made in the usual manner. The hot bead is then touched to sodium thiosulfate and reheated in the reducing flame. Easily volatile metals such as mercury and arsenic may be lost, and care must be exercised when they are under study.

FLAME TESTS

An input of thermal energy to atoms or ions may raise their electrons to excited levels (see p. 138). For many atoms this amount of thermal energy is available in an ordinary Bunsen flame and the wavelength of their emitted radiation is in the visible portion of the spectrum. As a consequence, the introduction of such elements to a flame imparts a color characteristic of the element to the flame.

Flame colorations may be observed if a platinum wire, cleaned by heating, is dipped into a solution of the sample and then held in the flame. Specimens to be tested in this manner should be powdered,

TABLE 5-5

Sodium Thiosulfate Bead Tests

Element	Color of Bead with $Na_2S_2O_3 \cdot 5H_2O$
Antimony, Sb	Orange
Arsenic, As	Yellow
Bismuth, Bi	Black
Cadmium, Cd	Yellow to orange
Chromium, Cr	Green
Cobalt, Co	Black
Copper, Cu	Black
Iron, Fe	Black
Lead, Pb	Black
Manganese, Mn	Light green
Mercury, Hg	Black
Molybdenum, Mo	Brown
Nickel, Ni	Black
Tin, Sn	Brown
Uranium, U	Black
Zinc, Zn	White

placed on a watch glass, and moistened with concentrated hydrochloric acid. The solution may then be used to moisten the platinum wire.

Another technique, which does not require dissolving the sample, is to introduce the powdered mineral into the air hole at the base of a Bunsen burner. This procedure is readily followed whenever samples are being ground in a mineralogy mortar. A few quick plunges of the pestle into a mortar containing finely powdered sample yields a fine air-borne dust which is readily entrained into the burner intake.

Flame colors may be produced quite unintentionally while performing other blowpipe operations. The student should always be alert for such flame colorations since they are very useful in correct identification. The flame colors which are characteristic of certain elements are given in Table 5-6.

OPEN- AND CLOSED-TUBE TESTS

Heating of a substance often results in the separation of volatile constituents which may occasionally be detected by their later sublimation or by their odor. Identification of the volatile material is often uncertain, but a considerable amount of control over the process of volatilization and positive identification of the volatile product may be obtained by heating the substance in a piece of glass tubing.

Two kinds of tubes are used. The "open tube" is simply a 4 to 6 inch piece of hard (Pyrex) glass tubing having a 5 to 7 mm diameter. A

TABLE 5–6

Flame Coloration

Element	Flame Color	Remarks
Antimony, Sb	Pale green	Usually observed when heated on charcoal. Color plays about assay.
Arsenic, As	Livid blue	Garlic odor.
Barium, Ba	Yellow green	Readily obtained.
Bismuth, Bi	Pale greenish-white	–
Boron, B	Yellow green	–
Calcium, Ca	Orange red	Readily obtained.
Copper, Cu	Emerald green	If the mineral is moistened with HCl, the flame will be azure blue. Readily obtained.
Lead, Pb	Pale "skim milk" blue	Usually observed on charcoal block.
Lithium, Li	Crimson	–
Molybdenum, Mo	Faint yellow green	–
Phosphorus, P	Pale bluish-green	Better results with H_2SO_4 than HCl
Potassium, K	Pale violet	Purplish-red when observed through cobalt glass. May be necessary to decompose mineral with a flux of gypsum to obtain a flame color.
Selenium, Se	Indigo blue	Horseradish odor.
Sodium, Na	Intense yellow	Readily obtained. Often obscures less sensitive elements.
Strontium, Sr	Crimson	Readily obtained. Residue is alkaline which differentiates from lithium.
Tellurium, Te	Grass green	–
Zinc, Zn	Bluish-green	Usually appears as bright streaks in the flame.

ground sample may be placed in such a tube by use of a paper spoon, as shown in Figure 5–3, or the tube may be bent to an angle, Figure 5–4, and the material slid in.

Testing is done by holding the tube over a Bunsen flame, as shown in Figure 5–5. Samples so heated are subjected to strong oxidizing reactions because the chimney effect of the tube continuously supplies air to the heated area. Volatile products move up the tube and are condensed in rings in the upper portion of the tube positioned with respect to their relative volatility. The color and position of the rings are indicative of the elements which form them and are tabulated in Table 5–7.

"Closed-tube" tests are performed in a similar manner, except that the tube is closed at one end. Closed tubes may be readily made by drawing

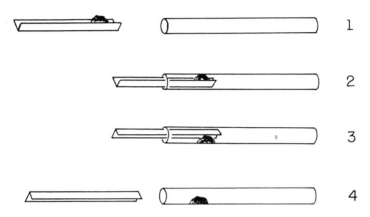

Fig. 5–3. Loading an open tube.

TABLE 5–7

Open Tube Reactions

Element	Result of Heating
Antimony, Sb	Dense white fumes condensing to a powder which is faint yellow when hot and white when cold.
Arsenic, As	White crystalline sublimate (observe with lens). Incomplete oxidation results in an arsenic mirror (see closed-tube test). Garlic odor.
Bismuth, Bi	Sublimate is brown while hot and yellow when cold. Bismuth sulfides yield a white sublimate which is fusible to yellow drops.
Lead, Pb	White sublimate which fuses to drops which are yellow while hot and white when cool.
Mercury, Hg	Minute metallic globules formed (observe with lens). Rapidly heated sulfides yield a brilliant black deposit.
Molybdenum, Mo	Deposits a delicate network of crystals, yellow while hot and white when cool.
Selenium, Se	Steel gray coating of radiating crystals. A reddish deposit of metallic selenium may form. Horseradish odor.
Sulfur, S	Rapid heating may deposit native sulfur which is yellow while hot and white when cool. Continued heating removes it. SO_2 odor.
Water, H_2O	Water droplets may condense on the upper portion of the tube. Adsorbed as well as formulary water may, of course, provide the source.

soft glass tubing and sealing off the drawn end. The arrangement of apparatus for making a test is shown in Figure 5–6.

The closed tube provides for heating under reducing (oxygen-poor) conditions. The sublimates which form are tabulated in Table 5–8.

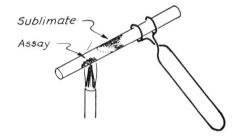

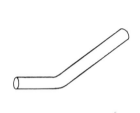

Fig. 5–4. An open tube.   Fig. 5–5. Use of an open tube.

Closed tubes are the same size as open tubes. Two at a time may be conveniently made by drawing out an 8-inch piece of soft glass tubing and sealing the necked ends. Ordinary test tubes may be used, but a closed tube test usually makes them unusable for other purposes.

TABLE 5–8

Closed-Tube Reactions

Element	Result of Heating
Antimony, Sb	Reddish-brown coating near assay.
Arsenic, As	Two rings: the lower is an "arsenic mirror" of silver gray crystalline arsenic; the upper is brilliant black arsenic sulfide.
Mercury, Hg	Minute droplets of metallic mercury (best developed when a $Na_2(CO_3)$ flux is used) accompanied by a black amorphous sublimate.
Selenium, Se	Fusible black globules which become red when rubbed.
Sulfur, S	Dark orange red liquid turning yellow to white on cooling.
Water, H_2O	Water droplets in upper portion of tube.

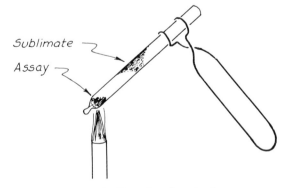

Fig. 5–6. Use of a closed tube.

WET CHEMICAL REACTIONS

The solution, precipitation, formation of complexes, gelatinization, etc., which may occur when minerals are treated with various chemical reagents properly lies in the field of analytical chemistry and will not be treated in detail here. However, some determinative reactions for the common elements and radicals found in minerals are described briefly in the following section. These chemical tests may be readily combined with the foregoing blowpipe reactions for further study of the various solutions and precipitates. A summary chart (Table 5–9) of the various tests for the elements is given at the end of this chapter.

Most of the chemical tests described on the following pages require that the mineral be dissolved prior to testing. Solution of some minerals is relatively easy, but others will require rather extensive pretreatment before they can be dissolved. The sequence to follow for getting minerals into solution is:

1. Test solubility in water.
2. Test solubility in nitric acid or in hydrochloric acid. Warm as necessary.
3. Test solubility in aqua regia. Heat gently. Use porcelain, silica, or vicor chemical ware. If soluble, evaporate to dryness, add concentrated nitric acid to residue, and evaporate again. Dissolve residue in water and filter.
4. Mix powdered sample with three volumes of sodium carbonate and fuse on charcoal. Cool fusion and dissolve it in a small amount of dilute nitric acid. Evaporate to dryness, add concentrated nitric acid, evaporate to dryness again, dissolve in water, and filter.
5. Substances not dissolved by one of the above treatments should be mixed with three volumes of potassium bisulfate and fused in a porcelain crucible. Cool the fusion, add a few drops of concentrated sulfuric acid, and remelt. Cool again, dissolve in cold water, and filter.

The various general and special reagents for chemical test work are listed below, with instructions for their mixing as required. All reagents are understood to be used in a diluted form unless concentrated reagents are specified.

Reagent List

Acetic acid CH_3COOH	Mix one volume of concentrated acid with nine volumes of water.
Ammonium hydroxide NH_4OH	Mix one volume of concentrated base with two volumes of water.
Ammonium molybdate $(NH_4)_2MoO_4$	Mix 10 grams of MoO_3 with 40 ml ° of water and 8 ml of concentrated NH_4OH. When dissolved, pour with constant stirring into a mixture of 40 ml of concentrated nitric acid and 60 ml of water. Let stand for several days. Decant or filter before using.

° ml, milliliter

Reagent List (Continued)

Ammonium oxalate (NH_4)$_2C_2O_4 \cdot H_2O$	Dissolve 4 grams of ammonium oxalate in water and dilute to 100 ml.
Ammonium thiocyanate (ammonium sulfocyanate) NH_4SCN	Dissolve 8 grams of the salt in 100 ml of water.
Aqua regia	Mix three volumes of concentrated HCl with one volume of concentrated HNO_3.
Barium chloride $BaCl_2 \cdot 2H_2O$	Dissolve 6 grams in 100 ml of water.
Barium hydroxide $Ba(OH)_2 \cdot 8H_2O$	Dissolve 6 grams in 100 ml of water.
Chloroplatinic acid $H_2PtCl_6 \cdot 6H_2O$	Dissolve 26.5 grams of chloroplatinic acid in water and dilute to 100 ml.
Cobalt nitrate $Co(NO_3)_2 \cdot 6H_2O$	Dissolve 7 grams in 100 ml of water.
Dibasic ammonium phosphate $Na_2HPO_4 \cdot 12H_2O$	Dissolve 6 grams of the salt in 100 ml of water.
Dimethylglyoxime $CH_3C(NOH)C(NOH)CH_3$	Dissolve 6 grams in 500 ml of 95 per cent ethyl alcohol.
Hydrochloric acid HCl	Mix two volumes of concentrated acid with three volumes of water.
Hydrogen peroxide H_2O_2	Use 3 per cent solution.
Lead acetate $Pb(C_2H_3O_2)_2 \cdot 3H_2O$	Dissolve 19 grams of lead acetate in water and dilute to 100 ml.
Methyl alcohol CH_3OH	
Nitric acid HNO_3	Mix one volume of concentrated acid with two volumes of water.
Potassium ferricyanide $K_3Fe(CN)_6$	Dissolve 5.5 grams of potassium ferricyanide in 100 ml of water.
Potassium ferrocyanide $K_4Fe(CN)_6 \cdot 3H_2O$	Dissolve 21 grams of potassium ferrocyanide in 100 ml of water.
Potassium nitrate KNO_3	Dry reagent.
Potassium bisulfate $HKSO_4$	Dry reagent.
Silver nitrate $AgNO_3$	Dissolve 4 grams in 100 ml of water. Keep in a dark bottle.
Sodium carbonate $Na_2(CO_3)$	Dry reagent.
Sodium fluoride NaF	Dry reagent.
Sodium hydroxide NaOH	2N. Dissolve 8 grams of NaOH in 100 ml of water.
Sodium sulfide $Na_2S \cdot 9H_2O$	Dissolve 12 grams of sodium sulfide in 100 ml of water.
Sulfuric acid H_2SO_4	Pour one volume of acid into six volumes of water.
Tannic acid $C_{14}H_{10}O_9$	Dissolve 10 grams of tannic acid in 10 ml of alcohol and dilute to 100 ml with water.
Tin, metallic	Dry reagent.
Turmeric paper	
Zinc, metallic	Dry reagent.

Tests for the Elements

Aluminum, Al

1. A flocculent white precipitate of aluminum hydroxide is obtained when an excess of ammonium hydroxide is added to an acidic solution containing aluminum. Iron hydroxide is precipitated under the same conditions (see p. 168). To separate aluminum and iron hydroxides, filter the precipitate and treat it with hot sodium hydroxide to dissolve aluminum hydroxide. Filter, acidify the filtrate, and add an excess of ammonium hydroxide to yield an aluminum hydroxide precipitate.
2. Heat light-colored, infusible, aluminous minerals intensely with the oxidizing flame on charcoal. Cool. Moisten with a drop of cobalt nitrate. Heat intensely with the oxidizing flame. A blue coloration on the sample indicates the presence of aluminum. The same reaction is obtained with zinc silicates.

Antimony, Sb

Heating of antimony-bearing minerals with concentrated nitric acid yields a white precipiate which is insoluble in water. Dilution and filtration allow antimony to be separated from combined substances.

Barium, Ba

The elements barium, strontium, and calcium have very similar chemical properties and it is recommended that their solutions or precipitates be tested for flame coloration.

1. An alkaline solution of barium, strontium, or calcium plus a 10 per cent aqueous solution of tannic acid produces a transitory yellow or yellow-green color.
2. An alkaline solution of barium, strontium, or calcium plus ammonium oxalate produces a finely divided white precipitate.
3. A concentrated hydrochloric acid solution of barium, strontium, or calcium plus dilute sulfuric acid yields a white precipitate. The calcium precipitate redissolves upon dilution of the solution with water, but the barium and strontium precipitates are insoluble.

Bismuth, Bi

Dissolve the mineral in hydrochloric acid (or in nitric acid, evaporate to a small volume, and add an excess of hydrochloric acid). Pour this solution into a test tube about one-third full of water. A white precipitate indicates bismuth.

Boron, B

1. Place a small amount of ground sample on a watch glass, cover with methyl alcohol, add an excess of concentrated sulfuric acid. Light with a match. A green flame indicates the presence of borates.
2. Moisten turmeric paper with a hydrochloric acid solution of the mineral. Dry paper at 100°C (on outside of test tube containing boiling water). The presence of boron is indicated by a reddish-

Tests for the Elements (Continued)

	brown color which turns inky-black upon the addition of ammonium hydroxide.
Bromine, Br	See test for chlorine.
Calcium, Ca	See tests for barium.
Carbon, C	As a carbonate.

1. Carbonates will dissolve with effervescence upon the addition of hydrochloric acid. The solution may require warming. The formation of an insoluble chloride (e.g., $PbCl_2$) may terminate the reaction. If this is suspected, add a small amount of nitric acid.

2. Carbon dioxide is heavier than air and when liberated as above it may be poured into a test tube containing barium hydroxide solution. A white precipitate of barium carbonate will form. Contamination from carbon dioxide in the air may interfere.

As a hydrocarbon.

Many hydrocarbons either burn alone in air or may be ashed on charcoal or in a closed tube. In each case the test is accompanied with pungent empyreumatic fumes.

Chlorine, Cl   A curdy white precipitate of silver chloride, which darkens with exposure to light, forms when silver nitrate is added to a dilute nitric acid solution of the mineral. This precipitate is soluble in ammonium hydroxide. Similar reactions for bromine and iodine.

Columbium, Cb   Fuse the mineral with two parts of sodium carbonate.
(Niobium)   Dissolve the fusion in a few drops of hydrochloric acid. Add a few grains of metallic tin and boil. The presence of columbium is indicated by the development of a dark blue color in the solution which does not readily turn brown on continued boiling and disappears on the addition of water. See also Tungsten.

Copper, Cu   An acidic solution containing copper assumes a deep blue color when neutralized with ammonium hydroxide.

Fluorine, F   Treat the ground mineral with concentrated sulfuric acid on a paraffin-coated glass surface. Scratch through the paraffin. After the reaction has proceeded for several minutes wash off the glass and remove the paraffin. Fluorine-bearing minerals, when treated with concentrated sulfuric acid, liberate hydrofluoric acid which will attack and etch glass.

Iodine, I   See test for chlorine.
Iron, Fe   1. A flocculent red-brown precipitate of iron hydroxide forms where an excess of ammonium hydroxide is added to an acid solution containing iron.

2. Ferrous and ferric iron may be distinguished by cyanide tests. If the mineral is soluble in a non-oxiding acid (e.g., hydrochloric acid) and is not a sulfide, a few drops of potassium ferricyanide added to a cold, dilute acid solution yields a heavy

Tests for the Elements (Continued)

dark blue precipitate with ferrous ions. A few drops of potassium ferrocyanide yields a heavy blue precipitate with ferric ions and a light blue precipitate with ferrous ions. A few drops of ammonium thiocyanate in a solution containing ferric ions yields a deep red color. No coloration is observed for ferrous ions.

Lead, Pb
A nitric acid solution of a lead mineral gives a white precipitate upon the addition of sulfuric acid.

Magnesium, Mg
1. A strongly ammoniacal solution containing magnesium ions yields a slowly forming white precipitate upon the addition of dibasic ammonium phosphate. Any precipitates forming before the addition of dibasic ammonium phosphate should be removed by filtration. Iron should be oxidized to the ferric state before the addition of ammonium hydroxide by the addition of a few drops of nitric acid. Calcium, barium, and strontium should be removed by precipitation as oxalates.

Nickel, Ni
Dissolve the mineral in nitric acid and neutralize with ammonium hydroxide. Filter if necessary. Add a few drops of dimethylglyoxime. A scarlet precipitate indicates nickel.

Oxygen, O
Oxides that contain an excess of oxygen generate chlorine gas when dissolved in hydrochloric acid.

Phosphorus, P
A canary-yellow precipitate is obtained when a few milliliters of a nitric acid solution of the mineral are added to cold or slightly warmed ammonium molybdate solution.

Potassium, K
A yellow, crystalline precipitate which is insoluble in water is obtained when chloroplatinic acid is added to a neutral or acidic solution containing potassium.

Silicon, Si
Dissolve the mineral in boiling hydrochloric acid, or if insoluble, fuse with sodium carbonate. Evaporate to dryness, producing first a jellylike material and then a sandy, insoluble residue. Add a small amount of aqua regia. Any residue is silica.

Silver, Ag
A white, curdy precipitate which darkens on exposure to light is obtained when a few drops of hydrochloric acid are added to a nitric acid solution of the mineral. The precipitate is soluble in ammonium hydroxide.

Strontium, Sr
See tests for barium.

Sulfur, S
1. Fuse mineral on charcoal with a reducing mixture. Place the fusion on a silver coin and wet it with a drop of water. A dark brown stain on the coin indicates sulfur. This test is very sensitive and clean equipment as well as a sulfur-free flame must be used.
2. A heavy white precipitate of barium sulfate is obtained when barium chloride is added to the solution of a soluble sulfate.

Tellurium, Te
A deep crimson color is developed when tellurium is heated in concentrated sulfuric acid. Use about 5 ml of acid. The color disappears if the acid is too hot. After cooling, the addition of water causes

Tests for the Elements (Continued)

	the color to disappear and a grayish-black precipitate of tellurium to be thrown down.
Tin, Sn	Warm the mineral with metallic zinc in dilute hydrochloric acid. Tin minerals will acquire a coating of metallic tin.
Titanium, Ti	1. Fuse the mineral with sodium carbonate and dissolve the fusion in equal parts of concentrated sulfuric acid and water. (Add the acid slowly to the water.) When the solution is cold, dilute it with water and add a few drops of hydrogen peroxide. A yellow to amber color indicates the presence of titanium.
	2. Fuse the mineral with sodium carbonate and dissolve the fusion in hydrochloric acid. Boil this solution with some metallic tin. A delicate violet color of the solution indicates the presence of titanium.
Tungsten, W (Wolfram)	Fuse the mineral with sodium carbonate. Dissolve the fusion in hydrochloric acid. A yellow precipitate indicates the presence of tungsten. Add a few grains of metallic tin or zinc and boil. The yellow precipitate will turn from yellow to blue to brown. Compare with columbium.
Uranium, U	Fuse the mineral with sodium fluoride in a platinum wire loop. Examine the bead under ultraviolet light. A fusion with sodium fluoride will fluoresce strongly.
Vanadium, V	1. A red-brown color is obtained when a small amount of hydrogen peroxide is added to an acidic solution of a vanadate.
	2. Fuse the mineral with four parts of sodium carbonate and two parts of potassium nitrate. Digest the fusion with warm water. Filter. Acidify filtrate with a slight excess of acetic acid. Add a small amount of lead acetate. A pale yellow precipitate indicates vanadium.
Zinc, Zn	1. Dissolve the mineral in hydrochloric acid. Add a few drops of nitric acid to oxidize any iron present. Make the solution slightly ammoniacal. Filter off any precipitates which form. Add sodium sulfide to the filtrate. A white precipitate indicates the presence of zinc.
	2. Mix the finely powdered mineral with one-half volume of sodium carbonate and make into a paste with water. Fuse in platinum wire loop and heat intensely with the loop held about 10 mm from the surface of a charcoal block. A deposit on the block which is pale yellow when hot and white when cold indicates zinc. If the block is first moistened with cobalt nitrate, a deposit with a characteristic green color forms.
Zirconium, Zr	Fuse the mineral with sodium carbonate. Dissolve the fusion in hydrochloric acid. A piece of turmeric paper placed in this solution assumes an orange color.

TABLE 5–9

Summary of Tests for the Elements

1 = excellent
2 = good
3 = fair

Element	Blowpipe tests					Tube tests		Wet Chemical Tests (page 167 ff.)	Remarks
	Fusibility (Table 5-1)	Globule (Table 5-3)	Sublimate (Table 5-2)	Bead Tests (Table 5-4)	Flame Tests (Table 5-6)	Open Tube (Table 5-7)	Closed Tube (Table 5-8)		
Aluminum								2	Special test with $CoNO_3$
Antimony	2		1			1	3	2	
Arsenic			1			2	1		Garlic odor when fused
Barium					1			3	
Bismuth	2	2	1					2	Imperfectly malleable globule with oxide coating
Boron					1			1	
Cadmium			2						
Calcium					2			2	
Carbon dioxide								1	
Chlorine					3			2	
Chromium				1					
Cobalt				1					
Columbium								3	
Copper		2		1	1			1	
Fluorine								3	
Gold	2	1							
Iron				1				1	Magnetic after heating
Lead	2	1	2		3			2	
Lithium					1				
Magnesium								3	
Manganese				1					$Na_2(CO_3)$ bead
Mercury						3	2		
Molybdenum			3		3	3			
Nickel				1				1	

171

TABLE 5–9 (Continued)

Element	Blowpipe tests					Tube tests		Wet Chemical Tests (page 167 ff.)	Remarks
	Fusibility (Table 5-1)	Globule (Table 5-3)	Sublimate (Table 5-2)	Bead Tests (Table 5-4)	Flame Tests (Table 5-6)	Open Tube (Table 5-7)	Closed Tube (Table 5-8)		
Oxygen								3	
Phosphorus					3			2	
Potassium					3			2	
Selenium			2			3	3		Decaying horseradish odor when heated
Silicon				3				3	
Silver		1						1	
Sodium					3				
Strontium					1			3	
Sulfur			3			2	2	1	
Tellurium			3			3	2	1	
Tin		2						2	
Titanium				1				2	
Tungsten				2				2	
Uranium				3				3	Radioactive
Vanadium				1					
Water							1		
Zinc			3		3			3	
Zirconium								2	

References

Brush, G. J., and S. L. Penfield. 1905. *Determinative Mineralogy and Blowpipe Analysis.* John Wiley & Sons, Inc., New York. An early but still excellent presentation of chemical procedures useful in mineral testing.

Hillebrand, W. F., and G. E. F. Lundell. 1929. *Applied Inorganic Analysis.* John Wiley & Sons, Inc., New York. Classical quantitative techniques of chemical analysis.

Hurlbut, C. S. 1952. *Dana's Manual of Mineralogy.* 16th ed. John Wiley & Sons, Inc., New York. Equipment, procedures, and useful tabulations for chemical mineralogy are given in Chap 3.

Kraus, E. H., W. F. Hunt, and L. S. Ramsdell. 1951. *Mineralogy.* McGraw-Hill Book Co., Inc., New York. Blowpipe and chemical mineralogy are treated in Chap. 15.

Smith, O. C. 1952. *Identification and Qualitative Chemical Analysis of Minerals.* D. Van Nostrand Co., Inc., New York. A thorough treatment of qualitative chemical testing covering the determination of elements in mineral compounds using simple equipment.

6

MINERALOGY

Classification of Matter

Matter, which constitutes the substance of the physical universe, may be classified in many different ways. It can occur in different physical forms as gases, liquids, and amorphous or crystalline solids, and can change from one form to another by such processes as crystallization, sublimation, solution, vaporization, and melting. Matter can be grouped chemically into those substances which make up or are similar to the chemical substances of living organisms and those which are not. The former are combinations of carbon chiefly with such elements as hydrogen, nitrogen, and oxygen. Such "organic" compounds include all compounds of carbon except the very simplest, such as C, CO, CO_2, or simple compounds containing the radicals CO_3^{-2}, CN^-, etc. All other substances are considered to be inorganic. Matter may also be subdivided according to whether it is formed into different compounds by artificial or natural means.

Minerals are a particular subdivision of matter defined as *naturally occurring solid inorganic substances, usually crystalline, which have fixed limits of chemical composition*. Minerals are thus by definition a relatively restricted grouping of the possible forms in which matter may be found. For example, the term *mineral* does not include water (liquid) but does include ice. Coal (an organic substance) is not a mineral, but the term does include graphite. Minerals do not include natural glasses, which have wide compositional limits, but do include quartz and feldspar. They do not strictly include artificial gems, although these are otherwise identical to natural gems.

The Crystalline State

Substances are considered to be crystalline when a regular atomic arrangement persists over distances which are very great as compared with the distances between the individual atoms. An assemblage of atoms arranged in a regular manner in three dimensions, together with the bonding of these atoms, constitutes the crystalline structure, and the imaginary geometrical framework to which the structure is related is the lattice. A fundamental characteristic of a crystal is that it can be subdivided into unit cells. These are small volumes of identical size, orientation, and constitution which, taken together, fill all the crystal.

Energetically, crystal structures are aggregates of atoms so combined as to equal or approach the lowest potential energy arrangement possible with the available constituents at the time of their crystallization.

Number and Abundance of Minerals

Minerals comprise perhaps 2,000 individual species of which only a few dozen are sufficiently abundant to be called common. Some of the more common or theoretically important species are described in this book, and the relation of many others to these more common species is indicated. It should be understood that the species described are often closely related to many other minerals, and the single description thus suffices for a group.

The number of possible mineral species is limited by three principal parameters: the abundance of the different elements in the earth's crust, the magnitude of naturally available energies, and the nature of the reacting atoms.

CRUSTAL ABUNDANCE OF ELEMENTS

Table 6–1 gives the abundance of the more common elements as determined by chemical analysis of crustal rocks, and Figure 6–1 shows the relative abundance of all the elements.

Oxygen is overwhelmingly the most abundant element in the crustal portion of the earth, and it is also a relatively large anion (ionic radius

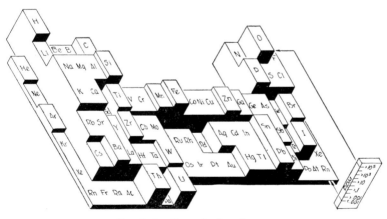

Fig. 6–1. Crustal abundance.

$\cong 1.40$ Å). Because of the size and abundance of oxygen ions, the rocks which form the crust of the earth and the minerals which compose these rocks must be essentially closely packed aggregates of oxygen ions with interstitial cations.

Oxygen forms complex ions with silicon, the next most abundant element. The resultant minerals—the silicates—are the largest mineral class in terms of volume. Other oxygen-bearing minerals which might be anticipated are oxides and any compounds in which oxygen is coordinated into a radical by some cation, e.g., carbonates, borates, phosphates, sulfates, and molybdates.

Aluminum, the next most abundant element after silicon, plays a unique role in minerals because of its size and charge. It can readily assume the role of silicon in the Si-O complex ions with four-fold coordination, or it

TABLE 6–1 *

Abundance of the More Common Elements
in the Crust of the Earth

Element	Per Cent by Weight
Oxygen	46.60
Silicon	27.72
Aluminum	8.13
Iron	5.00
Calcium	3.63
Sodium	2.83
Potassium	2.59
Magnesium	2.09
Titanium	.440
Hydrogen	.140
Phosphorus	.118
Manganese	.100
Sulfur	.0520
Carbon	.0320
Chlorine	.0314
Rubidium	.0310
Fluorine	.0300
Strontium	.0300
Barium	.0250
Zirconium	.0220
Chromium	.0200
Vanadium	.0150
Zinc	.0132

All other elements less than .0100

* Adapted from *Principles of Geochemistry* by B. Mason. Copyright, 1952, by John Wiley & Sons, Inc., New York.

can act as a cation in six-fold coordination linking oxygens or oxygen-bearing radicals together.

The other common cations—iron, magnesium, calcium, sodium, and potassium—fit into holes in the closely packed arrays of oxygen tetrahedra in silicates in such a way as to link the tetrahedra and to neutralize their excess negative charge. In other than silicate compounds these elements usually play similar cationic roles, linking anions or anionic groups. The principal exception is iron, which often enters into covalently and metalloidally bonded minerals.

Anions other than oxygen are rare in the earth's crust, their aggregate weight percentage being only about 0.1 per cent. The more important in the order of their abundance are sulfur, chlorine, and fluorine. The halogens, chlorine and fluorine, form simple ionic compounds with alkali metals and alkaline earths and occasionally enter into other compounds as essential components or as substitutions for hydroxyl groups or oxygen. Sulfur and, more rarely, arsenic, antimony, bismuth, tellurium, or selenium combine covalently or metalloidally with a number of the metals to form sulfides and arsenides. Combinations of antimony or arsenic with sulfur in a manner analogous to the silicon-oxygen combinations give rise to a complex series of sulfosalts.

Only a few elements, notably gold, silver, platinum, copper, sulfur, and carbon exist in the earth's crust as native elements.

An element of low abundance may be a principal element in a mineral, but only when it is markedly dissimilar to the major elements in its environment. If a minor element is geochemically similar to a major element, it will enter into minerals characterized by the major element and so be camouflaged, as in the case of rubidium which is camouflaged in potassium-bearing minerals or hafnium which is camouflaged by zirconium. Minor elements with distinctively different size, charge, or screening from associated major elements will, however, form distinct mineral species; examples are beryl (beryllium), uraninite (uranium), and cassiterite (tin). It is a remarkable commentary on the efficiency of natural processes of concentration that workable deposits of many very rare elements like copper, gold, mercury, or bismuth are found.

On the basis of their elemental abundance in the crust of the earth, minerals may be anticipated to comprise a relatively few common species composed of oxygen, silicon, and other major elements and a considerable number of rarer species containing the less common elements.

RESTRICTIONS IMPOSED BY ENVIRONMENT

The environments in which minerals form and change have definable limits of composition, temperature, pressure, and other parameters. These natural limits preclude the formation of a host of compounds which may be made synthetically. It may thus be anticipated that minerals will not contain elements in oxidation states very far removed from the valences discussed on p. 81 ff. Native elements will be rare. Forms representing extreme pressures and temperatures may exist, but many of these will transform displacively under near-surface conditions and will not be represented in collections.

RESTRICTIONS IMPOSED BY CRYSTAL CHEMICAL LAWS

The nature of the reacting atoms restricts the number of possible mineral species. Clearly, crystalline aggregates will form in nature only when (1) the elements will bond, (2) the elements combine into an electrically neutral array, (3) the array of atoms is consistent with the geometrical restrictions of symmetry, and (4) the elements combine into large aggregates and not into self-limiting groups which give rise to liquids or gases. It may be anticipated that minerals will be predominantly composed of element pairs from opposite sides of the periodic table. The number of different mineral structures will be small, but substitution will be common since ionic sizes and valence are not widely different.

The factors which set limits to the number of possible minerals and their abundance may be summarized as:

1. The nature of the element; principally size, charge, and screening efficiency.
2. The terrestrial abundance of elements.
3. Symmetry.
4. Levels of naturally available energy.

Mineral Classification

Minerals are subdivided on the basis of the anion or radical present and are further described in terms of the symmetry of their crystalline form and over-all chemistry. The terms in common use which describe minerals and mineralogical groupings are:

Mineral class—chemical grouping based on anion or anionic group, usually comprising:

Native elements	Nitrates
Sulfides (including selenides, tellurides)	
	Borates
Sulfosalts	Sulfates, chromates
Oxides, further distinguished as simple oxides, hydrated oxides and hydroxides, and multiple oxides	
	Phosphates, vanadates, arsenates
Halides	Wolframates, molybdates, uranates
Carbonates	Silicates

Mineral type or family—minerals showing a similarity of chemical type.

Mineral group—minerals showing a similarity of crystallography and structure. For example, the rhombohedral carbonates.

Mineral species—distinct individual mineral.

Mineral series—minerals related by isomorphism.

Mineral variety—variant of a mineral species, usually resulting from small amounts of chemical substitution or because of distinctive habit or color.

Crystal chemical laws can be utilized to establish a rational basis for mineral classification, but an arbitrary application of these laws could lead to an artificial system which disregards the important factor of mineral composition and which bears little resemblance to the commonly accepted mineral groupings. However, since the bases used for the classical subdivisions are ultimately dependent upon crystal chemical phenomena, a choice of crystal chemical parameters may be made in such a way that the classical mineralogical groupings are preserved in the main. This concept controls the arrangement of the mineral descriptions in Section II.

Minerals, of course, constitute only a small fraction of the number of possible compounds which may be classified by an application of crystal chemical principles. Mineral species, in turn, are restricted in number and type by the factors previously described. As a result, many crystal chemical divisions will not apply in the classification of minerals, and somewhat artificial distinctions must be made in order to provide equivalent populations in the various subdivisions. The following scheme has been adapted to provide, insofar as possible, a classification which can be utilized with a minimum of information concerning a given mineral, which will subdivide minerals into groups of roughly equivalent size, and which presents minerals in an order compatible with the usual schemes of classification.

The bases for the crystal chemical classification of minerals adopted here are predominant bond type, the presence or absence of radicals which indicate the relative strengths of cation-anion bonds (ionic structures only), the general chemical content, and the general structural geometry. A scheme designed on these principles is shown in Table 6–2 and will be described in the following sections.

The bond type has been treated previously. It is recognized that this parameter has some failings because of the gradational nature of the chemical bond, but since the major mineralogical groupings may be readily and naturally made on the basis of bond type, it is adopted as a primary division of minerals.

The relative strengths of the possible cation-anion bonds in an ionically bonded structure are of considerable importance in differentiating between the wide variety of substances which fall into the ionic group of minerals. (It will be remembered that the relative bond strength of a cation is defined as its valence divided by the number of anions to which it is bonded.) The strength of all the cation-anion bonds may be qualitatively equal. The direct test for this feature is to determine if the strength of each bond reaching an anion is numerically less than one-half of the anion valence. If there is no bond reaching the anion whose strength is more than one-half the anion charge, it follows that the anion is not linked more strongly to one cation than to another.

TABLE 6–2

Scheme of Classification

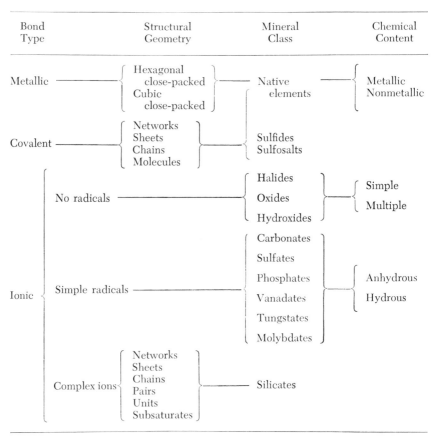

Bond Type	Structural Geometry	Mineral Class	Chemical Content
Metallic	Hexagonal close-packed, Cubic close-packed	Native elements	Metallic, Nonmetallic
Covalent	Networks, Sheets, Chains, Molecules	Sulfides, Sulfosalts	
Ionic — No radicals		Halides, Oxides, Hydroxides	Simple, Multiple
Ionic — Simple radicals		Carbonates, Sulfates, Phosphates, Vanadates, Tungstates, Molybdates	Anhydrous, Hydrous
Ionic — Complex ions	Networks, Sheets, Chains, Pairs, Units, Subsaturates	Silicates	

In contradistinction, there are other ionic structures which contain cation-anion bonds of different strengths. In such structures the strength of some bond reaching an anion is numerically greater than one-half the anion charge. It follows that no anion can be linked to two of these more powerful cations, and, therefore, this cation and its coordinated anions form a discrete group in the crystal. Such anionic groups or radicals are bound together by forces which are stronger than those which bind it into the rest of the structure, and the group may retain its identity even when the structure is broken down.

A special case of bond distribution arises when the cation-anion bond is equal to exactly one-half of the charge on the anion. Because of the importance of the minerals in which this circumstance is present—the silicates—a separate subdivision for these structures is made. Anionic groups occur, and intergroup sharing leads to interlocked radicals or complex ions.

Ionic structures which have all of their cation-anion bonds of approximately equal strength have formulae of the type A_mX_p or $A_mB_nX_p$, where A and B are cations, X an anion, and m, n, and p are integers. The former will be termed *simple structures* since they contain one cation type, for example, $NaCl$, CaF_2, Al_2O_3. The latter, which contain two or more kinds of cations, will be termed *multiple structures* and are represented by such compounds as $CaTiO_4$ and $MgAl_2O_4$.

Ionic structures in which the cation-anion bonds are not all of equal strength are always found to consist of an anionic group or radical coordinated by one cation with the groups being linked by the action of a different cation. Mineralogically, the anion is almost always oxygen. These structures might be subdivided on the basis of the shape of the anion group, but as a practical matter it is preferable to subdivide this type of mineral compound on the basis of whether or not it contains water or hydroxyl groups, that is, whether it is hydrous or anhydrous. No distinction is made here as to the role of water in the structure, and hydrous minerals may contain either structural water or coordinated water.*

In the special case of mineral structures in which the cation-anion bond strength equals one-half of the anion charge, the anionic groups link by sharing of anions to form complex ions. The resultant pairs, chains, sheets, and networks of complex ions are in turn bound together by other cations. The mode of development of complex ions is considered for borates in some detail below. The actual structures of borates are more complex than is indicated by the following section because of the ability of boron to coordinate four as well as three oxygen ions and the tendency of $(OH)^{-1}$ to substitute for O^{-2}.

Boron, valence $+3$, coordinates three oxygen ions, valence -2, in a plane triangular radical. The boron-oxygen bond strength, determined by the coordination of boron and its valence, is unity and is numerically equal to one-half the anion charge. The borate group which shares no

---

* Structural water merely occupies interstices in the structure and is essentially passive, contributing nothing of importance to the electrical picture. In some minerals, and especially in minerals undergoing weathering reactions, water may coordinate with a cation in a manner analogous to an ordinary anion.

oxygens with adjacent groups in the structure is shown in Figure 6–2a. Should one oxygen ion be shared between two of these triangular radicals, the pair of $(BO_3)^{-3}$ units has the group formula $(B_2O_5)^{-4}$, as shown in Figure 6–2b. For two shared oxygens per group, a single chain with the group formula $(BO_2)^{-1}$ is formed, as shown in Figure 6–2c. A sheet of borate groups results when all three of the oxygen ions are shared between adjacent triangular groups. The group formula is $(BO_{1\frac{1}{2}})^0$ or B_2O_3 and the sharing is illustrated in Figure 6–2d. Further sharing is possible among complex ions containing greater numbers of anions per cation, and in the silicates it will be seen that such sharing forms the foundation for classification of this extensive mineral class.

Covalently bonded structures are found only in a limited number of minerals. Simple covalent minerals usually have the formula type A_2X, AX, AX_2, or A_2X_3 and multiple covalent compounds have formulae of the type $A_mB_nX_p$. (Compare with simple and multiple ionic structures.)

Only a very few native metals are known as representatives of the group of metallically bonded minerals.

The subdivision in Table 6–2, structural geometry, will be discussed in detail in connection with the descriptions of the mineral groups.

Interrelationships Among Minerals

All mineral species are related more or less closely to other mineral species. The relationship may be one of symmetry, structure, chemical content, association, alteration, or several of these together. It is important to appreciate these relationships because properties of unknown species may be evaluated in terms of a known mineral if the relations of the two are known, or, conversely, variations in the properties of a given species may be rationalized.

Several of these relationships have been discussed in detail in Chapter 3. An isostructural relationship implies a common symmetry and hence external form shared by two species. Isomorphism and isotypism imply not only a common form, but also a chemical similarity. A polymorphic relationship is one of identical chemical content and different symmetry.

A common set of conditions often controls the formation of mineral assemblages, and this implies that only certain minerals may be found together in primary association. Two minerals cannot form at the same time and place if (1) a possible intermediate mineral exists (i.e., nepheline + quartz → albite, and therefore nepheline and quartz do not coexist), (2) the temperature or pressure of their formation are widely different, (3) they are polymorphous forms, or (4) they are isomorphous forms.

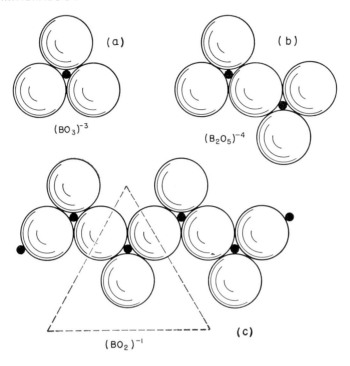

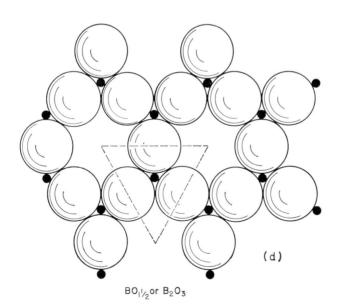

Fig. 6—2. Boron-oxygen linkages.

The close association of two or more minerals implies a common set of genetic parameters (it is, of course, here assumed that the minerals formed at essentially the same time). Since there is a somewhat restricted number of geological conditions under which mineral aggregates develop, it is often possible to characterize the geological process from the mineral suite or anticipate the mineral suite from the geological environment. A thorough description of geological processes is beyond the scope of this book, but since certain terms which have genetic significance will be used in the descriptions of individual minerals, a brief résumé of some typical geological environments follows.

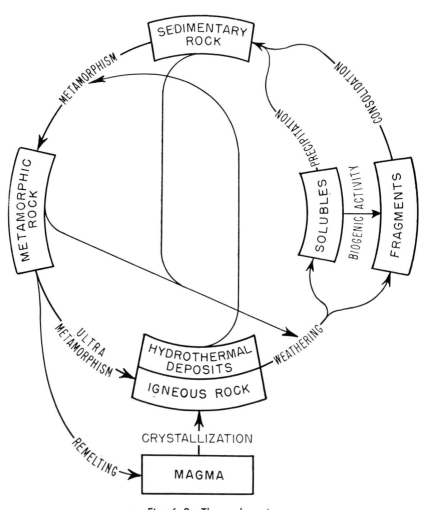

Fig. 6–3. The rock cycle.

No rock or mineral type has been excessively concentrated in the earth's crust over the whole of geological time. It follows that the processes of geology are essentially cyclic, as epitomized in Figure 6–3, in which the various products are boxed and processes shown on the arrows. A brief review of this "rock cycle" will serve to establish the environments which control mineral formation and change.

Magma is a complex melt-solution composed principally of silicates under high temperature and pressure. When released to the surface it is called *lava*. The composition of magma is approximately that given in Table 6–1. As magma cools, first one and then another mineral crystallizes and then reacts with the still liquid magma to form still a new solid phase. Two principal series of reactions which converge at lower temperature are simultaneously present. These reaction series are shown in Figure 6–4. The early formed minerals are rich in Mg, Fe, and Ca (are

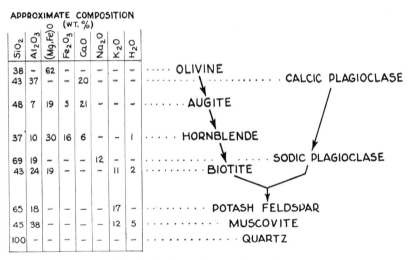

Fig. 6–4. Bowen's reaction series.

mafic), while the later minerals contain more alkalies and silicon (are salic). The left-hand limb is a discontinuous series and requires successive dissolution of the earlier formed solid phase for the development of the new solid phase. The right-hand limb is a continuous (isomorphous) series.

Minerals found close together on the reaction diagram may be expected to occur together in *igneous rocks* because they were either crystallizing at the same time (olivine and anorthite) or undergoing reaction (augite $\leftrightharpoons$ magma $\leftrightharpoons$ hornblende).

Differences in the initial composition of the magma or contamination from its walls could change the composition to such an extent that different reaction products are found. For example, a deficiency of silica could cause nepheline, $NaAlSiO_4$, to form in the place of albite, $NaAlSi_3O_8$.

Changes in the rate of cooling or physical separation of either solid or liquid phases can markedly modify the final mineral suite. Rapid cooling promotes disequilibrium and early formed minerals may not completely react. Sinking of heavy, early formed minerals depletes the magma of their constituents and is a means of obtaining mafic and salic rocks in the same chamber. Loss of the liquid portion of a crystallizing magma through its walls is another way of separating early and late mineral phases.

The fabric (grain size, shape, and arrangement) of a slowly cooled igneous rock is characteristically one with .1 mm to 3 cm interlocking equidimensional or stubby grains without preferred orientation.

Water and many exotic elements which do not readily substitute in rock-forming minerals are concentrated toward the end of magmatic crystallization. This hot, water-rich magma may react with earlier formed silicates (deuteric alteration), may react extensively with the walls of the magma chamber (contact metasomatism), or be emplaced as a body in the now solid portions of the igneous rock or chamber walls. In this latter instance the low viscosity of the water-rich solution allows crystals to attain large sizes, and the resultant coarsely crystalline *pegmatite* may contain rare minerals whose constituents were concentrated by magmatic cooling. Minerals such as lepidolite, beryl, spodumene, columbite, and a host of rare minerals are essentially restricted to this environment.

Pegmatitic crystallization still further concentrates the water fraction of the original magma, and this *hydrothermal solution* escapes into the roof rocks carrying metals, sulfur, chlorine, fluorine, carbon compounds, etc. Deposition of sulfides, fluorides, carbonates, and some silicates (especially quartz) takes place as these solutions reach levels of lower pressure and temperature or react chemically with the wall rocks. The final products of magmatic exhalation are deposited in hot springs, blended with ground waters, or are released into the atmosphere.

The following environmental terms are extensively used as mineralogical adjectives:

Magmatic—crystallization from a magma (a complex silicated melt-solution under considerable pressure).

Pegmatitic—crystallization from hot, hydrous end phases of magmatic crystallization or remelts of earlier formed rocks.

Hydrothermal—crystallization from hot water solutions, usually in veins.

Metamorphic—recrystallized without bulk chemical change.

Contact metasomatic—formed in the wall rock near the contact of intrusive magma by hot emanations from the magma.

Solfataric—sublimed from volcanic gases.

The minerals of igneous rocks and associated deposits are formed in a reducing environment, under pressure, and at relatively high temperatures. The environment at the surface of the earth, on the other hand, is one of low temperature and pressure and provides an abundance of water, oxygen, carbon dioxide, and organisms. Should minerals formed deep within the earth be brought to the surface by any of several geological means, it may be expected that extensive chemical and physical changes leading to equilibrium with the new environment will ensue. These changes are termed *weathering*. Physical disaggregation of rocks is accomplished by abrasion, the expansion of freezing water, chemical changes, etc. Chemical reactions generally leading to an increased volume and involving hydration, oxidation, or carbonation are common. The products of physical weathering processes are rock and mineral grains unchanged from their original state except in size and shape, e.g., quartz grains. The products of chemical weathering are secondary solids, e.g., clay minerals, iron oxides, which are formed at the site of weathering, colloids (principally silica from silicate destruction), and soluble ions (K^+, Na^+, Ca^{+2}, Mg^{+2}, etc.).

The products of weathering may remain *in situ* (residual aluminum hydrate deposits) or become the load of the geological transporting agents: wind, moving water, glaciers, etc. These agents have highly selective transporting abilities and can concentrate minerals according to physical properties. Gold placers are an example.

The transporting agents eventually deliver their sediment load to a permanent depositional site. Here layers of sediments are consolidated into sedimentary rocks by compaction, cementation, or interlocking of crystals precipitated from solution. The selective action of the transporting agents tends toward the development of monomineralic deposits. The principal sediments are clay minerals, quartz grains, rock fragments, and dissolved calcium and magnesium salts. The sedimentary rocks which form from these are shales, sandstones, and limestones. The latter may be inorganically deposited, but in most instances result from the fixation of calcium and magnesium carbonates into shells, etc.

Deep burial of sedimentary rocks, squeezing by earth movements, or the intrusion of igneous rocks raises the temperature and pressure until the minerals must make new adjustments to maintain equilibrium. If these adjustments are simply rearrangements of constituents already present the process is called *metamorphism*. *Metasomatism* is the more complex process wherein constituents are lost or gained by the system.

Metamorphism develops characteristic minerals (garnet, andalusite, staurolite, cummingtonite, and chloritoid), and metamorphic rocks often have a fabric which shows a high degree of preferred orientation of elongate or platy grains.

Continuing metamorphism (and metasomatism) may produce igneous-looking rocks without passing through a liquid phase, or the temperature may rise to such levels that remelting and magma formation occurs. Either process completes the cycle.

Rocks are aggregates of minerals formed by a common geological process. The intimate connection between rocks and the minerals occurring therein often requires the use of rock names in descriptive mineralogy. Rocks are classified into three principal groups according to their manner of formation, and each group is further subdivided in accordance with its mineralogical character. Figure 6–5 * shows the

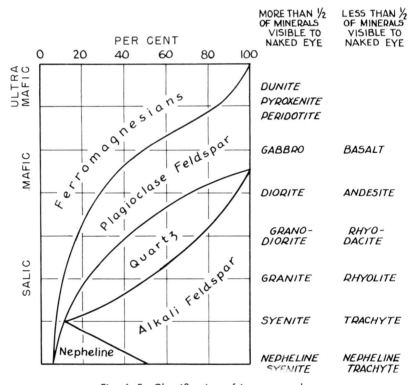

Fig. 6–5. Classification of igneous rocks.

classification of igneous rocks in a diagrammatic way. Rock names are assigned according to grain size and minerals present. It should be noted that the compositional divisions are arbitrary lines roughly corresponding to isotherms of the reaction series, Figure 6–4.

* Modified by permission from *Rocks and Rock-Minerals*, 3rd Ed., by L. V. Pirsson and Adolph Knopf. Copyright, 1947, by John Wiley & Sons, Inc., New York.

The classification of sedimentary rocks is made on the basis of grain size and composition as independent variables. Sedimentary rocks fall naturally into two principal classes according to whether they are composed of dominantly fragmental material or are not obviously fragmental. In the first case the rock is usually named for its predominant grain size and appropriate modifiers are used to specify its composition. Grain sizes and equivalent sedimentary rock types are:

GRAIN SIZE		ROCK TYPE
Pebbles	> 2 mm	Conglomerate
Sand	$\frac{1}{16}$ to 2 mm	Sandstone
Silt	$\frac{1}{256}$ to $\frac{1}{16}$ mm	Siltstone
Clay	$< \frac{1}{256}$ mm	Shale

As examples of terminology, sandstones could be further designated as:

Quartzose sandstone—predominantly quartz.
Arkose sandstone—predominantly quartz and feldspar.
Graywacke sandstone—mixture of rock and mineral fragments.

Sedimentary rocks which are not obviously fragmental are given compositional names. The principal sedimentary rocks of this type are:

Limestone—calcite predominant.
Dolostone—dolomite predominant.
Salinastone—gypsum, anhydrite, or halite predominant.
Chert—silica predominant.
Coal—carbonaceous material predominant.

Metamorphic rocks form from other rocks by recrystallization, sometimes accompanied by metasomatic changes, under increased heat and pressure. Classification of such rocks is often difficult, but is usually accomplished by a consideration of the fabric and composition. One such classification of metamorphic rocks is given in Table 6–3.

Minerals form in equilibrium with their environment, but the environment often changes after the mineral crystallizes. In consequence, there is a tendency for the mineral to change in structure, composition, or both in an attempt to maintain equilibrium. When the potential for change becomes sufficiently large, or when new elements become available, mineral alterations may take place whereby new, related mineral species arise from the old.

Mineral alteration is very common in species formed at high temperature and pressure which are later exposed at the surface of the earth. Here abundant oxygen, water, carbon dioxide, and numerous organic compounds promote rapid alteration of many minerals to oxidized, hydrated, or carbonated equivalents. These products of mineral alteration

TABLE 6–3

A Classification of Metamorphic Rocks

Grain Orientation	Grain Size or Composition	Metamorphic Rock	Examples
Preferred orientation of grains apparent	Banded or eyed structure of blocky grains	Gneiss	Granite gneiss Syenite gneiss Diorite gneiss
	Laminated structure of coarse grains	Schist	Muscovite schist Biotite schist Chlorite schist Amphibolite schist Graphite schist
	Laminated structure of very fine flakes	Phyllite	
	"Slaty" cleavage, no grains visible	Slate	
Nonoriented texture		Argillite	
		Hornfels	
Coarse, sutured texture	Predominantly quartz	Quartzite	
	Pebbly, any composition	Conglomerite	
	Calcite or dolomite	Marble	
	Calcium silicates	Skarn	

TABLE 6–4

Alteration Products

Primary Mineral		Alteration Product	
Galena	PbS	PbSO$_4$	Anglesite
Chalcopyrite	CuFeS$_2$	Cu$_2$CO$_3$(OH)$_2$	Malachite
Niccolite	NiAs	Ni$_3$(AsO$_4$)$_2$ • 8H$_2$O	Annabergite
Pyrite	FeS$_2$	Fe$_2$O$_3$ • nH$_2$O	Limonite
Anhydrite	CaSO$_4$	CaSO$_4$ • 2H$_2$O	Gypsum
Orthoclase	KAlSi$_3$O$_8$	Al$_2$Si$_2$O$_5$(OH)$_4$	Kaolin
Olivine	(Mg, Fe)$_2$SiO$_4$	Mg$_3$Si$_2$O$_5$(OH)$_4$	Serpentine
Spodumene	LiAlSi$_2$O$_6$	NaAlSi$_3$O$_8$	Albite

are, of course, minerals in their own right. A few examples of "primary" minerals and their alteration equivalents are given in Table 6–4.

Incipient alteration often provides a useful clue to the identity of an unknown mineral because many alteration products have a characteristic color. For example, oxidized and hydrated iron compounds are red brown to yellow brown, the alteration products of copper-bearing minerals are usually blue or green, nickel minerals alter to green products, cobalt to pink, and uranium to bright green, yellow, or orange products.

Ionic Minerals

Solids whose bonding is predominantly ionic comprise an overwhelming majority of those compounds which fall in the special category of minerals. The ionic group of minerals numbers among its members all the mineral families, with the exceptions of native elements, sulfides, and sulfosalts.

The primary feature underlying the classification of ionic minerals in terms of their structure is the purely geometrical arrangements of ions of characteristic radius ratios and charges in an energetically stable manner. This results in a limited number of geometrical arrangements common to a large number of mineral species. These arrangements are usually named for a common mineral or compound which contains them, and other isostructural minerals are described in terms of this common geometry.

Subdivision of the ionic minerals is made on the basis of the relative strength of the bonds present. Three categories of the ionic structures exist in which the strength of the cation-anion bond is either less, equal, or greater than one-half of the anion charge.

The distribution of mineral classes (chemically similar minerals) among the three groups of ionic structures are shown below in Table 6–5.

TABLE 6–5

Mineral Families Having Ionic Structures

Cation-Anion Bond Less Than One-half Anion Valence (No Radicals)	Cation-Anion Bond Greater Than One-half Anion Valence (Simple Radicals)	Cation-Anion Bond Equal to One-half Anion Valence (Complex Radicals)
Halides Oxides Hydroxides	Carbonates Sulfates Vanadates Molybdates Tungstates Phosphates	Silicates

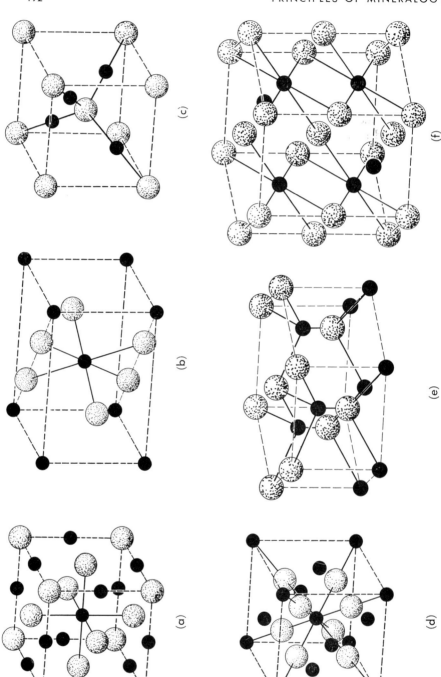

The more common structures found in these families and descriptions of the more important mineral representatives are given in the three following sections.

IONIC MINERALS NOT CONTAINING RADICALS

These minerals are divided into three mineralogical classes: halides, oxides, and hydrated oxides and hydroxides. These classes are further subdivided into two subgroups according to whether one or more cations are present in the mineral. Minerals with a single cation are classed as *simple minerals*, and those with two or more nonproxy cations are termed *multiple minerals*.

Illustrations of structures of some simple ionic minerals are presented in Figure 6–6, some multiple ionic minerals in Figure 6–7, and some

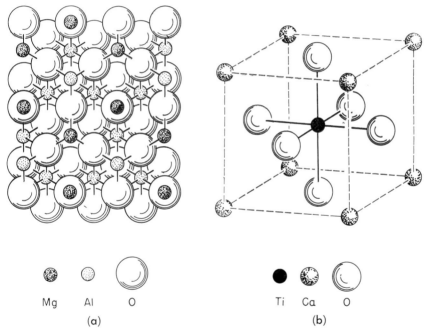

Mg   Al   O   Ti   Ca   O

(a)   (b)

Fig. 6–7. Structure of some multiple ionic minerals: (a) spinel, and (b) perovskite.

hydroxides in Figure 6–8. In most cases the structure of these minerals is an infinite three-dimensional array of alternating positive and negative ions. The different structures of these simple compounds are directly related to the radius ratio and charges of the constituent ions.

The geometrical arrangement of the nearest neighbors about an ion is, for these structures, always on the corners of a regular solid such as a tetrahedron, octahedron, or cube, and the structure may be envisaged as a stacking of these coordination solids.

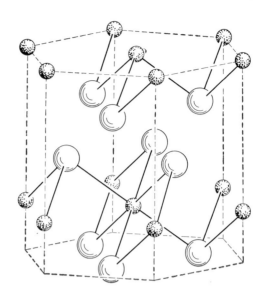

Brucite, Mg (OH)$_2$

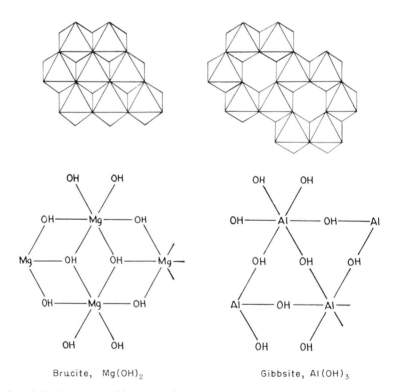

Brucite, Mg(OH)$_2$

Gibbsite, Al(OH)$_3$

Fig. 6–8. Structure of brucite (above); schematic coordination of brucite and gibbsite (below).

The final arrangement of ions must, of course, be electrically neutral and made up of alternating positive and negative ions. The relative number of each of the two kinds of ions in the structure is controlled by their valence and is shown in the mineral formula by the subscripts.

The critical radius ratios for the common coordinations are given in Table 2–4, and since ionic radii and valence are known (see Appendix), it is possible to obtain some idea concerning the structure of a compound of this type from these data.

As an example, the structure of cesium chloride may be predicted by the following argument: the radii of Cs^+ and Cl^- are, respectively, 1.65 and 1.81 Å and the radius ratio $Cs^+:Cl^-$ is thus 0.91. This radius ratio

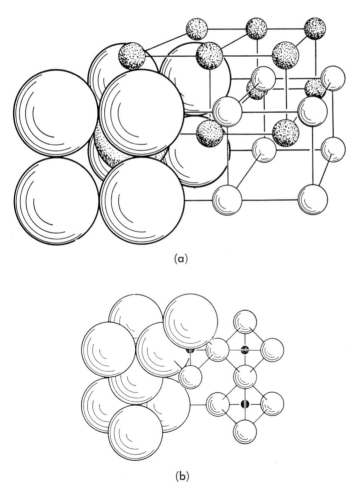

(a)

(b)

Fig. 6–9. (a) Structure of cesium chloride. (b) An arrangement of a linked SiO_4 tetrahedra.

requires a coordination of eight chlorine ions by each cesium ion. The valence of cesium is $+1$ and the valence of chlorine is -1, so each cesium ion in the structure must be electrically balanced by the presence of a chlorine ion. Therefore, chlorine must also have a coordination of eight. Eight symmetrically disposed ions will lie on the corners of a cube, and the cesium chloride structure must thus be a series of interpenetrating cubes composed alternately of cesium and chlorine ions, as shown in Figure 6–9a.

The structure of a silica group mineral, SiO_2, may be similarly deduced. Si^{+4} has a radius of 0.42 Å, and the radius of O^{-2} may be taken as 1.40 Å. The radius ratio $Si^{+4}:O^{-2}$ is then 0.30, and the silicon ion must coordinate four oxygen ions. Two oxygen ions are required per silicon ion in order to maintain electrical neutrality, and hence the number of silicon ions around each oxygen ion must be two. The oxygen neighbors of silicon will be located on the corners of a tetrahedron centered on the silicon ion, and the tetrahedra must be so arranged in space that each corner (oxygen) is equidistant from two tetrahedral centers (silicon). This arrangement requires that each oxygen be common to the coordination polyhedra of adjacent silicon ions. The structure will thus be a three-dimensional network of linked tetrahedra. There are several different ways in which this network can be arranged, one of which is illustrated in Figure 6–9b.

IONIC MINERALS CONTAINING SIMPLE RADICALS

These minerals comprise a large number of mineral classes, but the population of common species in each class is relatively small. The classes may be readily subdivided on the basis of whether or not the mineral contains water or hydroxyl groups.

Figures 6–10 and 6–11 illustrate the more common structures. Many of these minerals are geometrical equivalents of the previously described ionic minerals with a radical occupying the lattice position of an anion. The packing of radicals and radical-bonding ions is generally accomplished only by a decrease in symmetry from the analogous structures which do not contain radicals.

IONIC MINERALS CONTAINING COMPLEX IONS

Several mineral classes, namely borates, fluoroaluminates, and silicates, have sometimes been assigned to this general category. Borates and fluoroaluminates are poorly represented by common mineral species and are not well known structurally. In consequence, this category is here restricted to silicates, and the others are described with minerals containing simple radicals.

The relatively large size of oxygen atoms and their abundance in the earth's crust result in a variety of minerals which are essentially closely

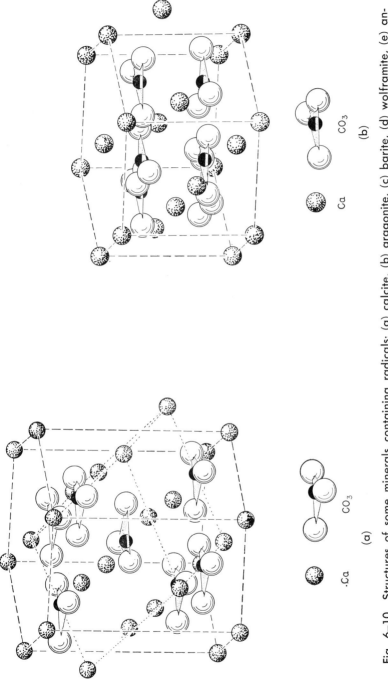

(a)

.Ca   CO₃

(b)

Ca   CO₃

Fig. 6–10. Structures of some minerals containing radicals: (a) calcite, (b) aragonite, (c) barite, (d) wolframite, (e) anhydrite, and (f) apatite.

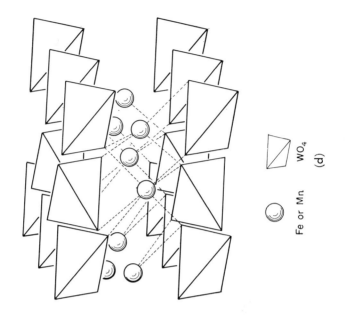

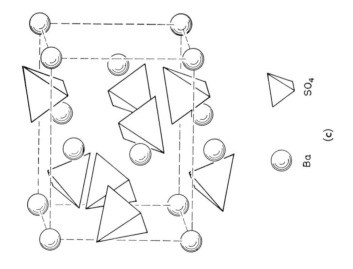

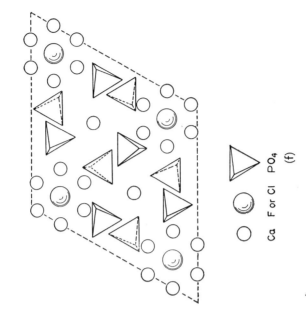

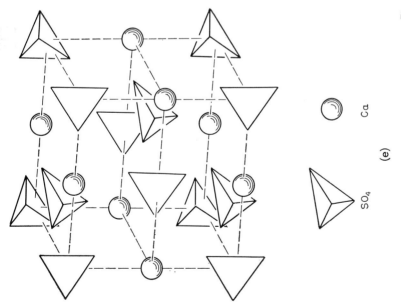

△ SO₄   ◎ Ca

(e)

▷ PO₄   ◎ Ca   ○ F or Cl

(f)

Fig. 6–10. (Continued)

199

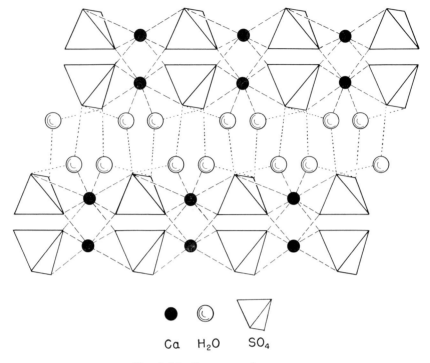

Ca   H₂O   SO₄

Fig. 6–11. Structure of gypsum.

packed oxygens held together by various cations in the interstices. The next most abundant element, silicon, joins with oxygen to form an extremely stable configuration, both geometrically and energetically, which is the fundamental unit of all silicate minerals. This unit consists of one silicon atom surrounded by four oxygen atoms disposed on the corners of a tetrahedron. The ionic radii of silicon and oxygen are such that all the atoms just touch.

The Si—O bond strength is 4 (the valence of silicon) divided by 4 (the coordination of Si), or unity. This is the strongest bond in silicate minerals. Each oxygen contributes one-half of its valence of -2 to silicon and there is thus a residual charge of -4 on each SiO_4 tetrahedron.

Diagrammatically, this SiO_4 unit may be represented as a tetrahedron

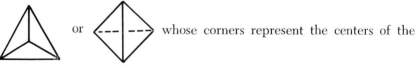

whose corners represent the centers of the oxygen atoms and whose sides equal two oxygen radii. Silicon is assumed as being centered within the tetrahedron.

The bonding of this SiO_4 tetrahedral unit may be represented as shown in the diagram following.

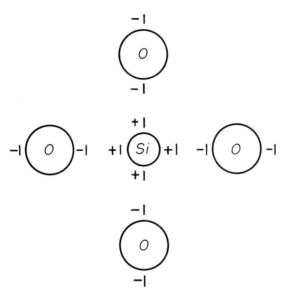

The valence requirements resulting from the unused charge of $- 1$ per oxygen in this fundamental unit are satisfied in one of a number of ways:

1. Cations may be used to neutralize the unit and join it to adjacent units. For example, in forsterite, Mg_2SiO_4, the bonding is as shown diagrammatically in Figure 6–9.

2. Units may share one or more oxygens with adjacent units. This is an important method of charge neutralization and is the basis for subdividing the silicate minerals into structural groups. One simple example of this sharing is for two tetrahedra to have a common oxygen, thus decreasing the total charge on the two units from $- 8$ to $- 6$.

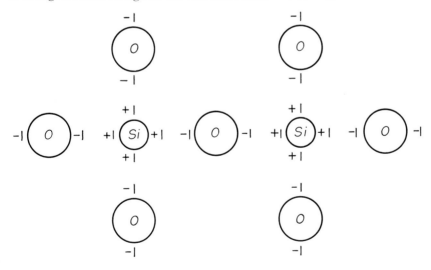

The sharing of the two or three oxygens (tetrahedral edge or face) between adjacent SiO₄ units is not energetically possible because of the mutual repulsion of silicon ions.

An extreme case of oxygen sharing is that of quartz in which all the oxygens are members of two tetrahedra (i.e., each oxygen is bonded to two silicon ions), and the result is a neutral network, SiO_2, shown diagrammatically:

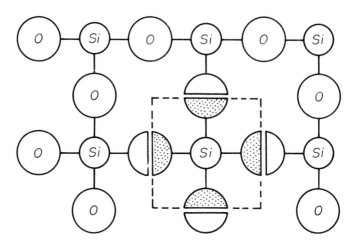

3. Oxygen sharing and charge balance by cations occur together in most silicate minerals. For example, in the paired tetrahedra discussed above the residual charge of -6 is neutralized by two Ca^{+2} and one Mg^{+2} in gehlenite, $Ca_2Mg(Si_2O_7)$.

4. Substitution of ions of different valence for O^{-2} or Si^{+4} may occur in silicates. The most common substitution is that of Al^{+3} for Si^{+4}. The resulting AlO₄ tetrahedron has a charge of -5 electrostatic units, and the excess of negative charge must be balanced by the addition of positive ions elsewhere in the structure. The usual cations are alkali metals and alkaline earths such as Na^{+1}, K^{+1}, and Ca^{+2}. The maximum amount of substitution of Al^{+3} for Si^{+4} is almost always 50 per cent or less. As examples of Al^{+3} substitution and charge balance by cations consider the minerals albite, $Na(AlSi_3O_8)$, and nepheline, $Na(AlSiO_4)$, wherein aluminum ions substitute in respectively one-quarter and one-half of the silicon ion sites.

5. Many silicate minerals have structures such that an hydroxyl group is accommodated in the center of a ring of tetrahedra. This $(OH)^{-1}$ group increases the net negative charge of the structure and requires the presence of positive ions elsewhere in the structure. For example, the mineral pyrophyllite, $Al_2(Si_2O_5)(OH)_4$, contains two Al^{+3} which neutralize the -2 charge per Si_2O_5 and -4 charge per four (OH) groups.

Silicate Structure Types. The divisions of silicates arising from the sharing of oxygen atoms between adjacent tetrahedra are shown in Table 6–6. This is a clean-cut breakdown of silicates because all known silicate minerals fall into one or another of these groupings. The only known exception is vesuvianite, $Ca_{10}(Mg, Fe)_2Al_4(Si_2O_7)_2(SiO_4)_5(OH)_4$, which contains both tetrahedral individuals and pairs. Only Si-O tetrahedra are considered here, but other tetrahedra could be included.

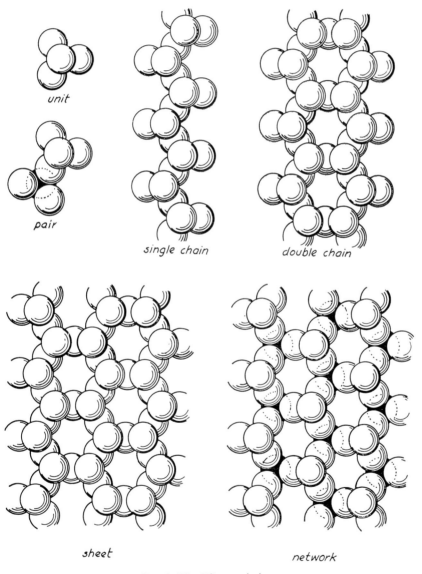

Fig. 6–12. Silicate skeleta.

TABLE 6-6

Structural Group	Diagrammatic Representation	Number of Shared Oxygens per Silicon	Si-O Repeat Unit	Si:O	Example
Tetrahedral subsaturate		0	$(SiO_4)O_x^{-(4+2x)}$	$1:(4+x)$	Kyanite, $Al_2(SiO_4)O$
Tetrahedral unit		0	$(SiO_4)^{-4}$	$1:4$	Forsterite, $Mg_2(SiO_4)$
Tetrahedral pair		1	$(Si_2O_7)^{-6}$	$1:3\frac{1}{2}$	Akermanite, $Ca_2Mg(Si_2O_7)$
Tetrahedral single chain		2	$(SiO_3)^{-2}$	$1:3$	Enstatite, $Mg(SiO_3)$ or $Mg_2(Si_2O_6)$
Tetrahedral ring		2	$(SiO_3)_n^{-2}$	$1:3$	Beryl, $Be_3Al_2(SiO_3)_6$ or $Be_3Al_2(Si_6O_{18})$

Tetrahedral double chain	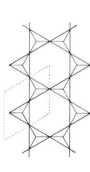	$2\frac{1}{2}$	$(Si_4O_{11})^{-6}$	$1:2\frac{3}{4}$	Tremolite, $Ca_2Mg_5(Si_8O_{22})(OH)_2$
Tetrahedral sheet	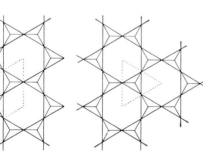	3	$(Si_2O_5)^{-2}$	$1:2\frac{1}{2}$	Kaolinite, $Al_2(Si_2O_5)(OH)_4$
Tetrahedral network	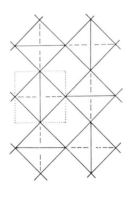	4	$(SiO_2)^0$	$1:2$	Quartz, SiO_2

205

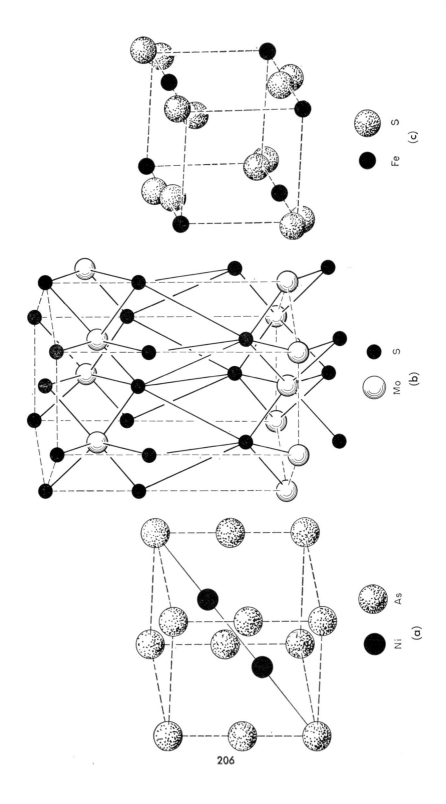

S

Fe

(c)

Mo

S

(b)

As

Ni

(a)

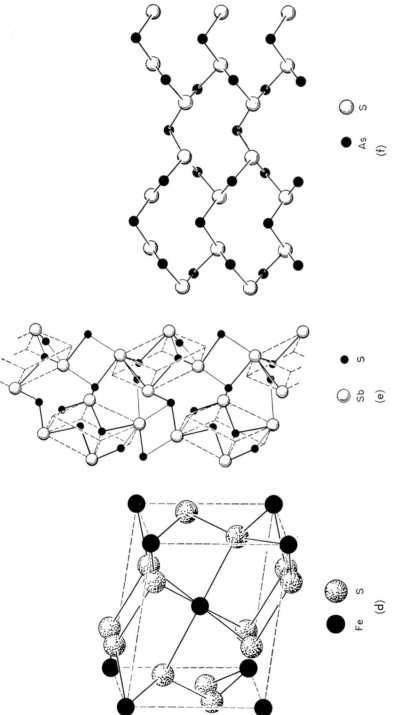

Fig. 6–13. Structures of some sulfides: (a) niccolite, (b) molybdenite, (c) pyrite, (d) marcasite, (e) stibnite, and (f) orpiment.

(d)

Fe ⬤   S ◌

(e)

Sb ◌   S ●

(f)

As ●   S ◌

It is interesting to note that this classification does not change the mineral groupings arrived at by physical and chemical measurements prior to a knowledge of crystal structure. This is, of course, because the structure imparts a characteristic set of physical, optical, and chemical properties to the mineral.

The complex Si—O ions which are the skeletons of silicate minerals are illustrated in Figure 6–12. These units, chains, sheets, etc., are held together by positive ions lying in and between them. Typical silicate structures are thus an alternation of complex ions and cation layers. Structures of some specific silicate minerals will be found in the following descriptive section.

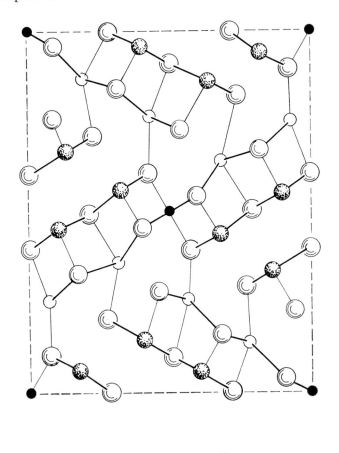

Fe   Pb   Sb   S

Fig. 6–14. Structure of jamesonite.

Covalent Minerals

The minerals in which covalent bonding predominates are restricted to compounds of metallic elements with sulfur or some chemically similar element and to some native elements. The distinction between pure covalent bonding and metallic bonding is not sharply defined, and the majority of the mineral compounds in this category have a pronounced metalloidal character.

The only mineral classes are the sulfides, sulfosalts, and nonmetallic native elements. The sulfides and sulfosalts are analogous to simple and

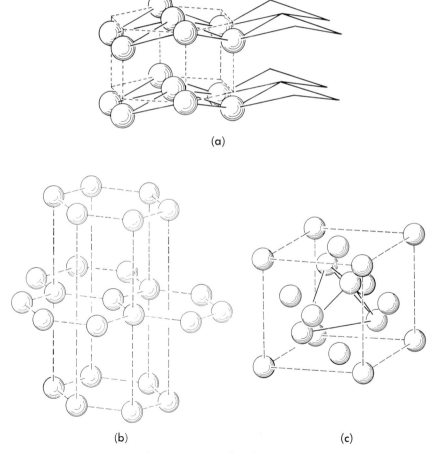

(a)

(b)   (c)

Fig. 6–15. Structures of some nonmetallic elements: (a) arsenic, (b) graphite, and (c) diamond.

multiple oxides with formulae of the type A_mX_n and $A_mB_nX_p$, respectively. The common elements participating in sulfide mineral formation are:

A: Ag, Cd, Co, Cu, Fe, Hg, Ni, Pb, Zn
X: As, S, Se, Te

The sulfosalts are complex compounds of a very few principal elements. These are:

A: Ag, Cu, Pb
B: As, Bi, Sb
X: S

Nonmetallic native elements of importance are limited to arsenic, sulfur, and the two forms of carbon, graphite and diamond. The principal structure types of covalently bonded minerals are illustrated in Figures 6–13 to 6–15.

Metallic Minerals

The only metallic minerals of importance are the native metals copper, gold, silver, and platinum. These minerals are all isostructural and, to a large extent, isomorphous.

The native metals are isometric and belong to the crystal class $\frac{4}{m}\bar{3}\frac{2}{m}$. Their structure is that of a face-centered cube, Figure 6–16. The

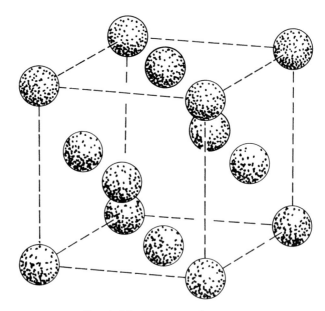

Fig. 6–16. Structure of copper.

variation in composition of these metals corresponds to their mutual solubility in binary systems.

References

CLARK, F. W. 1924. The data of geochemistry. *U. S. Geological Survey Bulletin 770.* 841 pp.

MASON, B. 1958. *Principles of Geochemistry.* 2d ed. John Wiley & Sons, Inc., New York. Geochemical, mineralogical, and geological topics are integrated.

NIGGLI, E. 1954. *Rocks and Mineral Deposits.* W. H. Freeman & Co., San Francisco. The position of mineralogical phenomena in the larger field of geology is developed. The chapters on "Elements of Crystal Chemistry," "Laws of Stability and Co-existence of Minerals in Mineral Aggregates," and "Preparatory Stages of the Crystallization Process" are especially pertinent.

PALACHE, C., H. BERMAN, and C. FRONDEL. Vol. I, 1944. Vol. II, 1951. *Dana's System of Mineralogy.* John Wiley & Sons, Inc., New York. A complete and detailed description of the known mineral species. These volumes constitute the ultimate reference source for most descriptive mineralogical information, and all serious students should familiarize themselves with Dana's system.

RANKAMA, K., and Th. G. SAHAMA. 1950. *Geochemistry.* The University of Chicago Press, Chicago. A thorough survey of the broad field of geochemistry.

Part II
MINERAL DESCRIPTIONS

7

MINERAL DESCRIPTIONS

Some 150 common, valuable, or theoretically important mineral species, series, or groups are described in the following pages. These descriptions are intended for the use of beginning students working with hand specimens and are therefore somewhat restricted in scope.* Descriptions are arranged in the following order:

* For supplementary details, students are referred to the following sources:

1. *Dana's System of Mineralogy.* 7th ed. C. Palache, H. Berman, and C. Frondel. John Wiley & Sons, Inc., New York. Vol. I—Native Elements, Sulfides, Oxides, Hydroxides. 1944. Vol. II—Halides, Nitrates, Borates, Carbonates, Sulfates, Phosphates, Arsenates, Tungstates, Molybdates, etc. 1951. This series together with an unfinished third volume covering silicates, constitutes the most complete tabulation of mineralogical data available.

2. *Dana's Textbook of Mineralogy.* 4th ed. 1926. W. E. Ford. John Wiley & Sons, Inc., New York. This text will be superseded on the completion of Vol. III of *Dana's System of Mineralogy.*

3. *Mineralogische Tabellen.* 1941. H. Strunz. Akademische Verlagsgesellschaft Becker & Erler Kom.-Ges.

4. *An Index of Mineral Species and Varieties Arranged Chemically.* 1950. M. H. Hey. Printed by order of the Trustees of the British Museum, London.

Each of these family groupings is preceded by a tabulation of included mineral groups, series, and species, only the more important of which are further described. General descriptions accompany each mineral family, and descriptive material is also presented for the more important subdivisions, as explained on the following page.

Crystallography, Structure, Habit
Crystal system. Crystal class. Crystal habit. Twinning.
Brief description of structure, including isostructural references.
Mineral habit.

Physical Properties
Manner of breaking—cleavage, parting, fracture, sectility.
Hardness. Specific gravity.
Luster. Diaphaneity. Color. Streak.
Miscellaneous properties—fusibility, fluorescence, taste, etc.

Distinctive Properties and Tests
Summary of the most valuable determinative properties.
Brief statement of useful blowpipe, chemical, or special confirmatory tests.

Association
Brief statement of the geological environment and rock types in which the mineral is found and a listing of other minerals which are often found with it.

Alteration: Minerals from or to which the mineral may readily change.
Formulae are given for species not elsewhere described.

Confused with: Minerals similar in general appearance are noted.

Variants
Many minerals have variants which differ from the norm in physical properties or appearance. Long usage has established special terms for these variants, and the more important are given as form varieties.

Most minerals have minor (isomorphic) variations in chemical content. The more important of these variations are included as chemical varieties.

All minerals contain small amounts of nonformulary elements. Such contaminants are noted when significant.

Related Minerals
Mineral species related by *isotypism, isomorphism,* and *polymorphism* are listed together with formulae.

Mineral species not related by the above phenomena but having generally similar composition are listed as *other similar species.*

Native Elements

METALS   NONMETALS

Gold group   Arsenic group
   Gold, Au   Arsenic, As
   Silver, Ag   Tellurium group
   Copper, Cu   Sulfur group
Platinum group   Sulfur, S
   Platinum, Pt   Carbon group
Iron group   Diamond, C
                                       Graphite, C

METALS

Gold Group. The gold group contains the native metals gold, silver, and copper. These metals have many physical similarities such as metallic luster, high electrical conductivity, easy malleability, high specific gravity, softness, similar melting points, etc. All three metals are isostructural and are based on a face-centered cubic cell containing four atoms, which is usually called the *copper structure*. The coordination of each metal atom in this structure is twelve, as is shown in Figure 7–1.

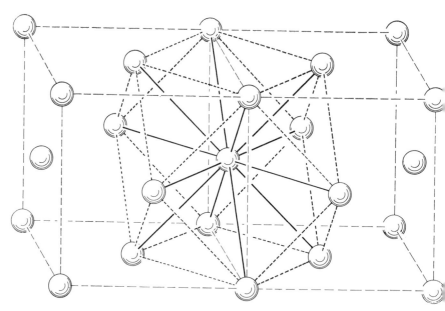

Fig. 7–1. Coordination in the copper structure.

There is a high degree of mutual solubility or isomorphism among these metals and also between them and certain other chemically similar

Native Elements (cont.)

elements such as mercury and palladium. The isomorphous relations in the gold group are illustrated in Figure 7–2.

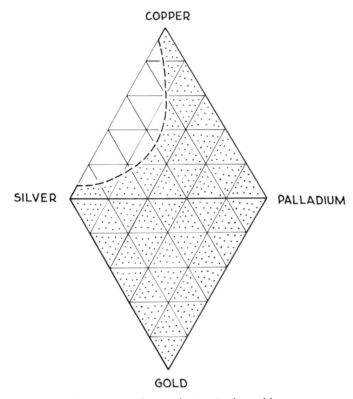

Fig. 7–2. Isomorphous relations in the gold group.

GOLD

Au

Crystallography, Structure, Habit

Isometric. $\frac{4}{m}\overline{3}\frac{2}{m}$. Crystals rough and distorted, usually octahedra and sometimes dodecahedra or cubes. Skeletal crystals common. Repeated twins common.

Copper structure, Figures 6–16 and 7–1. Face-centered cubic cell containing four Au atoms.

Usually in rounded irregular masses (nuggets), grains, or scales (colors).

Physical Properties

No cleavage. Hackly fracture. Sectile.

Hardness 2.5–3. Specific gravity 19.3.

Metallic luster. Opaque. Color and streak gold yellow.

Melting point 1062°.

Distinctive Properties and Tests

Sectility, color, specific gravity. Does not tarnish. Fuses easily (3) to a malleable globule. Insoluble in ordinary acids.

Association and Occurrence

Found with quartz, pyrite, chalcopyrite, galena, stibnite, sphalerite, arsenopyrite, tourmaline, molybdenite.

Widely distributed in small amounts. Usually (1) in quartz veins related to silica-rich igneous rocks or (2) concentrated by stream action into placer deposits.

Alteration: Resistant to change.

Confused with: Pyrite (fool's gold), chalcopyrite, weathered biotite.

Variants

Argentian (electrum), palladian (porpezite), rhodian, cuprian, bismuthian. Often contains considerable Fe and lesser amounts of Pt, Sn, Pb, or Zn.

Related Minerals

Isomorphs: Silver; copper; palladium, Pd.

Isotypes: Lead, Pb.

Other similar species: Maldonite, Au_2Bi.

SILVER

Ag

Crystallography, Structure, Habit

Isometric. $\frac{4}{m}\,\overline{3}\,\frac{2}{m}$. Distorted crystals. Sometimes cubes, octahedra, or dodecahedra but more commonly acicular forms. Twinning common as pairs or cyclic groups.

Copper structure, Figures 6–16 and 7–1. Face-centered cubic cell containing four Ag atoms.

Usually in irregular masses, plates, or coatings or in wirelike forms.

Physical Properties

No cleavage. Hackly fracture. Sectile.

Hardness 2.5–3. Specific gravity 10.5.

Metallic luster. Opaque. Color and streak silver white and shining on fresh surface, but tarnishing readily to gray or black.

Melting point 961°.

Distinctive Properties and Tests

Sectility, color, specific gravity. Fuses easily (2) to a bright, malleable globule.

Readily soluble in HNO_3. See wet chemical test for silver.

Association and Occurrence

Found with sulfides and arsenides of lead, silver, copper, cobalt, and nickel. Commonly associated nonore minerals are calcite, quartz, barite, fluorite, and uraninite.

Widely distributed in small amounts (more rare than native gold). Principal concentrations found in the oxidized zone of certain ore deposits: (1) Hydrothermal veins containing silver and other sulfides; (2) hydrothermal veins containing cobalt and nickel sulfides, arsenides, and sulfarsenides; (3) Hydrothermal veins containing metallic sulfides and uraninite.

Alteration: From silver halides, sulfides, and sulfosalts.

Confused with: Platinum group metals.

Variants

Aurian, mercurian (amalgam, arquerite), cuprian, arsenian, antimonian (dyscrasite). May also contain Bi, Pt, or Fe.

Related Minerals

Isomorphs: Gold; amalgam, (Ag, Hg).

Isotypes: Copper.

COPPER

Crystallography, Structure, Habit

Isometric. $\frac{4}{m}\bar{3}\frac{2}{m}$. Cubes, dodecahedra, octahedra. Crystals usually distorted and combined into branching groups. Dendritic. Contact, penetration, and cyclic twins are very common.

Copper structure, Figures 6–16 and 7–1. Face-centered cubic cell containing four Cu atoms.

Usually in irregular masses, plates, or scales; also flattened, elongate, and spearlike forms. Sometimes wirelike or arborescent.

Physical Properties

No cleavage. Hackly fracture. Sectile.

Hardness 2.5–3. Specific gravity 8.9.

Metallic luster. Opaque. Color and streak copper red on fresh surface darkening to brown on exposure.

Melting point 1083°.

Distinctive Properties and Tests

Sectility, color, specific gravity. See blowpipe and chemical tests for copper.

Association and Occurrence

Found with native silver, chalcopyrite, bornite, calcite, chlorite, zeolites, cuprite, malachite, and azurite (1) filling cracks and amygdules in and partially replacing the silicates of mafic lava flows or as a cement in associated conglomerates, sandstones, etc., and (2) in the oxidized zone above copper sulfide deposits.

Alteration: To cuprite, malachite, azurite.

Confused with: Red gold.

Variants

Arsenian. Often contains such elements as Ag, Fe, Bi, Sb, Hg, Ge, Sn, and Pb.

Related Minerals

Isotypes: Gold; silver; platinum; lead, Pb; iridium, Ir.

PLATINUM

Crystallography, Structure, Habit

Isometric. $\frac{4}{m} \bar{3} \frac{2}{m}$. Rare and distorted cubes.

Copper structure, see Figures 6–16 and 7–1. Face-centered cubic cell containing four Pt atoms.

Found in small grains and scales and, more rarely, in larger nuggets.

Physical Properties

No cleavage. Hackly fracture. Sectile.

Hardness 4–4.5. Specific gravity 14–19.

Metallic luster. Opaque. Color and streak steel gray to dark gray.

Infusible. Insoluble. May be weakly magnetic.

Distinctive Properties and Tests

Sectility, color, specific gravity. Infusible.

Association and Occurrence

Found with chromite, olivine, and magnetite in mafic and ultramafic rocks.

Alteration: Resistant to change.

Confused with: Native silver.

Variants

Ferrian, cuprian, palladian, rhodian, iridian. Also may contain Os and, less commonly, Cu, Au, or Ni.

Related Minerals

Isotypes: Copper; iridium, Ir; osmiridium, (OsIr).

Other similar species: Palladium, Pd.

Crystallography, Structure, Habit

Hexagonal. $\bar{3}\frac{2}{m}$. Crystals rare, usually acicular, and sometimes pseudocubes.

The simple cell of arsenic is an acute rhombohedron containing two atoms, one at each lattice point and one at the center of the cell. These two atoms are structurally dissimilar. The unit cell of the arsenic structure is a multiple cell containing six As atoms. See Figures 6–15a and 7–3.

Usually granular massive, often in concentric layers.

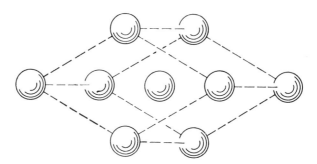

Fig. 7–3. A simple cell of the arsenic structure.

Physical Properties

Perfect basal (0001) and fair (10$\bar{1}$4) cleavage. Uneven fracture. Brittle. Hardness 3.5. Specific gravity 5.7.

Submetallic luster. Opaque. Color tin white on fresh surface tarnishing to dark gray. Streak gray.

Distinctive Properties and Tests

Luster, habit. Tests for arsenic.

Association and Occurrence

Found with silver-cobalt-nickel ores in veins.

Alteration: Oxidizes to form a black crust of arsenolite, As_2O_3.

Confused with: Manganese oxides.

Variants

Usually contains such contaminants as Sb, Fe, Ni, Ag, and S.

Related Minerals

Isotypes: Allemontite, AsSb; antimony, Sb; bismuth, Bi.
Other similar species: Graphite.

SULFUR   (α-sulfur)   S

Crystallography, Structure, Habit
Orthorhombic. $\dfrac{2}{m}\dfrac{2}{m}\dfrac{2}{m}$. Usually imperfectly crystalline. Crystals pyramidal, bipyramidal, thick tabular. Rare twinning.

Massive, colloform, encrusting, powdery.

Physical Properties
Imperfect (001), (110), (111) cleavage. Conchoidal to uneven fracture. Brittle to subsectile.

Hardness 1.5–2.5. Specific gravity 2.1.

Resinous to greasy luster. Translucent to transparent. Color yellow of various shades.

Melting point 113°. Negatively electrified by friction.

Distinctive Properties and Tests
Hardness, specific gravity, color. Melts and burns with a blue flame liberating acrid SO_2.

Association and Occurrence
Found with celestite, gypsum, aragonite, and calcite (1) in sedimentary rocks, (2) as a volcanic sublimate, and (3) as a decomposition product of sulfides in metallic veins.

Alteration: From sulfides and possibly sulfates.

Confused with: Orpiment, sphalerite.

Variants
Selenian (selensulfur). May contain small amounts of Te. Inclusions of clay, bitumen, etc., are common.

Related Minerals
Polymorphs: Sulfur is known in three forms; the common orthorhombic (α) modification and two rare monoclinic modifications known as β- and γ-sulfur.

DIAMOND

Crystallography, Structure, Habit

Isometric. $\bar{4}$ 3m. Usually octahedra, often distorted; also dodecahedra, cubes, tetrahedra. Simple and multiple contact twins very common. Also penetration twins and cyclic groups.

Face-centered cubic unit cell containing eight carbon atoms. Each carbon atom is linked tetrahedrally to four neighbors. See Figure 6–15c.

Crystal grains, often with curved faces. Inclusions common.

Physical Properties

Perfect (111) cleavage. Conchoidal fracture. Brittle.

Hardness 10. Specific gravity 3.5

Adamantine luster. Transparent to translucent. Color blue white, yellow, brown, black, etc.

Triboelectric. Sometimes strongly fluorescent under ultraviolet light. Often fluoresces when rubbed on wood. Infusible.

Distinctive Properties and Tests

Hardness, habit. Unattacked by acids and alkalies.

Association and Occurrence

Found with pyrope garnet, kyanite, olivine, and zircon in altered ultramafic rocks or in placers.

Alteration: Resistant to change.

Confused with: Quartz, topaz.

Variants

Form varieties: Bort—granular to cryptocrystalline diamond; carbonado—massive black or gray bort.

May contain minute quantities of such elements as Si, Fe, Mg, Al, Ca, and Ti.

Related Minerals

Polymorphs: Graphite.

GRAPHITE

Crystallography, Structure, Habit

Hexagonal. $\dfrac{6}{m}\dfrac{2}{m}\dfrac{2}{m}$. Hexagonal tablets. Glide twinning may produce striae on the base.

Structure somewhat similar to that of arsenic. The unit cell contains four C atoms. See Figure 6–15b.

Embedded foliated masses, scales, columns, grains, earthy.

Physical Properties

Perfect (0001) cleavage. Sectile.

Hardness 1–2. Specific gravity 2.2.

Metallic to earthy luster. Opaque (transparent in extremely thin flakes). Color black to steel gray. Streak black.

Cleavage laminae are pliable but not elastic. Greasy feel. Thermoelectric.

Distinctive Properties and Tests

Softness (greasy feel, soils fingers, marks paper), cleavage. Infusible and unattacked by acids.

Association and Occurrence

Found with calcite, quartz, orthoclase, pyroxene, garnet, spinel, amphibole, etc., in metamorphic rocks and, less commonly, in igneous rocks.

Alteration: Resistant to change.

Confused with: Molybdenite, pyrolusite.

Variants

Often contains a small amount of Fe.

Related Minerals

Polymorphs: Diamond.

Other similar species: Arsenic.

Sulfides

A_mX_n Type $(m{:}n > 3{:}1)$
   Tetradymite group
   Copper arsenide group

A_3X Type

A_2X Type
   Argentite group
     Argentite, Ag_2S
   Chalcocite group
     Chalcocite, Cu_2S

A_3X_2 Type
   Bornite, Cu_5FeS_4

A_4X_3 Type

AX Type
   Galena group
     Galena, PbS
   Sphalerite group
     Sphalerite, ZnS
   Chalcopyrite group
     Chalcopyrite, $CuFeS_2$
   Wurtzite group
   Niccolite group
     Pyrrhotite, $Fe_{1-x}S$
     Niccolite, $NiAs$

AX Type (cont.)
   Covellite group
     Covellite, CuS
     Cinnabar, HgS
     Realgar, AsS

A_3X_4 Type
     Orpiment, As_2S_3
   Stibnite group
     Stibnite, Sb_2S_3

AX_2 Type
   Pyrite group
     Pyrite, FeS_2
   Cobaltite group
     Cobaltite, $CoAsS$
   Loellingite group
     Marcasite, FeS_2
   Arsenopyrite group
     Arsenopyrite, $FeAsS$
   Molybdenite group
     Molybdenite, MoS_2
   Krennerite group

AX_3 Type
   Skutterudite series, $(CoNi)As_{3-x}$

Sulfides are generally soft and fusible minerals, often heavy, opaque, and with a metallic luster. These family characteristics are shared with the native elements and the sulfosalts since they are a macroscopic indication of their composition and bonding.

Luster	Cleavage	Hardness	Minerals
Metallic	Present	> 5.5	Arsenopyrite, skutterudite series
		2.5–5.5	Galena, cobaltite
		< 2.5	Covellite, stibnite, molybdenite
	Absent	> 5.5	Pyrite, marcasite
		2.5–5.5	Chalcocite, bornite, chalcopyrite, pyrrhotite, niccolite
		< 2.5	Argentite
Non-metallic	Present	> 5.5	
		2.5–5.5	Sphalerite, cinnabar
		< 2.5	Realgar, orpiment
	Absent		

Sulfides (cont.)

Chemically, sulfides are combinations of one or more metals with either sulfur or a chemically similar element such as arsenic, selenium, or tellurium. A few isomorphous series exist, but most sulfide species exhibit a restricted amount of isomorphous replacement.

The identification of the sulfide minerals can be readily accomplished by use of their physical properties alone. The easily recognized properties of luster (metallic or nonmetallic), hardness, and cleavage, for example, can be used to separate the sulfide minerals into groups as given in the table at the bottom of the previous page.

These mineral groupings may be subdivided into individual species by color and miscellaneous properties as follows:

Mineral	Fresh Color	Distinctive Characteristics
Chalcocite	Shining lead gray	Subsectile
Bornite	Brown bronze	Iridescent tarnish
Chalcopyrite	Brass yellow	Greenish-black streak
Pyrrhotite	Brown bronze	Magnetic
Niccolite	Pale copper red	Brown black streak

The identification of a sulfide is readily confirmed by means of simple blowpipe or wet chemical tests. For example, sulfides may be divided into groupings based on their fusibility coupled with the magnetic properties of the resulting fusion:

Infusible	Fusible with a Magnetic Residue	Fusible with a Non-magnetic Residue	Volatile
Sphalerite	Bornite	Argentite	Cinnabar
Molybdenite	Chalcopyrite	Chalcocite	Realgar
	Pyrrhotite	Galena	Orpiment
	Pyrite	Niccolite	
	Marcasite	Covellite	
	Arsenopyrite	Stibnite	
		Cobaltite	
		Skutterudite series	

A magnetic residue gives positive evidence of the presence of iron in the mineral, and the simple chemical manipulations described in Chapter 5 should resolve any remaining difficulties.

ARGENTITE (silver glance) Ag_2S

Crystallography, Structure, Habit

Isometric. $\frac{4}{m}\bar{3}\frac{2}{m}$ (at 179°C). Cubes, octahedra, and rarely dodecahedra. Penetration twins.

Usually massive, also groups of parallel individuals, arborescent, coatings.

Physical Properties

Poor (001) and (011) cleavage. Subconchoidal fracture. Sectile.

Hardness 2–2.5. Specific gravity 7.3.

Metallic luster. Opaque. Color dark lead gray, darkening on exposure to light. Streak shining.

Fuses readily (1.5) with intumescence.

Distinctive Properties and Tests

Hardness, specific gravity, sectility. Easy fusion which, if done on charcoal, produces a silver button. Tests for silver.

Association and Occurrence

Found with other silver minerals and cobalt-nickel sulfides in veins and as inclusions in "argentiferous galena."

Alteration: To native silver and silver sulfosalts.

Confused with: Chalcocite, tetrahedrite

Variants

Chemical varieties: Cuprian (jalpaite), selenian (aguilarite).

Related Minerals

Polymorphs: Acanthite, an orthorhombic form of Ag_2S stable below 179°C. It is likely that all argentite is really acanthite.

Other similar species: Hessite, Ag_2Te; petzite, $(AuAg)_2Te$; naumannite, Ag_2Se; eucairite, CuAgSe.

CHALCOCITE   (copper glance) Cu_2S

Crystallography, Structure, Habit

Orthorhombic. $\frac{2}{m}\frac{2}{m}\frac{2}{m}$. Crystals rare, usually short prismatic to thick tabular. Twinning produces a stellate grouping of three individuals or a cruciform penetration twin.

Massive, compact, impalpable.

Physical Properties

Indistinct (110) cleavage. Conchoidal fracture. Subsectile.

Hardness 2.5–3. Specific gravity 5.7.

Metallic luster. Color and streak black lead gray. Often tarnished.

Easily fusible (2–2.5).

Distinctive Properties and Tests

Hardness, color, sectility. Tests for copper.

Association and Occurrence

Found with covellite, cuprite, native copper, azurite, malachite, bornite, etc., (1) in secondarily enriched zone in copper-bearing sulfide deposits, and (2) in hydrothermal sulfide veins.

Alteration: To native copper, covellite, malachite, azurite.

Variants

Often contains some Ag and Fe.

Related Minerals

Isomorphs: Berzelianite, Cu_2Se.

Isotypes: Stromeyerite, $(AgCu)_2S$.

Polymorphs: Hexagonal modification above 105°.

Other similar species: Digenite, $Cu_{2-x}S$.

BORNITE (peacock ore) Cu_5FeS_4

Crystallography, Structure, Habit

Isometric. $\frac{4}{m} \bar{3} \frac{2}{m}$. Rare cubes or dodecahedra with rough and curved faces. Penetration twins common.

The unit cell contains eight formulary units.

Usually massive, occasionally granular or compact.

Physical Properties

(111) cleavage in traces. Conchoidal to uneven fracture. Brittle. Hardness 3. Specific gravity 5.1.

Metallic luster. Opaque. Color copper red tarnishing to give a purplish iridescent coating. Streak gray black.

Fusible at 2.5.

Distinctive Properties and Tests

Color and peacock tarnish. Tests for copper and iron.

Association and Occurrence

Widespread in copper deposits usually with chalcopyrite and quartz. Also with chalcocite, enargite, covellite, pyrite, pyrrhotite, marcasite, arsenopyrite, etc.

Found in (1) sulfide veins, (2) zone of secondary enrichment in copper-bearing sulfide deposits, (3) possibly as a magmatic segregation, (4) as an accessory in pegmatites, and (5) in black shales.

Alteration: To chalcocite, chalcopyrite, covellite, cuprite, chrysocolla, malachite, azurite.

Confused with: Niccolite, pyrrhotite, chalcocite.

Variants

Often contains small amounts of Pb, and less commonly Au and Ag.

Related Minerals

Other similar species: Pentlandite, $(FeNi)_9S_8$.

GALENA   PbS

Crystallography, Structure, Habit

Isometric. $\frac{4}{m}\overline{3}\frac{2}{m}$. Commonly in cubes or cubo-octahedra. Rarely octa-hedra. Penetration and contact twins common, also repeated lamellar twins.
Isostructural with halite, NaCl, Figure 6–6a. 4 PbS per unit cell.
Crystal aggregates, massive, fine granular to impalpable, plumose.

Physical Properties

Perfect (001) cleavage yielding cubic fragments. Parting on (111). Sub-conchoidal fracture. Brittle.
Hardness 2.5. Specific gravity 7.6.
Metallic luster. Opaque. Color and streak lead gray.
Melting point 1115°.

Distinctive Properties and Tests

Cubic crystals and cleavage, specific gravity. Tests for lead.

Association and Occurrence

Widely distributed. Found with sphalerite, chalcocite, pyrite, quartz, silver ores, fluorite, and barite in (1) sulfide veins; (2) replacement deposits, usually in limestone.

Alteration: To cerussite, anglesite, and pyromorphite.

Confused with: Stibnite.

Variants

Often contains Sb and As. Native silver or argentite may be included as an exsolved phase.

Related Minerals

Isotypes: Altaite, PbTe; clausthalite, PbSe; alabandite, MnS; oldhamite, CaS.

SPHALERITE (zinc blende, black jack) ZnS

Crystallography, Structure, Habit
Isometric. $\overline{4}3m$. Tetrahedron, dodecahedron, and cubes as basic forms, but crystals are often highly modified, distorted, or rounded. Twins usually as simple or multiple contact twins or lamellar intergrowths, occasionally penetration twins.

Isostructural with diamond, Figure 6–15c. Zn and S atoms occupy alternate C atom sites. The cell contains four ZnS.

Usually in cleavable masses or crystal aggregates, also coarse to fine granular, fibrous, colloform.

Physical Properties
Perfect (011) cleavage. Conchoidal fracture. Brittle.

Hardness 3.5–4. Specific gravity 3.9–4.1.

Resinous to adamantine luster. Translucent to transparent. Color yellow, brown, black (deepening with increasing iron content). Streak white, pale yellow, pale brown.

Pyroelectric. Occasionally triboluminescent and fluorescent. Infusible.

Distinctive Properties and Tests
Cleavage, luster. Powdered mineral decomposed by warm hydrochloric acid with the evolution of H_2S gas.

Association and Occurrence
Found with galena, chalcopyrite, pyrite, barite, fluorite, siderite, rhodochrosite, quartz.

Sphalerite is a common mineral. It is found as replacements in (1) dolostone, limestone, and other sedimentary rocks, (2) in sulfide veins, and (3) in contact metamorphic deposits.

Alteration: To goslarite, $ZnSO_4 \cdot 7H_2O$; hemimorphite, smithsonite.

Confused with: Siderite, ankerite, sulfur, enargite.

Varieties
Cadmian (přibramite), ferroan (marmatite).

Related Minerals
Isomorphs: Christophite, (ZnFe)S with up to 26 per cent Fe.

Isotypes: Metacinnabarite, (HgFeZn)S; tiemannite, HgSe; coloradoite, HgTe; onofrite, Hg(SSe); guadalcazarite (HgZn)(SSe).

Polymorphs: Wurtzite, stable form above $1020°$.

CHALCOPYRITE   (copper pyrites) $CuFeS_2$

Crystallography, Structure, Habit

Tetragonal. $\bar{4}2m$. Usually in pseudotetrahedra with prominent sphenoidal faces. Sphenoidal faces (112) are dull, oxidized, or striated, and the ($\bar{1}$12) faces are brilliant and unstriated. Penetration twins.

Isostructural with diamond and sphalerite (see Figure 6–1c). Cu and Fe atoms alternate in the sites occupied by Zn in sphalerite. The unit cell contains four formulary units. The crystals of chalcopyrite are pseudoisometric due to the nearly isometric cell dimensions ($c \approx 2a$) and its orthogonal angular relations.

Usually massive and crystal aggregates not rare.

Physical Properties

Indistinct cleavage parallel to (012). Uneven fracture. Brittle.

Hardness 3.5–4. Specific gravity 4.2.

Metallic luster. Opaque. Color brass yellow, sometimes showing an iridescent tarnish on exposure. Streak green black.

Readily fusible (2).

Distinctive Properties and Tests

Color, streak. Tests for copper and iron.

Association and Occurrence

Widespread in occurrence and found in most rock types. Usually found with pyrite, sphalerite, bornite, galena, chalcocite, quartz, or calcite in (1) magmatic segregation with pentlandite, pyrrhotite; (2) vein deposits of wide temperature range; (3) pyrometasomatic deposits; and (4) black shales.

Alteration: To chalcocite, covellite, chrysocolla, malachite, iron oxides.

Confused with: Pyrite, gold, bornite, pyrrhotite.

Variants

Commonly contains small amounts of Ag and Au.

Related Minerals

Isotypes: Stannite, Cu_2FeSnS_4.

PYRRHOTITE

$$Fe_{1-x}S$$

Crystallography, Structure, Habit

Hexagonal. $\dfrac{6}{m}\dfrac{2}{m}\dfrac{2}{m}$. Rare tabular to platy crystals.

Isostructural with niccolite, Figure 6–13a. The unit cell contains two formulary units. Some of the Fe sites are vacant and the Fe:S ratio varies from about 0.85 to 1.0.

Usually massive, also disseminated grains.

Physical Properties

No cleavage. Parting parallel to (0001) and (11$\bar{2}$0). Uneven to sub-conchoidal fracture. Brittle.

Hardness 3.5–4.5. Specific gravity 4.6.

Metallic luster. Opaque. Color bronze yellow. Streak black.

Weakly magnetic. Fusible (3).

Distinctive Properties and Tests

Color, magnetism. Yields H_2S when decomposed by HCl.

Association and Occurrence

Found with pyrite, chalcopyrite, pentlandite, galena, and magnetite in (1) mafic igneous rocks, (2) pegmatites, (3) metamorphic rocks, and (4) hydrothermal veins.

Alteration: To sulfates, oxides, or carbonates of iron.

Confused with: Bornite, pyrite.

Variants

Chemical varieties: Troilite, FeS. Exsolution of pyrrhotite into Fe-rich and Fe-poor phases may occur. Ni, Co, Mn, and Cu are common impurities.

Related Minerals

Isotypes: Niccolite; jaipurite, CoS; arite, Ni(AsSb); breithauptite, NiSb.

Polymorphs: Orthorhombic modification above 138°.

NICCOLITE

NiAs

Crystallography, Structure, Habit

Hexagonal. $\frac{6}{m}\frac{2}{m}\frac{2}{m}$. Crystals rare, usually pyramidal. Cyclic twins (fourlings).

Niccolite structure, see Figure 6–13a. There are 2 NiAs per unit cell. Usually massive, sometimes colloform or columnar.

Physical Properties

No cleavage. Uneven fracture. Brittle.
Hardness 5–5.5. Specific gravity 7.8.
Metallic luster. Opaque. Color pale copper red. Streak brownish black. Fusible (2).

Distinctive Properties and Tests

Color, association, alteration, tests for nickel and arsenic.

Association and Occurrence

Found with skutterudite series minerals, native silver, silver sulfosalts, pyrrhotite, chalcopyrite, etc., (1) in veins with silver and cobalt minerals and (2) in copper–iron–nickel sulfide deposits associated with mafic igneous rocks (norite).

Alteration: To annabergite, $Ni_3As_3O_8 \cdot 8H_2O$, a green, earthy powder.

Confused with: Bornite, pyrrhotite.

Variants

Usually contains some Sb, and often Fe, Co, and S.

Related Minerals

Isomorphs: Breithauptite, NiSb.
Isotypes: Pyrrhotite; arite, Ni(AsSb); jaipurite, CoS.
Other similar species: Millerite, NiS; pentlandite, $(FeNi)_9S_8$.

237

Crystallography, Structure, Habit

Hexagonal. $\dfrac{6}{m}\dfrac{2}{m}\dfrac{2}{m}$. Crystals rare, hexagonal plates when found.

Structure closely related to that of niccolite, but three niccolite cells high and the cell contains 6 CuS.

Usually massive or in tabular aggregates.

Physical Properties

Perfect (0001) cleavage, flexible in very thin laminae.

Hardness 1.5–2. Specific gravity 4.7.

Submetallic luster. Opaque. Color indigo blue, sometimes with a purple tarnish. Streak lead gray to black.

Fusible (2.5) giving sulfurous fumes.

Distinctive Properties and Tests

Color, association, tests for copper.

Association and Occurrence

Found with other copper minerals in veins and secondarily enriched zones.

Alteration: From chalcopyrite, chalcocite, enargite, bornite, etc.

Variants

Usually contains some iron.

Related Minerals

Isomorph: Klockmannite, CuSe.

Crystallography, Structure, Habit

Hexagonal. 32. Crystals as rhombohedra, thick tablets, and prisms. Contact twins fairly common, also six-pointed stellate forms and penetration twins. The structure is that of distorted halite. The unit cell contains 3 HgS.

Usually found as crystalline incrustations, granular, massive, or earthy.

Physical Properties

Perfect $(10\bar{1}0)$ cleavage. Subconchoidal to uneven fracture. Subsectile. Hardness 2–2.5. Specific gravity 8.1.

Luster may be adamantine to metallic in dark-colored crystalline varieties or earthy to dull in friable varieties. Color is a tint or shade of red. Streak red brown to scarlet.

Distinctive Properties and Tests

Color and streak, specific gravity, tests for mercury. Wholly volatile before the blowpipe.

Association and Occurrence

Found with pyrite, marcasite, realgar, calcite, stibnite, quartz, opal, fluorite, barite in (1) veins, (2) disseminated, and (3) in masses in sedimentary and volcanic rocks.

Confused with: Hematite, cuprite, realgar.

Variants

Often contains admixed clay, iron oxide, bitumen, etc.

Related Minerals

Polymorphs: Metacinnabarite.

Other similar species: Coloradoite, HgTe; tiemannite, HgSe.

REALGAR

Crystallography, Structure, Habit

Monoclinic. $\dfrac{2}{m}$. Short prismatic crystals striated vertically. Contact twins with irregular composition surface.

Found as crystalline aggregates or crusts, coarse to fine granular, and compact.

Physical Properties

Good (010) cleavage and less good (001), ($\bar{1}$01), and (120). Conchoidal fracture. Sectile.

Hardness 1.5–2. Specific gravity 3.6.

Luster resinous to greasy. Transparent (fresh) to translucent. Color and streak red to orange yellow.

Melting point approximately 310°. AsS is unstable in the presence of light and alters to As_2S_3 and As_2O_3.

Distinctive Properties and Tests

Color, low melting point, tests for arsenic. Wholly volatile when heated on charcoal.

Association and Occurrence

Found with orpiment, arsenic minerals, stibnite, and lead, gold, and silver ores (1) in hydrothermal veins, (2) in replacement deposits in sedimentary rocks, and (3) as a volcanic sublimate.

Alteration: Readily to a reddish-yellow powder which is a mixture of orpiment, As_2S_3, and arsenolite, As_2O_3.

Confused with: Cinnabar, hematite, cuprite.

Related Minerals

Other similar species: Orpiment.

ORPIMENT

As_2S_3

Crystallography, Structure, Habit

Monoclinic. $\frac{2}{m}$. Small and poor, short tabular crystals.

Structure is crumpled As_2S_3 sheets, Figure 6–13f. Four formulary units per unit cell.

Many habits, usually in foliated or columnar masses.

Physical Properties

Perfect (010) cleavage; cleavage laminae are flexible but not elastic. Sectile. Hardness 1.5–2. Specific gravity 3.5.

Pearly to resinous luster. Transparent to translucent. Color yellow, streak yellow.

Melting point approximately 300°.

Distinctive Properties and Tests

Hardness, color, tests for arsenic. Orpiment is wholly volatile before the blowpipe.

Association and Occurrence

Found with stibnite, realgar, native arsenic, calcite, barite, gypsum in (1) low-temperature hydrothermal veins, (2) hot springs, (3) volcanic sublimates, and (4) in replacement deposits in sedimentary rocks.

Alteration: From realgar.

Confused with: Native sulfur.

Related Minerals

Other similar species: Realgar.

STIBNITE

Sb_2S_3

Crystallography, Structure, Habit

Orthorhombic. $\frac{2}{m}\frac{2}{m}\frac{2}{m}$. Stout to slender prismatic crystals, often striated vertically and sometimes bent.

Stibnite structure, Figure 6–13b. Four Sb_2S_3 per cell.

Usually found in aggregates of acicular to columnar crystals, also granular to impalpable.

Physical Properties

Perfect (010) cleavage and imperfect (100) and (110) cleavage. Subconchoidal fracture. Subsectile.

Hardness 2. Specific gravity 4.6.

Metallic luster. Opaque. Color and streak lead to steel gray, often with a black tarnish.

Specimens are readily bent or twisted. Melting point 550°. Transparent to infrared light.

Distinctive Properties and Tests

Hardness, habit, cleavage. Tests for antimony. A drop of concentrated KOH produces a yellow coating and a brown spot on stibnite.

Association and Occurrence

Stibnite is widely distributed. It is found with realgar, orpiment, galena, marcasite, pyrite, cinnabar, calcite, barite, and chalcedonic quartz (1) in low-temperature hydrothermal veins, (2) in replacement deposits, and (3) in hot-spring deposits.

Alteration: To kermesite, Sb_2S_2O; cervantite, $Sb_2O_3 \cdot Sb_2O_5$; senarmontite, Sb_2O_3; valentinite, Sb_2O_3; and stibiconite, $H_2Sb_2O_5$.

Confused with: Jamesonite, enargite, galena.

Variants

May be contaminated with traces of Fe, Pb, or Cu and, less often, with Zn, Co, Ag, or Au.

Related Minerals

Isotypes: Bismuthinite, Bi_2S_3, and guanajuatite, Bi_2Se_3.

PYRITE

FeS_2

Crystallography, Structure, Habit

Isometric. $\frac{2}{m}\bar{3}$. Crystals common, usually in cubes, less often in pyrito-hedra and rarely in octahedra. Crystals usually striated. Penetration twins common, contact twins rare.

Pyrite structure (see Figure 6–13c). The unit cell contains 4 FeS_2.

Usually in crystals or crystal aggregates, also massive, granular.

Physical Properties

Indistinct (001) cleavage. Indistinct (011) and (111) parting. Conchoidal to uneven fracture. Brittle.

Hardness 6–6.5. Specific gravity 5.0.

Metallic luster. Opaque. Color pale brass yellow, sometimes with an iridescent tarnish. Streak green black to brown black.

Thermoelectric. Sparks when struck with steel. Fusible (2.5–3) to magnetic globule.

Distinctive Properties and Tests

Crystal form, hardness, color.

Association and Occurrence

Pyrite is the most widespread and abundant of the sulfides. It may be associated with most other minerals and is found over a wide range of environments.

Alteration: To sulfates and oxides of iron.

Confused with: Chalcopyrite, marcasite.

Variants

Chemical varieties: Nickelian, cobaltian. Often contaminated with small amounts of V, Mo, Cr, W, etc.

Related Minerals

Isomorphs: Bravoite, $(NiFe)S_2$.

Isotypes: Laurite, RuS_2; sperrylite, $PtAs_2$; hauerite, MnS_2; cobaltite; gersdorffite, NiAsS; ullmanite, NiSbS.

Polymorphs: Marcasite.

Other similar species: Arsenoferrite, $FeAs_2$.

Crystallography, Structure, Habit

Isometric. 23. In cubes or pyritohedra with striated faces.

Isostructural with pyrite (Figure 6–13c) with As and S pairs occupying alternate sites of sulfur pairs in pyrite. The unit cell contains 4 CoAsS.

Crystal aggregates, granular, compact.

Physical Properties

Perfect (001) cleavage. Uneven fracture. Brittle.

Hardness 5.5. Specific gravity 6.3.

Metallic luster. Opaque. Color usually silver white, sometimes tending toward reddish, violet gray, or gray black. Streak gray black.

Thermoelectric. Fusible (2–3).

Distinctive Properties and Tests

Color, cleavage, crystal habit. Tests for cobalt and arsenic.

Association and Occurrence

Found with cobalt and nickel sulfides and arsenides, pyrrhotite, chalcopyrite, galena, and magnetite in high-temperature deposits, either disseminated or in veins.

Alteration: To erythrite, $Co_3(AsO_4)_2 \cdot H_2O$, a pink, powdery coating or "bloom."

Confused with: Skutterudite series.

Variants

Chemical varieties: Ferrian. Nickel may be present as a minor contaminant.

Related Minerals

Isomorphs: Gersdorffite, NiAsS; ullmanite, NiSbS.

Isotypes: Pyrite.

Polymorphs: Orthorhombic modification above 850°.

Crystallography, Structure, Habit

Orthorhombic. $\frac{2}{m}\frac{2}{m}\frac{2}{m}$. Crystals tabular and frequently with curved faces. Twinning produces coxcomb arrays, spear shapes, and occasionally stellate fivelings.

Structure illustrated in Figure 6–13d. Two FeS_2 per unit cell.

Crystal aggregates, fine grained to impalpable, stalactitic, colloform, and concentric.

Physical Properties

Poor (101) cleavage. Uneven fracture. Brittle.

Hardness 6–6.5. Specific gravity 4.9.

Metallic luster. Opaque. Color tin white on fresh surface deepening on exposure to pale bronze yellow. Streak gray black.

Fusible (2.5–3) to magnetic globule.

Distinctive Properties and Tests

"Coxcomb" habit, color. Distinguished from pyrite by the following test: Treat finely ground mineral with cold HNO_3 and boil the solution. Marcasite is decomposed with the liberation of sulfur, yielding a milky solution. Pyrite treated in the same manner is completely dissolved.

Association and Occurrence

Found with lead and zinc ores. It is deposited at low temperatures from acid solutions (1) in metalliferous veins and (2) in sedimentary rocks, especially limestones, shales, and coals.

Alteration: To iron sulfates and iron oxides, native sulfur.

Confused with: Pyrite.

Variants

May contain traces of Fe or Cu.

Related Minerals

Isotypes: Loellingite, $FeAs_2$; safflorite, $(CoFe)As_2$; rammelsbergite, $NiAs_2$. Polymorph: Pyrite.

ARSENOPYRITE

Crystallography, Structure, Habit

Monoclinic. $\frac{2}{m}$. Prismatic and stout striated crystals. Pseudo-orthorhombic shapes produced by twinning. Penetration, contact and cyclic twins.

Superstructure of the marcasite structure Figure 6–13d. Eight FeAsS units per cell.

Found as disseminated crystals, crystal aggregates, granular and compact masses.

Physical Properties

Distinct (101) cleavage. Uneven fracture. Brittle.

Hardness 5.5–6. Specific gravity 6.1.

Metallic luster. Opaque. Color silver white. Streak black.

Readily fusible (2). May be thermoelectric.

Distinctive Properties and Tests

Color, tests for arsenic, crystal form.

Association and Occurrence

Most abundant and widespread arsenic-bearing mineral. Found with pyrite, chalcopyrite, sphalerite, and ores of tin, cobalt, nickel, silver, gold, and lead (1) in high-temperature veins, (2) in pegmatites, (3) in contact metamorphic rocks, and (4) disseminated in marble or slate.

Alteration: To scorodite, $FeAsO_4 \cdot 2H_2O$.

Confused with: Skutterudite series.

Variants

Chemical varieties: Cobaltian (danaite), bismuthian. Usually contains some Co and may contain traces of Ni, Fe, Bi, Sb, Au, or Ag.

Related Minerals

Isomorphs: Glaucodot, $(CoFe)AsS$.

Isotypes: Gudmundite, $FeSbS$.

Other similar species: Wolfachite, $Ni(AsSb)S$; lautite, $CuAsS$.

Crystallography, Structure, Habit

Hexagonal. $\frac{6}{m}\frac{2}{m}\frac{2}{m}$. Crystals as hexagonal plates or short prisms. Molybdenite structure, Figure 6–13e. The unit cell contains 2 MoS_2. Usually found in foliated masses or in discrete scales.

Physical Properties

Perfect (0001) cleavage, laminae flexible but not elastic. Sectile. Hardness 1–1.5. Specific gravity 4.7.

Metallic luster. Opaque. Color lead gray. Streak grayish-black (greenish on glazed porcelain).

Infusible.

Distinctive Properties and Tests

Cleavage, hardness, greenish streak on glazed porcelain.

Association and Occurrence

Found with scheelite, wolframite, topaz, fluorite, chalcopyrite, cassiterite, epidote, etc., (1) in veins, (2) in pegmatites, (3) in granite, and (4) in contact metamorphic deposits.

Alteration: To ferrimolybdite, $Fe_2O_3 \cdot 3MoO_3 \cdot 8H_2O$.

Variants: May contain traces of Au or Ag.

Related Minerals

Isotype: Tungstenite, WS_2.

Crystallography, Structure, Habit

Isometric. $\frac{2}{m}\bar{3}$. Cubes, cubo-octahedra, and octahedra, frequently with curved faces. Cyclic twins and complex and distorted shapes.

The structure is illustrated in Figure 7–4. The unit cell contains eight formulary units.

Usually massive, dense to granular.

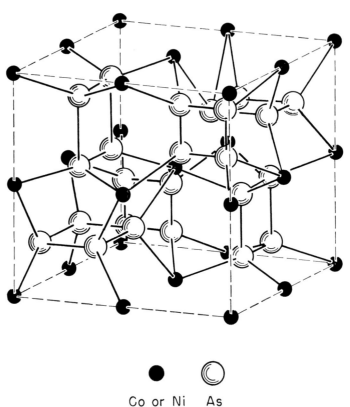

Co or Ni   As

Fig. 7–4. Skutterudite structure.

Physical Properties

Distinct (011) and (111) cleavage, but this cleavage is variable and not characteristic. Variable cleavage may be due to parting in these directions. Fracture conchoidal to uneven. Brittle.

Hardness 5.5–6. Specific gravity 6.5.

Metallic luster. Opaque. Color tin white to silver gray. Streak black.

Thermoelectric. Fusible (2–2.5).

Skutterudite Series (cont.)

Distinctive Properties and Tests

Color, tests for Co, Ni, and As.

Association and Occurrence

Usually found in veins with cobalt and nickel minerals, especially cobaltite and niccolite, also arsenopyrite, native silver, silver sulfosalts, native bismuth, calcite, siderite, barite, and quartz.

Alteration: Cobalt-rich types alter to pink erythrite, $Co_3As_2O_8 \cdot 8H_2O$. Nickel-rich types alter to green annabergite, $Ni_3As_2O_8 \cdot 8H_2O$.

Confused with: Arsenopyrite, cobaltite.

Variants

Chemical varieties: Ferrian, bismuthian. S commonly replaces a small amount of the As.

Related Minerals

The skutterudite series includes the following isomorphous pairs: Skutterudite, $(CoNi)As_{3-x}$ to nickel skutterudite $(NiCo)As_{3-x}$ with $x = 0$ to 0.5; smaltite, $(CoNi)As_{3-x}$ to chloanthite, $(NiCo)As_{3-x}$ with $x = 0.5$ to 1.0.

Sulfosalts

$A_mB_nX_p$ Type ($m:n > 4:3$)
  Polybasite group
  Argyrodite series

A_3BX_3 Type
  Ruby silver group
  Pyrargyrite, Ag_3SbS_3
  Tetrahedrite series, $Cu_{12}(SbAs)_4S_{13}$

A_3BX_4 Type
  Sulvanite group
  Enargite group
  Enargite, Cu_3AsS_4

A_2BX_3 Type
  Bournonite group
  Bournonite, $PbCuSbS_3$

ABX_2 Type ($A:B \sim 1:1$)
  Jamesonite, $Pb_4FeSb_6S_{14}$

$A_2B_3X_6$ Type ($A + B:X \sim 5:6$)
  Andorite group
  Plagionite group

AB_2X_4 Type ($A:B \sim 1:2$)

AB_4X_7 Type

The general physical characteristics of sulfosalts are the same as those of the sulfides, to which they are closely related. The principal difference between the two families is the presence in sulfosalts of chains, sheets, etc., of sulfur and arsenic, antimony, or bismuth as contrasted to sulfur (or arsenic, selenium, etc.), either singly or paired in sulfides.

Sulfosalts are always composed of a limited number of elements. As-S, Bi-S, or Sb-S are coordinated by silver, copper, or lead. Only rarely are other elements present. A generalized formula for the sulfosalts might thus be written:

$$(Ag, Cu, Pb)(As, Bi, Sb)S$$

The limited number of elements found in sulfosalts is not a criterion of the number of species. Various combinations in different proportions result in many species.

Distinction between the various sulfosalts described may be best made by use of the properties of cleavage, color, and streak, together with the mineral habit as indicated by the table below.

Mineral	Hardness	Cleavage	Color	Streak	Habit, etc.
Pyrargyrite ...	2.5	Yes	Red to black	Red	
Tetrahedrite ..	3–4.5	No	Gray black	Brown to black	Brittle, tetrahedral crystals
Enargite	3	Yes	Black	Black	
Bournonite ...	2.5–3	No	Steel gray to black	Steel gray to black	Tubular crystals, cogwheel twins
Jamesonite ...	2–3	Yes	Steel gray to black	Steel gray to black	Feathery appearance

The sulfosalt family may be distinguished from the sulfide family on the basis of fusibility. Only two sulfides, argentite and stibnite,[*] melt at less than 2 on the scale of fusibility, whereas all sulfosalts fuse at less than 2.

[*] Stibnite may be considered as a metalless sulfosalt.

PYRARGYRITE

Ag_3SbS_3

Crystallography, Structure, Habit

Hexagonal. $3m$. Striated prisms. Twins by growth into complex aggregations, also repeated and cyclic twins.

Crystal aggregates, massive, compact.

Physical Properties

Distinct $(10\overline{1}1)$ cleavage. Conchoidal to uneven fracture. Brittle. Hardness 2.5. Specific gravity 5.8. Adamantine luster. Translucent. Color deep red. Streak red. Melting point $486°$.

Distinctive Properties and Tests

Color, diaphaneity, fusibility, tests for silver and antimony. Decomposed by HNO_3 with the formation of S and Sb_2O_3.

Association and Occurrence

Found with silver sulfosalts, native silver, galena, sphalerite, calcite, dolomite, and quartz (1) in low-temperature metalliferous veins and (2) in secondarily enriched zones.

Alteration: To argentite, native silver, and rarely to cerargyrite or stibnite. From argentite, native silver.

Confused with: Proustite, Ag_3AsS_3.

Variants

Some As may replace Sb.

Related Minerals

Isotype: Proustite, Ag_3AsS_3.
Polymorphs: Pyrostilpnite; xanthoconite.

TETRAHEDRITE SERIES $\quad Cu_{12}(SbAs)_4S_{13}$

Crystallography, Structure, Habit

Isometric. $\bar{4}\,3m$. Tetrahedral crystals. Penetration twins, often repeated twins.

Structure is a distorted version of the sphalerite structure. Cu and some Sb or As atoms occupy equivalent positions to zinc in sphalerite, while the remaining antimony and all of the sulfur atoms are in sites equivalent to sulfur in sphalerite. The unit cell contains two formulary units.

Crystal aggregates, massive, granular, compact.

Physical Properties

No cleavage. Subconchoidal to uneven fracture. Brittle.

Hardness 3–4.5, increasing with As content. Specific gravity 4.6–5:1, increasing with Sb content.

Metallic luster. Opaque. Color gray to black. Streak black to brown to red.

Fuses readily (1.5). Very thin splinters are cherry red in transmitted light.

Distinctive Properties and Tests

Crystal form, lack of cleavage, color.

Association and Occurrence

One of the most common sulfosalts with widespread occurrence and varied association. Found with chalcopyrite, sphalerite, galena, pyrite, quartz, siderite, barite, etc.

Alteration: To azurite, malachite, antimony oxides, and occasionally to cuprite, limonite, and chrysocolla.

Confused with: Chalcocite, argentite.

Variants

Chemical varieties: Zincian, ferroan (coppite), argentian (freibergite), mercurian (schwatzite), plumbian (malinowskite), bismuthian, nickelian, and cobaltian.

Related Minerals

Isomorphs: The tetrahedrite series exhibits complete isomorphism from tetrahedrite, $Cu_{12}Sb_4S_{13}$, to tennantite, $Cu_{12}As_4S_{13}$. Limited replacement of many different elements for Cu is very common.

Other similar species: Germanite, Cu_3GeS_4; colusite, $Cu_3(AsSnFe)S_4$; sulvanite, Cu_3VS_4.

Crystallography, Structure, Habit

Orthorhombic. $2mm$. Tabular or prismatic striated crystals. Cyclic twins. Sphalerite structure. Two formulary units per unit cell. Crystal aggregates, massive, granular, bladed.

Physical Properties

Perfect (110) and distinct (100) and (010) cleavage. Uneven fracture. Brittle.

Hardness 3. Specific gravity 4.4.

Metallic luster. Opaque. Color and streak gray black to iron black.

Readily fusible (1). Dull black tarnish on exposed surfaces. Insoluble.

Distinctive Properties and Tests

Cleavage, color, tests for copper and arsenic.

Association and Occurrence

Found with copper sulfides and pyrite (1) in intermediate temperature veins and (2) in replacement deposits.

Alteration: To tennantite, copper arsenates, arsenic oxides.

Confused with: Sphalerite, stibnite, bournonite, jamesonite.

Variants

Chemical varieties: Antimonian. Commonly contains some Fe and more rarely Zn or Ge.

Related Minerals

Isomorphs: Famatinite, Cu_3SbS_4.

Polymorphs: Luzonite.

Other similar species: Tetrahedrite; sulvanite, Cu_3VS_4; germanite, Cu_3GeS_4; and colusite, $Cu_3(AsSnFe)S_4$.

BOURNONITE

$PbCuSbS_3$

Crystallography, Structure, Habit

Orthorhombic. $\frac{2}{m}\frac{2}{m}\frac{2}{m}$. Short prisms and tablets. Striated. Twins to form cruciform or wheel-like aggregates.

Subparallel crystal aggregates, massive, granular, compact.

Physical Properties

Imperfect (010) cleavage. Subconchoidal to uneven fracture. Brittle. Hardness 2.5–3. Specific gravity 5.8.

Metallic luster. Opaque. Color and streak steel gray to black.

Easily fusible (1).

Distinctive Properties and Tests

Crystal form, tests for lead, copper, and antimony.

Association and Occurrence

One of the commonest sulfosalts. Found with galena, sphalerite, stibnite, chalcopyrite, siderite, chalcocite, quartz, dolomite, pyrite, etc., in hydrothermal veins formed at moderate temperature.

Alteration: To lead antimonate (bindheimite), cerussite, malachite, azurite.

Confused with: Enargite, stibnite, jamesonite.

Variants

Chemical varieties: Arsenian. Often contains small amounts of Ag, Zn, and Fe.

Related Minerals

Isomorphs: Seligmannite, $PbCuAsS_3$.

Other similar species: Aikinite, $PbCuBiS_3$.

Crystallography, Structure, Habit

Monoclinic. $\frac{2}{m}$. Acicular to fibrous crystals. Striated.

Structure illustrated in Figure 6–14. Two formulary units per unit cell. Felted masses, massive, columnar, plumose.

Physical Properties

Good (001) cleavage. Brittle.

Hardness 2.5. Specific gravity 5.6.

Metallic luster. Opaque. Color and streak gray black, sometimes tarnishing iridescent.

Easily fusible (1).

Distinctive Properties and Tests

Pulmose habit ("feather ore"), tests for lead, iron, and antimony.

Association and Occurrence

Found in moderate- to low-temperature hydrothermal veins with lead sulfo-salts, pyrite, sphalerite, galena, tetrahedrite, stibnite, quartz, siderite, dolomite, calcite, rhodochrosite, etc.

Alteration: To lead antimonate (bindheimite).

Confused with: Stibnite, enargite, bournonite.

Variants

May contain significant amounts of Cu and Zn and traces of Ag and Bi.

Related Minerals

Other similar species: Dufreynosite, $Pb_2As_2S_5$; cosalite, $Pb_2Bi_2S_5$; zinkenite, $PbS \cdot Sb_2S_3$; and boulangerite, $5PbS \cdot 2Sb_2S_3$.

Halides

The halogen elements in column VII of the periodic table are characterized by unit negative valences and poor screening. These elements, therefore, tend to form strong ionic bonds with well-screened alkali and alkali metal elements. The minerals which are formed are called halides. Only two of the halides, halite and fluorite, are common minerals. Bromine and iodine are geochemically rare, and so are minerals which contain them. Many multiple halides are known but none are common.

Halide structures are ordinarily quite simple, and the first mineral structure to be worked out (by W. H. Bragg) was that of halite.

Halides as a family are characterized by low specific gravity, light colors, softness, and especially by their solubility in water.

The halides are widely used in industry. Halite, in addition to its direct use as salt, is used in the manufacture of HCl and as a source of sodium and chlorine. Sylvite, KCl, provides an important source of potassium. Fluorite yields fluorine for numerous fluorine bearing compounds and is in demand by both the steel and aluminum industry as a flux. (The name fluorite is from the Latin *fluere*, to flow, and not from the property of fluorescence or the element fluorine.) Fluorite, usually artificial, is also used as a component in spherically and chromatically corrected compound lenses and in spectrographic prisms which must transmit ultraviolet or infrared light.

HALITE (rock salt)   NaCl

Crystallography, Structure, Habit

Isometric. $\frac{4}{m}\bar{3}\frac{2}{m}$. Crystals as cubes, sometimes "hopper" forms, rarely octahedra.

Halite structure, see Figures 6–6a and 7–5. Four NaCl per unit cell.

Crystalline aggregates, massive, coarsely granular to compact.

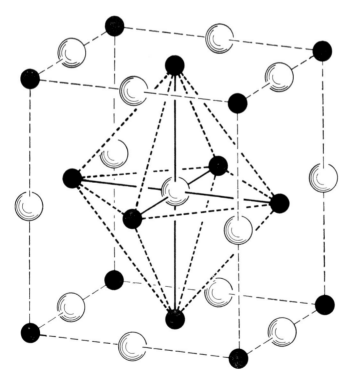

Fig. 7–5. Coordination in the halite structure.

Halite (cont.)

Physical Properties
Perfect cubic cleavage. Conchoidal fracture. Brittle.
Hardness 2. Specific gravity 2.2.
Vitreous luster. Transparent to translucent. Colorless or white, also yellowish, reddish, bluish, or purplish.
Soluble with a salty taste. Highly diathermanous. Melting point 804°.

Distinctive Properties and Tests
Crystal form, cleavage, taste.

Association and Occurrence
Found (1) as extensive sedimentary beds with associated kainite, $MgSO_4 \cdot KCl \cdot 3H_2O$; polyhalite, $K_2SO_4 \cdot MgSO_4 \cdot 2CaSO_4 \cdot 2H_2O$; carnallite, $KCl \cdot MgCl_2 \cdot 6H_2O$; gypsum, anhydrite, clay minerals, etc., (2) as a precipitate from saline waters from oceans and springs, and desert efflorescence, and (3) as a volcanic sublimate.

Alteration: Readily dissolves in water.

Confused with: Sylvite, KCl.

Variants
Chemical varieties: Argentian (huantajayite).
Often mechanically mixed with $CaSO_4$, $CaCl_2$, $MgCl_2$, or $MgSO_4$.

Related Minerals
Isotypes: Bromyrite, AgBr; sylvite, KCl; villiaumite, NaF; and cerargyrite.
Other related species: Sal ammoniac, NH_4Cl.

CERARGYRITE (horn silver) $\qquad$ AgCl

Crystallography, Structure, Habit

Isometric. $\frac{4}{m}\bar{3}\frac{2}{m}$. Crystals rare, cubes.

Halite structure, Figures 6–6a and 7–5. With 4 AgCl per unit cell.

Usually massive and encrusting, sometimes columnar.

Physical Properties

No cleavage. Poor conchoidal fracture. Tough. Highly sectile.

Hardness 2–3. Specific gravity 5.5.

Resinous luster. Translucent to transparent. Color pearl gray to gray green to colorless. The color deepens with increasing amounts of iodine. The color deepens on exposure to light.

Resembles horn or wax. Melting point 445°.

Distinctive Properties and Tests

Sectility, waxy appearance, readily fusible to globule of metallic silver.

Association and Occurrence

Cerargyrite is a secondary silver mineral associated with native silver, cerussite, galena, limonite, calcite, barite, jarosite, wulfenite, etc.

Alteration: From other silver minerals.

Variants

Chemical varieties: Bromian (embolite), iodian, chlorian. May sometimes contain Hg or Fe.

Related Minerals

Isomorphs: Bromyrite, AgBr.

Isotypes: Halite; sylvite, KCl; villiaumite, NaF.

Other similar species: Iodyrite, AgI.

FLUORITE

CaF_2

Crystallography, Structure, Habit

Isometric. $\frac{4}{m}\,3\,\frac{2}{m}$. Crystals usually cubes and rarely octahedra or dodecahedra.

Fluorite structure, see Figure 6–6b, with 4 CaF_2 per unit cell.

Usually in crystals, also cleavable, granular, and columnar masses.

Physical Properties

Perfect octahedral cleavage. Rare and indistinct parting on (011). Flat conchoidal fracture, may be splintery for compact kinds. Brittle.

Hardness 4. Specific gravity 3.2.

Vitreous luster. Transparent to translucent. Color usually a tint or shade of violet or green, also white, yellow, pink, and colorless.

Frequently strongly fluorescent or phosphorescent when heated, scratched, or exposed to various kinds of electromagnetic radiation. Melting point 1360°.

Distinctive Properties and Tests

Crystal form, cleavage, color. Loses color on heating.

Association and Occurrence

Found (1) as a vein mineral associated with tourmaline, celestite, quartz, cassiterite, topaz, galena, sphalerite, calcite, barite, (2) as a minor constituent of limestone and dolomite, (3) as a minor accessory in igneous rocks, and (4) as a volcanic sublimate.

Confused with: Calcite, quartz.

Variants

Chemical varieties: Yttrian (yttrofluorite), cerian (yttrocerite).

Cl replaces F in minute quantities.

Related Minerals

Similar species: Sellaite, MgF_2.

Oxides

SIMPLE OXIDES

A_2O TYPE
    Cuprite, Cu_2O
    Ice, H_2O

AO TYPE
    Periclase group
    Zincite group

A_3O_4 TYPE
    Hematite group
        Corundum, Al_2O_3
        Hematite, Fe_2O_3
        Ilmenite series, $(FeMgMn)TiO_3$
    Arsenolite group

AO_2 TYPE
    Rutile group
        Rutile, TiO_2
        Pyrolusite, MnO_2
        Cassiterite, SnO_2
    Uraninite group
        Uraninite, UO_2

MULTIPLE OXIDES

ABO TYPE
AB_2O_4 TYPE
    Spinel group
        Spinel series
            Spinel, $MgAl_2O_4$
        Magnetite series
            Magnetite, $FeFe_2O_4$
        Chromite series
            Chromite, $FeCr_2O_4$
    Hausmannite group

AB_4O_7 TYPE
ABO_3 TYPE
A_2BO_5 TYPE
AB_2O_5 TYPE
AB_3O_7 TYPE
ABO_4 TYPE
AB_2O_6 TYPE
    Columbite-tantalite series
        $(FeMn)(CbTa)_2O_6$

Oxides comprise a mineral class whose members have widely different physical properties. They are, however, usually harder than any other class except the silicates, heavier than other classes except the sulfides, generally nonreactive to common acids, often opaque, and not uncommonly have a high luster.

The physical characteristics of greatest usefulness in distinguishing between the various oxide minerals are hardness, color, and streak. This class is about equally divided into species whose hardness is less, approximately equal, and greater than the hardness of a knife blade. Many species have a constant color, usually black or reddish, and streaks are often distinctive. These properties together with some miscellaneous features are given in the following table.

The oxides are, for the most part, simple in both composition and in structure. Simple oxides are composed of one kind of metal and oxygen in ratios from A_2O to AO_2. Multiple oxides have two nonequivalent metal ions coordinated by oxygen. The metal-oxygen bond strengths are always about the same, and no discrete structural groups are found.

Oxides (cont.)

Some Physical Properties of the Oxides

Mineral	Hardness with Respect to Steel	Color	Streak	Miscellaneous
Cuprite	−	Red	Red brown	Red crystals
Ice	−	Colorless	None	
Corundum ..	+	Various	None	Very hard
Hematite ...	− to =	Red brown to black	Red	
Ilmenite	=	Black	Red to black	
Rutile	+	Red to black	Light brown	High luster
Pyrolusite ..	−	Black	Black	Sooty
Cassiterite ..	+	Brown to black	None	Heavy
Uraninite ...	=	Black	Brown black	Pitchy luster
Diaspore ...	+	White	None	Perfect cleavage
Goethite ...	−	Brown	Yellow brown	
Spinel	+	Various	None	Octahedral crystals
Magnetite ..	+	Black	Black	Magnetic
Chromite ...	=	Black to brown black	Dark brown	
Columbite ..	+	Black	Red to black	High luster

CUPRITE Cu_2O

Crystallography, Structure, Habit
Isometric. 432. Usually in octahedra, rarely dodecahedra, cubes, or capillary forms.

Cuprite structure (see Figure 6–6c). Two Cu_2O per unit cell. The structure of cuprite is unique among inorganic crystal structures in that it consists of two completely interpenetrating and identical networks which are not cross-connected by any Cu–O bonds.

Usually in crystals or crystal aggregates, also massive, granular, or earthy.

Physical Properties
Interrupted (111) cleavage. Conchoidal to uneven fracture. Brittle.
Hardness 3.5–4. Specific gravity 6.1.
Luster metallic to adamantine to earthy. Subtransparent to subtranslucent.
Color shades of red. Streak shining brown red.
Fusible (3).

Distinctive Properties and Tests
Crystals, luster, color, tests for copper.

Association and Occurrence
Found in the oxidized portion of copper veins associated with limonite, native copper, malachite, azurite, and chrysocolla.

Alteration: To malachite, native copper. From tetrahedrite, chalcopyrite.

Confused with: Cassiterite, hematite, cinnabar.

Variants
Form varieties: Capillary (chalcotrichite)—plushlike aggregates; earthy (tile ore).

Related Minerals
Similar species: Tenorite, CuO.

Crystallography, Structure, Habit

Hexagonal. $3m$. Crystals as lacy hexagonal plates (snowflakes), hexagonal prisms. Twinning with basal plane as twin plane.

Ice structure, see Figure 7–6. Twelve H_2O per unit cell. This structure is closely related to several other structures. The O atoms occupy the sites of the Zn and O atoms of zincite, Figure 6–6e, or the Si positions in tridymite.

Found in crystals, massive, and granular forms.

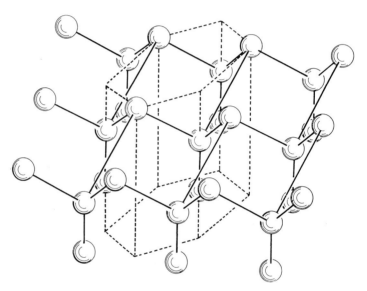

Fig. 7–6. Center of gravity of H_2O molecules in ordinary ice.

Physical Properties

No cleavage. Conchoidal fracture. Brittle, especially at low temperatures. Hardness 1.5. Specific gravity 0.92.

Vitreous luster. Transparent. Colorless to white.

Melting point $0°$.

Distinctive Properties and Tests

Melting point, taste, specific gravity.

Association and Occurrence

Forms whenever temperature falls below the freezing point of water as precipitation (snow, hail) and as a coating over bodies of water. It is also a semipermanent feature of snowfields and glaciers.

Some of the water adsorbed on the surface of minute mineral grains, e.g., clay minerals, is probably a monolayer of ice.

Ice (cont.)

Alteration: Melts to water.

Related Minerals

Polymorphs: There are many polymorphic forms of ice. At atmospheric pressure three forms, Ice I, Ice II, and Ice III are known in the range of 0° to −160°. High-pressure polymorphs are also known.

CORUNDUM Al_2O_3

Crystallography, Structure, Habit

Hexagonal. $\bar{3}\frac{2}{m}$. Crystals usually hexagonal prisms with tapered ends and flat terminations. Twinning common, producing a lamellar structure and basal striae, also penetration twins.

Corundum structure, Figure 6–6f. The cell contains two formulary units. Found as crystals, massive, granular, and in rounded grains.

Physical Properties

No cleavage. Good to perfect basal (0001) and rhombohedral (10$\bar{1}$1) parting. Uneven to conchoidal fracture. Brittle.

Hardness 9. Specific gravity 4.0.

Adamantine to vitreous luster. Transparent to translucent. Color various, usually brown, pink, or blue.

Sometimes shows color zones. May change color on heating. Some varieties fluorescent and phosphorescent. Melting point 2050°.

Distinctive Properties and Tests

Crystal form, hardness.

Association and Occurrence

Found as (1) an accessory mineral in alumina-rich metamorphic rocks, (2) as a rare accessory mineral in silica-poor igneous rocks, and (3) as a contact-metamorphic mineral, especially around peridotites. The usual associates are chlorite, micas, olivine, serpentine, magnetite, spinel, kyanite, and diaspore.

Alteration: Resistant, but may change to other aluminous minerals such as zoisite, sillimanite, kyanite, margarite, etc.

Confused with: Cordierite.

Variants

Form varieties: Ordinary—corundum; gems—sapphire (blue), ruby (red), oriental topaz (yellow), oriental emerald (green), oriental amethyst (purple), and several others; emery—granular black corundum with magnetite, hematite, or spinel.

Minor amounts of Fe, Ti, Cr, and Mn may replace Al.

Related Minerals

Isotypes: Hematite; ilmenite series.

Polymorphs: α-alumina (corundum), β-alumina, γ-alumina, δ-alumina.

HEMATITE $\qquad$ Fe_2O_3

Crystallography, Structure, Habit
Hexagonal. $\bar{3}\frac{2}{m}$. Thick to thin tabular crystals. Penetration and lamellar twins.

Corundum structure, see Figure 6–6f. Two Fe_2O_3 per unit cell.

Hematite is found in a wide range of habits; as crystal groupings, often in parallel position or as rosettes, columnar, granular, colloform, lamellar, compact, earthy, micaceous.

Physical Properties
No cleavage. Parting on (0001) and $(10\bar{1}1)$ due to twinning. Subconchoidal to uneven fracture. Brittle in compact forms, elastic in thin plates, and soft and unctuous in loose scaly kinds.

Hardness 5–6. Specific gravity 5.3.

Metallic to earthy luster. Translucent to opaque. Color reddish brown to black. Streak light to dark brick red.

Melting point 1350°. Becomes magnetic after heating.

Distinctive Properties and Tests
Streak, tests for iron.

Association and Occurrence
A very common and widespread mineral. Found (1) as extensive sedimentary beds, (2) in contact metamorphic deposits, (3) as a minor accessory in igneous rocks, (4) as coatings and nodules derived by alteration from other iron minerals, (5) in hydrothermal veins, and (6) in the oxidized zone above metalliferous veins.

Alteration: From magnetite (called martite if pseudomorphous), siderite, pyrite, marcasite, etc.

Confused with: Cinnabar.

Variants
Form varieties: Specular—micaceous flakes with a splendent metallic luster; compact columnar, fibrous, or colloform (kidney ore); ocherous—red and earthy.

Ti may replace small amounts of Fe. Up to several per cent water may be present in fibrous or ocherous varieties.

Related Minerals
Isotypes: Corundum; ilmenite series.

Other similar species: Turgite, $2Fe_2O_3 \cdot nH_2O$; goethite, $FeO(OH)$; limonite, $Fe_2O_3 \cdot nH_2O$; bixbyite, $(FeMn)_2O_3$.

Ilmenite $FeTiO_3$
Geikielite $MgTiO_3$
Pyrophanite $MnTiO_3$

Crystallography, Structure, Habit

Hexagonal. $\bar{3}$. Thick tabular crystals with prominent basal planes and small rhombohedral terminations. Lamellar twins.

Corundum structure (see Figure 6–6f) with Fe, etc., and Ti alternating in the Al sites of corundum. Two formula units per cell.

Crystal aggregates, massive, granular, compact, scaly.

Physical Properties

No cleavage for ilmenite, good to excellent cleavage for geikielite and pyrophanite. Parting on (0001) and ($10\bar{1}1$) due to twinning. Conchoidal to subconchoidal fracture. Brittle.

Hardness 5–6. Specific gravity 4.7.

Metallic to submetallic luster. Opaque. Color black (Fe rich) to brownish-black (Mg rich) or deep red (Mn rich). Streak black to brownish-red to yellow.

Sometimes weakly magnetic due to the mechanical mixture or exsolution of magnetite.

Distinctive Properties and Tests

Color and streak, association, tests for titanium.

Association and Occurrence

Ilmenite is found (1) as an accessory mineral in igneous rocks, especially mafic types, (2) as segregations of large extent from such igneous rocks, (3) in high-temperature hydrothermal veins, (4) in pegmatites, (5) as large dike-like masses, and (6) as a principal constituent of black beach sands.

Ilmenite is often associated with magnetite in its primary occurrences. It is accompanied by magnetite, rutile, zircon, monazite, and quartz in the black sands.

Alteration: Relatively stable. Sometimes changes to a yellowish-white powdery material called *leucoxene* which is a mixture of titanium oxides.

Confused with: Magnetite, chromite, hematite.

Variants

Chemical varieties: Ilmenite—ferrian (menaccanite), magnesian, manganoan; geikielite—ferroan; pyrophanite—ferroan.

Related Minerals

Isomorphs: Complete isomorphism between common ilmenite and rare geikielite and pyrophanite.

Isotypes: Hematite; corundum.

Other similar species: Senaite, $(FeMnPb)TiO_3$.

RUTILE

TiO_2

Crystallography, Structure, Habit

Tetragonal. $\dfrac{4}{m}\dfrac{2}{m}\dfrac{2}{m}$. Prismatic crystals with pyramidal terminations, prism zone vertically striated. Commonly twinned as contact twins or cyclic twins, occasionally polysynthetic.

Rutile structure, see Figure 6–6d. Two TiO_2 per cell.

Commonly as crystals, also compact massive.

Physical Properties

Distinct (110) and fair (100) cleavage. Parting on (092) due to twin gliding and also on (011). Subconchoidal to uneven fracture. Brittle.

Hardness 6–6.5. Specific gravity 4.2.

Metallic adamantine luster. Transparent to opaque. Color reddish-brown, red, black, and rarely other colors. Streak pale brown, yellowish, and rarely grayish.

Turns black on heating and regains color on cooling.

Distinctive Properties and Tests

Crystal form and twins. Luster, pale streak. Tests for titanium.

Association and Occurrence

Rutile is typically formed at high temperatures. It is found (1) in hornblende-rich igneous and metamorphic rocks as an accessory mineral, (2) as a vein mineral, (3) in pegmatites, and (4) as a constituent of black beach sands. The "blue quartz" found in metamorphic and igneous rocks owes its color to the inclusion of minute rutile needles.

Alteration: From other titanium minerals such as sphene, ilmenite, and Ti-rich hornblende. To leucoxene, a yellowish-white earthy material.

Confused with: Cassiterite, sphene.

Variants

Form varieties: Sagenite—complexly twinned intergrowth of acicular crystals; Venus' hair-stone—smoky quartz penetrated with acicular crystals.

Chemical varieties (all black in color): Ferrian (nigrine), tantalian (strüverite), and columbian (ilmenorutile). Small amounts of Sn, Cr, and V may be present.

Related Minerals

Isotypes: Cassiterite; pyrolusite; plattnerite, PbO_2.

Polymorphs: Anatase (octahedrite), brookite.

Other similar species: Baddelyite, ZrO_2.

PYROLUSITE $\qquad$ MnO$_2$

Crystallography, Structure, Habit

Tetragonal. $\dfrac{4}{m}\dfrac{2}{m}\dfrac{2}{m}$. Usually found as pseudomorphs after orthorhombic manganite. Rarely in prismatic crystals. Twinning rare as repeated twins.

Isostructural with rutile, Figure 6–6d. Two MnO$_2$ per cell.

Usually in massive columnar, fibrous, or divergent forms. Also colloform, granular, and powdery. Often observed as dendritic growths on fracture surfaces in rocks.

Physical Properties

Perfect (110) cleavage (rarely observed). Uneven fracture. Brittle.

Hardness 6–6.5 for crystals, 2–6 for massive forms. Fibrous or pulverulent forms may be soft enough to soil the fingers. Specific gravity 5.0.

Metallic luster. Opaque. Color light to dark steel gray. Streak black.

Distinctive Properties and Tests

Color, hardness, streak, habit, low water content, tests for manganese. Chlorine gas evolved when treated with HCl. Oxygen evolved when heated in the closed tube (a glowing splinter of wood which flares up when placed at the mouth of the tube tests for oxygen).

Association and Occurrence

Pyrolusite is one of the most common manganese minerals. It is always formed under strongly oxidizing conditions and is always a secondary mineral. It is found as coatings, nodules, and beds, probably resulting from the devitrification of manganese colloids transported by waters.

Pyrolusite is usually accompanied by iron oxides and other manganese oxides.

Alteration: From other manganese minerals, e.g., manganite, rhodochrosite.

Confused with: Manganite, psilomelane, graphite.

Variants

Form varieties: Ordinary; crystallized (polianite).

Pyrolusite may be relatively impure due to mechanical admixture of clay, silica, iron oxides, etc., and adsorbed contaminants or proxy elements including water, heavy metals, phosphorus, alkali metals, and alkaline earths, especially barium.

Related Minerals

Isotypes: Rutile; cassiterite; plattnerite, PbO$_2$.

Other similar species: Manganite, MnO(OH); psilomelane.

CASSITERITE

SnO_2

Crystallography, Structure, Habit

Tetragonal. $\frac{4}{m}\frac{2}{m}\frac{2}{m}$. Crystals as low pyramids or as prisms, sometimes striated. Contact and penetration twins very common.
Isostructural with rutile, Figure 6–6d. Two SnO_2 per cell.
Crystals, colloform with radiating fibers, massive, granular.

Physical Properties

Imperfect (100) cleavage. Distinct parting on (111) or (011). Subconchoidal to uneven fracture. Brittle.
Hardness 6–7. Specific gravity 7.0.
Luster metallic adamantine, often splendent. Transparent to opaque. Color usually brown or black, rarely gray, red, white, or yellow. Streak white to brown.
Infusible.

Distinctive Properties and Tests

Crystal form, specific gravity, luster, association, tests for tin.

Association and Occurrence

Characteristically found (1) in high-temperature hydrothermal veins or contact metamorphic deposits genetically related to quartzose igneous rocks. Also noted (2) in pegmatites, (3) as an accessory mineral in igneous rocks, and (4) in the zone of oxidation over tin deposits. The resistance of cassiterite to weathering and its high specific gravity often cause it to be concentrated in stream and beach placers.

Associated with B- and F-containing minerals such as topaz, tourmaline, fluorite, muscovite, and lepidolite in the mineral aggregation called *greisen.* Also assocated with wolframite, quartz, arsenopyrite, and molybdenite.

Alteration: Resistant to change.

Confused with: Rutile.

Variants

Form varieties: Ordinary—in crystals or massive; stream tin—rounded pebbles or sand in placers; wood tin—in concentric, radiating forms with a colloform surface, brown in color, and looking like dry wood.
Chemical varieties: Ferrian, tantalian (ainalite). Small amounts of Cb, W, Ti, and Mn may be present.

Related Minerals

Isotypes: Rutile; pyrolusite; plattnerite, PbO_2.

URANINITE

UO_2

Crystallography, Structure, Habit

Isometric. $\frac{4}{m}\bar{3}\frac{2}{m}$ (?). Rare octahedral, cubic, or cubo-octahedral crystals. Rarely twinned.

Isostructural with fluorite, Figure 6–6b. Face-centered isometric cell with 4 UO_2 per cell.

Usually massive, often colloform.

Physical Properties

No cleavage. Uneven to conchoidal fracture. Brittle.

Hardness 5–6. Specific gravity 10.8 but decreasing as U^{+4} is oxidized to U^{+6}.

Luster submetallic to pitchlike and dull. Opaque. Color black. Streak brownish-black.

Highly radioactive. Infusible.

Distinctive Properties and Tests

Habit, association, high specific gravity, tests for uranium.

Association and Occurrence

Found (1) in pegmatites with zircon, tourmaline, monazite, and carbonaceous material, (2) in high-temperature hydrothermal tin veins with cassiterite, pyrite, chalcopyrite, arsenopyrite, galena, and Co-Ni arsenide minerals, (3) in hydrothermal veins formed at moderate temperatures with Co-Ni-Bi-Ag-As minerals and pyrite, chalcopyrite, galena, various carbonates, barite, fluorite, etc., (4) as (3), but without the Co-Ni minerals, and (5) replacing wood or other reducing precipitants in sedimentary rocks.

Alteration

Alters readily to a variety of highly colored secondary uranium compounds, usually yellow, orange, or green.

Auto-oxidation produces UO_3, so the mineral formula is $U_{4-x}U_xO_8$.

Confused with: Columbite.

Variants

Form varieties: Crystallized. Structure is always more or less damaged by radioactive bombardment. Massive (pitchblende).

Chemical varieties: Thorian (bröggerite), cerian and yttrian (cleveite). Products of radioactive decay are always present, i.e., Pb, He, Ra. Other common contaminating elements are N, A, Fe, rare earths, and water.

Related Minerals

Isomorphs: Thorianite, ThO_2.

Other similar species: Gummite, $UO_3 \cdot nH_2O$; baddelyite, ZrO_2.

SPINEL $MgAl_2O_4$

Crystallography, Structure, Habit

Isometric. $\frac{4}{m}\bar{3}\frac{2}{m}$. Octahedral crystals. Contact twins common.

Spinel structure, Figure 6–7a. Eight formula units per cell. Mg in 4- and Al in 6-fold coordination.

Usually as crystals, also massive, granular, and compact.

Physical Properties

No cleavage. Indistinct (111) parting. Conchoidal to splintery fracture. Brittle.

Hardness 7.5–8. Specific gravity 3.6.

Vitreous to dull luster. Transparent. Variously colored. White streak.

Melting point 2135°.

Distinctive Properties and Tests

Crystals, hardness. Red spinel turns brown or black and opaque when heated, and on cooling changes color from black to green to colorless to red.

Association and Occurrence

Spinel is a high-temperature mineral found as (1) an accessory in mafic igneous rocks, (2) in alumina-rich schists, (3) in contact metamorphosed limestone, and (4) in placer deposits.

The usual mineral associates are chondrodite, diopside, chalcopyrite, pyrite; magnetite, garnet, vesuvianite; sillimanite, andalusite, cordierite; forsterite, chondrodite, scapolite; or plagioclase, corundum, zircon.

Alteration: Resistant to change but may alter to talc, mica, or serpentine.

Confused with: Rutile, garnet, zircon.

Variants

Form varieties: Ordinary; gems—ruby spinel, ballas ruby (red), rubicelle (yellow to orange red), almandine spinel (violet), and many blue varieties.

Chemical varieties: ferroan (ceylonite), zincian, ferrian, chromian (picotite).

Related Minerals

Isomorphs: Hercynite, $FeAl_2O_4$; gahnite, $ZnAl_2O_4$; galaxite, $MnAl_2O_4$.

Isotypes: Magnetite, chromite.

MAGNETITE

$FeFe_2O_4$

Crystallography, Structure, Habit

Isometric. $\frac{4}{m}\bar{3}\frac{2}{m}$. Crystals usually octahedra. Contact twins.

Isostructural with spinel, Figure 6–7a. Fe^{+2} occupies the Mg sites in the spinel structure and Fe^{+3} occupies the Al sites. Four formula units per cell.

Massive, granular, and as crystals.

Physical Properties

No cleavage. Good (111) parting. Subconchoidal to uneven fracture. Brittle.

Hardness 5.5–6.5. Specific gravity 5.2.

Metallic luster, splendent to dull. Opaque. Color and streak black.

Melting point 1591°. Strongly magnetic, sometimes with polarity (lodestone).

Association and Occurrence

Magnetite is one of the most abundant and widespread of oxide minerals. It is found as (1) magmatic segregations in igneous rocks with apatite and pyroxene, (2) as an accessory mineral in all igneous rocks, (3) in metamorphic rocks, especially marble with garnet, diopside, olivine, pyrite, and chalcopyrite, (4) in high-temperature sulfide veins, and (5) in placers.

Alteration: To hematite (martite), goethite.

Confused with: Ilmenite, chromite.

Variants

Chemical varieties: Magnesian, manganoan, nickelian, aluminian, chromian, titanian, vanadian.

Related Minerals

Isomorphs: Magnesioferrite, $MgFe_2O_4$; franklinite, $ZnFe_2O_4$; jacobsite, $MnFe_2O_4$; trevorite, $NiFe_2O_4$.

Isotypes: Spinel, chromite.

Other similar species: Hausmannite, $MnMn_2O_4$.

CHROMITE $FeCr_2O_4$

Crystallography, Structure, Habit

Isometric. $\frac{4}{m}\bar{3}\frac{2}{m}$. Crystals rare, usually as octahedra.

Isostructural with spinel, Figure 6–7a. Fe in 4- and Cr in 6-fold coordination. Eight formula units per cell.

Usually massive or granular.

Physical Properties

No cleavage. Uneven fracture. Brittle.

Hardness 5.5. Specific gravity 4.6.

Metallic luster. Opaque. Color black. Streak brown.

Sometimes weakly magnetic.

Distinctive Properties and Tests

Streak. Tests for chromium. Association.

Association and Occurrence

Found with olivine, pyroxene, spinel, chlorite, magnetite, pyrrhotite, or niccolite (1) in ultramafic rocks and their derived serpentines as an accessory mineral and in segregations, and (2) in placers.

Alteration: To goethite.

Confused with: Magnetite, ilmenite.

Variants

Chemical varieties: Magnesian, aluminian.

Related Minerals

Isomorphs: Magnesiochromite, $MgCr_2O_4$.

Isotypes: Spinel, magnetite.

COLUMBITE-TANTALITE SERIES

$$(FeMn)(CbTa)_2O_6$$
$$(FeMn)(TaCb)_2O_6$$

Crystallography, Structure, Habit

Orthorhombic. $\dfrac{2}{m}\dfrac{2}{m}\dfrac{2}{m}$. Short prismatic or equant crystals. Contact twins common, also penetration twins and stellate forms.

Structure, Figure 7–7. Chains of $(FeMn)O$ and $(CbTa)O$ octahedra. Crystal aggregates, massive.

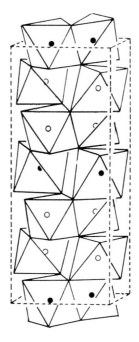

○　　　●

Fe or Mn　Cb or Ta

Fig. 7–7. Columbite structure.

Physical Properties

Distinct (010) cleavage. Subconchoidal to uneven fracture. Brittle.

Hardness 6–6.5. Specific gravity 5.2 (columbite) to 7.9 (tantalite), increasing linearly with an increase in Ta_2O_5.

Luster metallic splendent to submetallic. Translucent to transparent. Color black to brownish-black, often with an iridescent tarnish. Streak dark red to black.

Infusible.

Columbite-Tantalite Series (cont.)

Distinctive Properties and Tests
Luster, streak, specific gravity, association.

Association and Occurrence
Found (1) in granitic pegmatites with albite, lithium silicates such as lepidolite and spodumene, and phosphates and (2) in placers.

Alteration: Resistant to change.

Confused with: Uraninite, wolframite.

Variants
Chemical varieties: Ferroan (Fe:Mn $>$ 3:1), manganoan (Fe:Mn $<$ 3:1). Small amounts of Sn (for Fe or Mn) and W (for Cb or Ta) may be present.

Related Minerals
Other similar species: Tapiolite, $(FeMn)(TaCb)_2O_6$; brookite, TiO_2.

Hydroxides

SIMPLE HYDROXIDES	MULTIPLE HYDROXIDES

SIMPLE HYDROXIDES

$A(OH)_2$ Type
 Brucite group
  Brucite, $Mg(OH)_2$
 Lepidochrocite group
 Hydrotalcite group
 Sjorgrenite group
$A(OH)_3$ Type
 Miscellaneous
  Gibbsite, $Al(OH)_3$

MULTIPLE HYDROXIDES

$AO(OH)$ Type
 Goethite group
  Goethite, $FeO(OH)$
  Diaspore, $AlO(OH)$
 Miscellaneous
  Psilomelane, $BaMnMn_8O_{16}(OH)_4$

The true hydroxides are differentiated from other hydroxyl-bearing minerals by the fact that the hydroxyl radical is a necessary component of the basic structure in which it alternates with cations. In a clay mineral, *per contra*, the hydroxyl groups occupy interstices in the sheets of linked Si-O tetrahedra and are required by the structure only for charge balance.

Several members of the hydroxide family are very common because they represent stages in the weathering of common primary minerals. Goethite and the closely related hydrous iron oxides which are termed "limonite" are found nearly everywhere in consequence of the breakdown of iron-bearing minerals. These iron hydroxides may occur in amounts ranging from surface films on rocks up to deposits minable as iron ore. Goethite is also used as a natural yellow or brown pigment to which the names ocher, umber, and sienna are applied.

Gibbsite and diaspore are two of the several hydroxides of aluminum which result from the chemical weathering of aluminous rocks. Mechanical mixtures of such minerals are called "bauxite" and are exploited as aluminum ore.

The oxides and hydroxides of manganese tend to transform into one another and are sometimes found as complex mixtures. A widespread hydroxide of manganese is psilomelane; and this mineral, together with manganite, $MnO(OH)$, and the oxide pyrolusite, MnO_2, is a notable scavenger of dissolved metallic ions from the waters in which it forms. This scavenging action is due to the flocculent nature of the precipitating minerals and the consequent very large surface which is available.

BRUCITE   (nemalite) $Mg(OH)_2$

Crystallography, Structure, Habit

Hexagonal. $\bar{3}\frac{2}{m}$. Platy crystals.

Brucite structure, see Figure 6–8b. One $Mg(OH)_2$ per unit cell.

Found as crystals, foliated masses, and fibrous aggregates.

Physical Properties

Perfect (0001) cleavage yielding flexible folia. Sectile.

Hardness 2.5. Specific gravity 2.4.

Pearly luster on cleavage faces, vitreous elsewhere. Transparent. Color white to pale green, gray, or blue. Streak white.

Infusible. Water lost at 410°.

Distinctive Properties and Tests

Perfect cleavage and flexible folia. Softness. Soluble in acids. Association.

Association and Occurrence

Found in low-temperature veins in magnesium-rich metamorphic rocks such as serpentine, chlorite, and dolomite schists associated with calcite, aragonite, talc, and magnesite.

Alteration: From periclase, MgO. To hydromagnesite, $3MgCO_3 \cdot Mg(OH)_2 \cdot 3H_2O$; serpentine.

Confused with: Gypsum, gibbsite.

Variants

Form varieties: Ordinary, fibrous.

Chemical varieties: Ferroan, manganoan. Zinc may substitute in minor amounts for Mg.

Related Minerals

Isotypes: Pyrochroite, $Mn(OH)_2$; portlandite, $Ca(OH)_2$.

GIBBSITE   (hydrargillite) $Al(OH)_3$

Crystallography, Structure, Habit

Monoclinic. $\frac{2}{m}$. Rare tabular pseudohexagonal crystals. Contact twins.

Gibbsite structure, see Figure 6–8a. Eight formula units per cell.

Usually crystals or crystal aggregates, also colloform with radiating structure, encrusting, earthy, compact, and enamel-like.

Physical Properties

Perfect (001) cleavage. Tough.

Hardness 2.5–3.5. Specific gravity 2.4.

Pearly luster on cleavages, otherwise vitreous. Transparent. Color white but often colored by impurities.

Strong earthy smell when breathed on. Infusible. Not readily soluble in acids.

Distinctive Properties and Tests

Good cleavage, earthy smell, yields water in the closed tube.

Association and Occurrence

Found with diaspore and boehmite in bauxite deposits and with corundum in talc schists.

Alteration: From aluminous minerals.

Confused with: Kaolin, brucite.

Variants

May contain a little Fe.

Related Minerals

Polymorphs: Boehmite.

Other similar species: "Bauxite," a mechanical mixture of gibbsite, boehmite, and diaspore.

GOETHITE α-FeO(OH)

Crystallography, Structure, Habit
Orthorhombic. $\dfrac{2}{m}\dfrac{2}{m}\dfrac{2}{m}$. Striated prisms, tablets, or scales. Acicular to filiform crystals.

Isostructural with diaspore, Figure 7–8. Four FeO(OH) per cell.

Usually massive, colloform, or stalactitic showing concentric banding and a radial fibrous structure.

Physical Properties
Perfect (010) and fair (100) cleavage. Uneven fracture. Brittle. Hardness 5–5.5. Specific gravity 4.3 (crystals), 3.3–4.3 (massive material). Adamantine-metallic to dull luster, sometimes silky on fibrous kinds. Translucent to transparent. Color a shade of brown. Streak brownish-yellow.

Distinctive Properties and Tests
Habit, streak. Soluble in HCl. Evolves water in the closed tube.

Association and Occurrence
One of the most common minerals. Occurs as the oxidation product from iron-bearing minerals and is found concentrated in the sedimentary beds, in gossans, and lateritic soils. It is commonly associated with hematite, pyrolusite, psilomelane, calcite, quartz, clay minerals, and limonite.

Alteration: From iron-minerals, especially siderite, pyrite, and magnetite.

Confused with: Hematite.

Variants
Form varieties: Bog iron ore; limonite (ocherous and poorly crystallized). Usually contains Mn and has adsorbed water.

Related Minerals
Isotypes: Diaspore, AlO(OH).

Polymorphs: Lepidochrosite, γ-FeO(OH).

Other similar species: Turgite, $2Fe_2O_3 \cdot nH_2O$; manganite, MnO(OH); and stainerite, CoO(OH).

DIASPORE   α-AlO(OH)

Crystallography, Structure, Habit

Orthorhombic. $\frac{2}{m}\frac{2}{m}\frac{2}{m}$. Thin platy, bladed, or acicular crystals. Twinning is rare.

Diaspore structure, Figure 7–8. Four formula units per cell.

Usually in crystals, may be foliated massive, scaly, stalactitic.

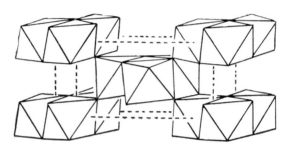

Fig. 7–8. Diaspore structure.

Physical Properties

Perfect (010) cleavage, fair (110) cleavage. Conchoidal fracture. Very brittle.

Hardness 6.5–7. Specific gravity 3.4.

Brilliant to vitreous luster. Transparent. Color white or colorless, sometimes variously tinted.

Distinctive Properties and Tests

Brittleness, luster, association.

Association and Occurrence

Found (1) in emery deposits with corundum, magnetite, spinel, and chlorite, (2) in bauxite deposits, lateritic soils, and with aluminous clays, and (3) as a late hydrothermal mineral in alkali pegmatites.

Alteration: From corundum (?). To kaolinite (?).

Confused with: Brucite.

Variants

Chemical varieties: Ferrian, color brown, manganoan, color red. Admixed phosphorus or silica may be present.

Related Minerals

Isotypes: Goethite.

Polymorphs: Boehmite.

Other similar species: "Bauxite," a mechanical mixture of gibbsite, boehmite, and diaspore.

282

PSILOMELANE

$BaMnMn_8O_{16}(OH)_4$

Crystallography, Structure, Habit

Orthorhombic. Never shows distinct crystals.
Massive, in colloform crusts, and earthy.

Physical Properties

Hardness 5–6. Specific gravity 4.7.
Submetallic to dull luster. Opaque. Color black to gray. Shining black streak.
Infusible.

Distinctive Properties and Tests

Color, luster and habit. Chlorine gas evolved when dissolved in HCl. Tests for manganese.

Association and Occurrence

Psilomelane is a secondary mineral formed by weathering of other manganese minerals and often associated with pyrolusite, goethite, calcite, etc.

Alteration: From manganous carbonates and silicates.

Confused with: Pyrolusite.

Variants

A number of contaminants either admixed, adsorbed, or replacing Ba or Mn may be present. Small amounts of Cu, Co, Ni, Mg, Ca, W, and alkali metals are usually found.

Related Minerals

Similar species: Pyrolusite; manganite, $MnO(OH)$; wad, (mixture of manganese oxides and hydroxides).

Carbonates

ANHYDROUS CARBONATES

$A(CO_3)$ Type
  Calcite group
    Calcite, $Ca(CO_3)$
    Magnesite, $Mg(CO_3)$
    Siderite, $Fe(CO_3)$
    Rhodochrosite, $Mn(CO_3)$
    Smithsonite, $Zn(CO_3)$
  Aragonite group
    Aragonite, $Ca(CO_3)$
    Witherite, $Ba(CO_3)$
    Strontianite, $Sr(CO_3)$
    Cerussite, $Pb(CO_3)$

$AB(CO_3)_2$ Type
  Dolomite group
    Dolomite, $CaMg(CO_3)_2$

HYDROUS CARBONATES

$A_m(CO_3)_p(OH)_q$ Type
  Malachite, $Cu_2(CO_3)(OH)_2$
  Azurite, $Cu_3(CO_3)_2(OH)_2$

The carbonate minerals are easily distinguished from other mineral families by their softness, distinctive colors, and effervescence in warm dilute HCl.

Members of the calcite group are usually well crystallized, have a blocky habit, and cleave into rhombshaped fragments (with the exception of smithsonite which is usually colloform). Members of the aragonite group have an elongated or massive habit. The hydrous carbonates have distinctive colors and a colloform habit.

The simplest distinguishing tests for the various carbonate minerals are given in the following table. The colors of siderite, rhodochrosite, malachite, and azurite are essentially constant. Colors of the other carbonates are usually white, but they may take on a wide range of tints. Reactions with cold HCl are quite distinctive if the sample is coarse grained. Flame colors are distinctive.

Distinctive Tests for the Carbonate Minerals

Mineral	Color	Reaction with Cold Dilute HCl	Flame Color
Calcite	Various	Effervesces	Brick red
Magnesite	White	No action	None
Siderite	Brown	No action	None
Rhodochrosite	Pink	No action	None
Smithsonite	White	Effervesces	Blue-green streaks
Dolomite	White	No action	Brick red
Aragonite	White	Effervesces	Brick red
Witherite	White	Effervesces	Yellowish green
Strontianite	White	Effervesces	Crimson
Cerussite	White	No action	Pale bluish white
Malachite	Green	Effervesces	Green
Azurite	Blue	Effervesces	Green

Carbonates (cont.)

All of the members of the calcite group are isotypic and, to some extent, isomorphic. These relations are illustrated by Figure 7–9.

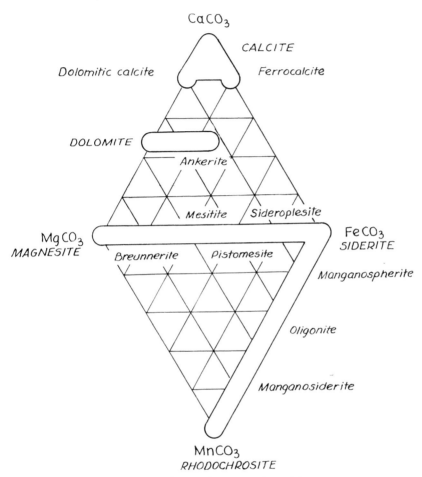

Fig. 7–9. Isomorphous relations in the calcite group.

Minerals in the aragonite group are all isotypic, but isomorphism between the species is limited.

Most $A(CO_3)$ salts are isostructural with either calcite or aragonite. In general, the calcite arrangement is utilized by small cations such as Li, Na, Mg, Ca, Fe, Zn, Co, or Cd, while the aragonite structure better accommodates large cations such as K, Ba, Sr, and Pb. Polymorphs utilizing the two structures are found when the cation-oxygen radius ratio is near the critical value of 0.73, e.g., polymorphs of $CaCO_3$ or KNO_3.

CALCITE

$$Ca(CO_3)$$

Crystallography, Structure, Habit

Hexagonal. $\bar{3}\frac{2}{m}$. The crystal habit is extremely varied and some 300 different forms have been reported. There are three important habits: (1) short to long prisms, (2) rhombohedra, and (3) scalenohedra. Repeated parallel twinning is common.

Calcite structure, see Figure 6–10a. This structure resembles that of halite with planar CO_3 groups taking the place of Cl ions. The CO_3 groups are arranged in parallel position normal to the three-fold axis [0001], which corresponds to a cube diagonal.

Crystals and crystal aggregates, coarse granular to impalpable, stalactitic, nodular, encrusting, and as a component of shells.

Physical Properties

Perfect rhombohedral cleavage ($10\bar{1}1$). Parting on ($01\bar{1}2$) and sometimes on (0001). Conchoidal fracture. Brittle.

Hardness 3 [approximately 2.7 on (0001) and 3.5 on (1011)]. Specific gravity 2.7.

Vitreous luster. Transparent. Colorless or white but may assume various colors. White streak.

Sometimes fluorescent or phosphorescent under electromagnetic radiation (X rays, ultraviolet, sunlight). Often thermoluminescent. Infusible.

Distinctive Properties and Tests

Cleavage, crystals, hardness. Soluble in cold dilute HCl with effervescence. Tests for calcium.

Association and Occurrence

One of the most common and widely distributed of all minerals. It is (1) the principal constituent of certain sedimentary rocks (limestone, chalk) and their metamorphic equivalents (marble), (2) found as a hydrothermal vein mineral with sulfides, barite, quartz, fluorite, dolomite, siderite, etc. Calcite is also formed by (3) carbonation during weathering of most rocks, and is (4) utilized by organisms in their shells.

Alteration: To solution. From calcium-bearing minerals.

Confused with: Dolomite, aragonite.

Calcite (cont.)

Variants

Form varieties: Ordinary, fibrous, lamellar, concretionary, oölitic, fetid (contains H_2S which is liberated when broken), and numerous others.

Chemical varieties: Manganoan, ferroan, zincian, cobaltian, plumbian, barian, strontian, and magnesian.

Related Minerals

Isomorphs: Rhodochrosite.

Isotypes: Magnesite; siderite; sphærocobaltite, $CoCO_3$; smithsonite; otavite, $CdCo_3$; soda niter, $NaNO_3$; and dolomite.

Polymorphs: Aragonite, vaterite or μ-calcite.

MAGNESITE

$Mg(CO_3)$

Crystallography, Structure, Habit

Hexagonal. $\bar{3}\frac{2}{m}$. Crystals rare.

Isostructural with calcite, see Figure 6–10a.

Usually massive, also granular, compact, earthy, fibrous.

Physical Properties

Perfect rhombohedral cleavage ($10\bar{1}1$). Conchoidal fracture. Brittle. Hardness 4. Specific gravity 3.0.

Vitreous to earthy luster. Translucent to transparent. Color white or colorless. Streak white.

Sometimes shows green or blue fluorescence or phosphorescence in ultraviolet light. Triboluminescent. Infusible.

Distinctive Properties and Tests

Chalky or porcelain-like appearance. Effervesces in warm HCl.

Association and Occurrence

(1) Massive magnesite forms by alteration of magnesium-rich rocks. (2) Limestone and dolomite may be replaced by $MgCO_3$. (3) Rarely found as a hydrothermal vein mineral, as an accessory in igneous rocks, and filling the cavities of lava.

Alteration: From magnesium-rich rocks such as serpentine, dunite, or peridotite by carbonation. Replaces calcite and dolomite.

Confused with: Calcite, dolomite, kaolin.

Variants

Chemical varieties: Ferroan (breunnerite), manganoan, calcian. May contain minor amounts of Zn.

Related Minerals

Isomorphs: Siderite.

Isotypes: See calcite.

Other similar species: hydromagnesite, $Mg_4(CO_3)_3(OH)_2 \cdot 3H_2O$.

SIDERITE

$$Fe(CO_3)$$

Crystallography, Structure, Habit

Hexagonal. $\bar{3}\frac{2}{m}$. Usually rhombohedral crystals, also tablets, prisms, and scalenohedra. Faces often curved or composite. Parallel repeated twinning.
Isostructural with calcite, see Figure 6–10a.
Massive, crystal aggregates, granular, colloform, fibrous, and earthy.

Physical Properties

Perfect rhombohedral cleavage $(10\bar{1}1)$. Uneven to conchoidal fracture. Brittle.
Hardness 3.7–4.5. Specific gravity 4.0.
Vitreous luster. Translucent to transparent. Color yellow brown or grayish-brown to brown and red brown. Streak white.
Fusible (4–4.5).

Distinctive Properties and Tests

Color, cleavage. Blackens and becomes magnetic when heated in a closed tube. Effervesces in warm HCl.

Association and Occurrence

Siderite is a common mineral found usually (1) in bedded deposits with clay or shale, coal, and quartz, (2) as a constituent of some hydrothermal veins, (3) in bogs, and less commonly in lava cavities, pegmatites, metamorphosed sedimentary rocks, and (4) as a replacement of limestone.

Alteration: To goethite.

Confused with: Sphalerite.

Variants

Chemical varieties: Calcian, magnesian (sideroplesite), manganoan (manganospherite), cobaltian.

Related Minerals

Isomorphs: Rhodochrosite, magnesite.
Isotypes: See calcite.

RHODOCHROSITE

$Mn(CO_3)$

Crystallography, Structure, Habit

Hexagonal. $\bar{3}\frac{2}{m}$. Crystals are rare, usually rhombohedral.

Isostructural with calcite, see Figure 6–10a.

Usually massive, also granular, compact, and columnar.

Physical Properties

Perfect rhombohedral cleavage $(10\bar{1}1)$. Parting parallel to $(10\bar{1}2)$. Uneven to conchoidal fracture. Brittle.

Hardness 3.5–4. Specific gravity 3.7.

Vitreous to pearly luster. Subtranslucent to transparent. Color is shade of pink. Streak white.

Infusible, but dissociates at 300°.

Distinctive Properties and Tests

Color. Soluble with effervescence in warm HCl. Tests for manganese.

Association and Occurrence

Found (1) as a primary gangue mineral in sulfide veins where it is also associated with calcite, siderite, dolomite, fluorite, barite, quartz, and manganese oxides, (2) in high-temperature metamorphic deposits with rhodonite, garnet, and manganese oxides, and (3) as a secondary mineral in residual deposits of iron or manganese oxides.

Alteration: To manganese oxides, e.g., pyrolusite, which change the color to brown or black in the early stages of change.

Confused with: Rhodonite.

Variants

Chemical varieties: Calcian, ferroan (manganosiderite), magnesian, zincian.

Related Minerals

Isomorphs: Siderite; calcite.

Isotypes: See calcite.

SMITHSONITE (calamine) $Zn(CO_3)$

Crystallography, Structure, Habit

Hexagonal. $\bar{3}\frac{2}{m}$. Crystals rare, rhombohedral.

Isostructural with calcite, see Figure 6–10a.

Usually colloform encrusting; also stalactitic, earthy.

Physical Properties

Good $(10\bar{1}1)$ cleavage. Uneven to subconchoidal fracture. Brittle.

Hardness 4–4.5. Specific gravity 4.4.

Vitreous to pearly luster. Translucent. Color various—grayish white, gray, greenish white, brownish white, green, blue green, yellow, brown, white. Streak white.

Infusible.

Distinctive Properties and Tests

Habit, often color, association. Tests for zinc. Soluble in cold HCl with effervescence.

Association and Occurrence

Found (1) as a secondary mineral in the oxidized zone of ore deposits containing sphalerite, or (2) replacing adjacent calcareous rocks. Usually associated with hemimorphite, cerussite, malachite, azurite, anglesite, etc.

Alteration: From sphalerite.

Confused with: Hemimorphite.

Variants

Chemical varieties: Ferroan, calcian, cobaltian (pink), cuprian (apple green), cadmian (yellow), magnesian, plumbian. May also contain small amounts of Mn, Ge.

Related Minerals

Isotypes: See calcite.

ARAGONITE

$$Ca(CO_3)$$

Crystallography, Structure, Habit

Orthorhombic. $\dfrac{2}{m}\dfrac{2}{m}\dfrac{2}{m}$. Crystals acicular, prismatic, or tabular. Twinning common as contact or cyclic twins, sometimes pseudohexagonal.

Aragonite structure, see Figure 6–10b.

Found as crystals and crystal aggregates, columnar, colloform, fibrous, and pisolitic.

Physical Properties

Imperfect (010) and (110) cleavage. Subconchoidal fracture. Brittle. Hardness 3.5–4. Specific gravity 2.9.

Vitreous to resinous luster. Transparent to translucent. Colorless to white.

Sometimes fluorescent under X rays or ultraviolet light. Sometimes thermoluminescent. Infusible, but decrepitates at red heat as it transforms to calcite.

Distinctive Properties and Tests

Crystals. Effervesces with cold dilute HCl.

Association and Occurrence

Always formed under near-surface low-temperature conditions. Found as (1) crystals, pisolites, and sinter from hot springs or on recent sea bottoms, (2) as disseminated crystals and masses in gypsum or clay beds, (3) with sedimentary limonite and siderite, (4) in the oxidized zone of ore deposits with limonite, calcite, malachite, azurite, smithsonite, cerussite, etc., and (5) as the constituent of certain shells.

Alteration: To calcite.

Confused with: Strontianite, calcite.

Aragonite may be distinguished from calcite by the following stain tests: Boil fragments in cobalt nitrate solution, wash. Aragonite assumes a lilac rose tint more rapidly than does calcite. Wash with ammonium sulfide solution. Aragonite turns black, calcite gray. It should be noted that these tests are not reliable for very fine-grained material.

Variants

Chemical varieties: Plumbian (tarnowitzite), strontian, zincian (nicholsonite), barian (altstonite).

Related Minerals

Isotypes: Strontianite, witherite, cerussite.
Polymorphs: Calcite, vaterite.

WITHERITE

$$Ba(CO_3)$$

Crystallography, Structure, Habit

Orthorhombic. $\frac{2}{m}\frac{2}{m}\frac{2}{m}$. Crystals always twinned forming pseudohexagonal pyramids. Deep horizontal striations sometimes make the crystals look like a stack of pyramids.

Isostructural with aragonite, see Figure 6–10b.

As crystals, globular, colloform, columnar, or granular.

Physical Properties

Distinct (010) and imperfect (110) cleavage. Uneven fracture.
Hardness 3–3.5. Specific gravity 4.3.

Vitreous to resinous luster. Transparent to translucent. Colorless to white often with tints of yellow, brown, or green. Streak white.

May fluoresce or phosphoresce in X rays or ultraviolet light. May be thermoluminescent. Fusible (2.5–3).

Distinctive Properties and Tests

Specific gravity, crystals. Soluble with effervescence in cold dilute HCl. Flame test for barium. Even very dilute solutions give a precipitate of barium sulfate when sulfuric acid is added.

Association and Occurrence

Found in low-temperature hydrothermal veins associated with barite and galena.

Confused with: Barite.

Variants

Usually contains some Ca or Sr.

Related Minerals

Isotypes: See aragonite.

Polymorphs: Transforms at 811° to a hexagonal form, and at 982° to an isometric form.

STRONTIANITE

$$Sr(CO_3)$$

Crystallography, Structure, Habit

Orthorhombic. $\frac{2}{m}\frac{2}{m}\frac{2}{m}$. Short to long prismatic crystals, often acicular. Commonly twinned into pseudohexagonal forms.

Isostructural with aragonite, see Figure 6–10b.

Found as crystals, massive, and columnar to fibrous.

Physical Properties

Good (110) cleavage. Uneven to subconchoidal fracture. Brittle.

Hardness 3.5. Specific gravity 3.8.

Vitreous to resinous luster. Transparent to translucent. Colorless to gray with tints of yellow, green, or red.

May fluoresce or phosphoresce under X rays or ultraviolet light. Sometimes thermoluminescent. Fuses at 1497°.

Distinctive Properties and Tests

Crystals. Flame test for strontium. Swells and sprouts when strongly heated. Effervesces in cold dilute HCl.

Association and Occurrence

Strontianite is a low-temperature hydrothermal mineral associated with barite, celestite, and calcite in (1) veins in limestone and marl, (2) sulfide veins, and (3) in geodes or as concretionary masses in limestone or clay beds.

Alteration: To celestite.

Confused with: Aragonite.

Variants

Usually contains Ca or Ba.

Related Minerals

Isotypes: See aragonite.

Polymorphs: Transforms to hexagonal form at 929°.

CERUSSITE

$$Pb(CO_3)$$

Crystallography, Structure, Habit

Orthorhombic. $\frac{2}{m}\frac{2}{m}\frac{2}{m}$. Crystals varied, but often tabular. Almost always twinned into pseudohexagonal forms.

Isostructural with aragonite, see Figure 6–10b.

Found as crystal clusters, massive, granular to compact, and earthy.

Physical Properties

Distinct (110) cleavage. Conchoidal fracture. Very brittle.

Hardness 3–3.5. Specific gravity 6.6.

Luster adamantine to vitreous, resinous, or pearly. Transparent to translucent. Colorless to white, gray, blue, or green, streak white.

May be fluorescent (yellow) under X rays or ultraviolet light. Readily fusible (1.5) and yields a lead globule when heated on charcoal.

Distinctive Properties and Tests

Specific gravity, luster, ready fusion. Tests for lead. Soluble with effervescence in nitric acid.

Association and Occurrence

Cerussite is a common secondary lead mineral found in the oxidized portion of ore deposits, where it is associated with anglesite, iron oxides, etc.

Alteration: From galena, anglesite.

Confused with: Anglesite.

Variants

May contain trace amounts of Sr, Ag, or Zn.

Related Minerals

Isotypes: See aragonite.

Other similar species: Hydrocerussite, $Pb_3(CO_3)_2(OH)_2$.

DOLOMITE

$CaMg(CO_3)_2$

Crystallography, Structure, Habit

Hexagonal. $\bar{3}$. Crystals usually rhombohedra or prisms, often with curved faces. Repeated parallel twinning.

Isostructural with calcite, see Figure 6–10a. The Ca and Mg atoms of dolomite alternate in the Ca sites of calcite.

Massive, granular, and as crystals.

Physical Properties

Perfect rhombohedral cleavage $(10\bar{1}1)$. Parting parallel to $(02\bar{2}1)$. Subconchoidal fracture. Brittle.

Hardness 3.5–4. Specific gravity 2.9.

Vitreous to pearly luster. Translucent. Colorless to white. Streak white.

May fluoresce under ultraviolet light. May be thermoluminescent. Infusible.

Distinctive Properties and Tests

Cleavage. Effervesces in hot dilute HCl.

Association and Occurrence

Found (1) as massive sedimentary rock, often mixed with calcite, (2) in hydrothermal veins with fluorite, barite, calcite, siderite, quartz, and metallic ores, (3) in cavities in limestone with calcite, celestite, gypsum, and quartz, and (4) as grains in serpentine and talcose rocks.

Alteration: From calcite by action of Mg-rich solutions. Under thermal metamorphism dolomite may break down into calcite and periclase, MgO, or combine with silica to form diopside or other calcium-magnesium silicates.

Confused with: Calcite.

Variants

Chemical varieties: Cobaltian (reddish), plumbian, manganoan, ferroan (brown), calcian, magnesian, and cerian.

Related Minerals

Isomorphs: Ankerite, $Ca(FeMg)(CO_3)_2$; kutnahorite, $Ca(MnMg)(CO_3)_2$.

Isotypes: Calcite; huntite, $Ca_3Mg(CO_3)_4$.

Other similar species: Alstonite, $CaBa(CO_3)_2$; barytocalcite, $CaBa(CO_3)_2$.

MALACHITE $Cu_2(CO_3)(OH)_2$

Crystallography, Structure, Habit
Monoclinic. Crystals rare, prismatic acicular, or rounded. Commonly contact twinned.

Massive, encrusting, colloform.

Physical Properties
Perfect (001) cleavage. Subconchoidal to uneven fracture.

Hardness 3.5–4. Specific gravity 4.1.

Adamantine to vitreous luster. Translucent to opaque. Bright green in color. Streak pale green.

Readily fusible (2). Loses water at 315°.

Distinctive Properties and Tests
Habit, color. Soluble with effervescence in cold dilute HCl. Evolves much water in the closed tube. Tests for copper.

Association and Occurrence
Malachite is a secondary copper mineral formed by oxidation and carbonation. It is usually associated with azurite, cuprite, limonite, calcite, chalcedony, chrysocolla, etc.

Alteration: From azurite, cuprite.

Confused with: Garnierite, melanterite, chrysocolla, and other secondary copper minerals.

Variants
May contain small amounts of zinc.

Related Minerals
Similar species: Azurite; phosgenite, $Pb_2(CO_3)Cl_2$; hydrozincite, $Zn_5[(CO_3)_2(OH)_3]_2$; aurichalcite $(ZnCu)_5[(CO_3)_2(OH)_3]_2$.

AZURITE $\qquad$ $Cu_3(CO_3)_2(OH)_2$

Crystallography, Structure, Habit

Monoclinic. $\frac{2}{m}$. Crystals varied in habit and often distorted. Twinning is rare.

Massive, encrusting, and earthy.

Physical Properties

Perfect but interrupted (100) cleavage. Conchoidal fracture. Brittle. Hardness 3.5–4. Specific gravity 3.8.

Vitreous to adamantine luster. Transparent to opaque. Azure blue. Streak blue.

Fusible (3). Loses water at 410°.

Distinctive Properties and Tests

Color, habit. Soluble with effervescence in cold dilute HCl. Tests for copper.

Association and Occurrence

Azurite, like malachite, is a secondary copper mineral formed by oxidation and carbonation of copper oxides and sulfides.

Alteration: To malachite.

Related Minerals

Similar species: Hydrocerussite, $Pb_3(CO_3)_2(OH)_2$; hydromagnesite, $Mg_4(CO_3)_3(OH)_2 \cdot 3H_2O$; malachite.

Borates

Boron is a very small $+3$ cation whose mineralogical role is analagous to that of chemically related aluminum in that boron is capable of entering structures as a simple cation or as a radical-former. In the former instance, it is a typical component of high-temperature minerals such as tourmaline, axinite, $HCa(MnFe)Al_2B(SiO_4)_4$, or danburite, $CaB_2Si_2O_8$. In low-temperature minerals, boron is capable of coordinating either three or four oxygen anions into triangular $(BO_3)^{-3}$ or tetrahedral $(BO_4)^{-5}$ radicals. In addition, the oxygens may be shared between these radicals to form B_mO_n complex ions. In consequence of these coordination and sharing possibilities, the borates may be anticipated to be, and are, structurally complex.

Borates have a volcanic association. The extensive deposits of the present desert areas of the world such as the American Southwest, Tibet, and Chile are reconcentrated from boron-containing volcanic emanations by the action of ground waters. Waters rich in boron are drawn to the surface by capillary action and deposit borates upon evaporation. The existence of similar conditions in the geological past is indicated by the presence of borates in many saline deposits which developed by evaporation in volcanic regions. For example, borates are found in the extensive salt deposits at Stassfurt in Germany, in the salt domes of Louisiana, and in brine springs of northern Italy.

Borates, usually transformed into borax or boric acid, find wide use in industry. Borax has a very low melting point and is much used as a flux in such applications as welding or soldering and the manufacture of tile and porcelain enamels for coating iron. Borax is a solvent for casein; this property is exploited in the production of plaster, paint, calcimine, and in the manufacture of plywood and coated paper.

Borax is easily soluble in water and the resulting boric acid solution is mildly antiseptic. Wide use of this property is made in medicine, in the manufacture of soaps, disinfectants, and deodorants, and for food preservation.

$$Na_2B_4O_7 \cdot 10H_2O$$

Crystallography, Structure, Habit

Monoclinic. $\frac{2}{m}$. Tabular to short prismatic crystals, often poorly formed. As crystals, massive and cellular, and encrusting.

Physical Properties

Perfect (100) cleavage, less good (110). Conchoidal fracture. Brittle. Hardness 2–2.5. Specific gravity 1.7.

Vitreous to resinous luster. Translucent to opaque. Colorless to white or tints of gray, blue, or green. Streak white.

Sweetish alkaline taste. Fusible (1–1.5) with swelling.

Distinctive Properties and Tests

Sweetish taste, water soluble, low specific gravity, association. Evolves much water in the closed tube. Tests for boron.

Association and Occurrence

Borax is the most widespread of the borate minerals. It is found (1) in evaporite deposits and muds of saline lakes and playas with halite, other borates, gypsum, and calcite, (2) as an efflorescence on soils in arid regions, and (3) as a deposit from hot springs.

Alteration: Readily dissolves.

Confused with: Other borates.

Related Minerals

Similar species: Kernite, $Na_2B_4O_7 \cdot 4H_2O$; tincalconite, $Na_2B_4O_7 \cdot 5H_2O$; colemanite; ulexite, $NaCaB_5O_9 \cdot 8H_2O$.

COLEMANITE

$Ca_2B_6O_{11} \cdot 5H_2O$

Crystallography, Structure, Habit
Monoclinic. Short prismatic crystals.
Massive, granular, compact.

Physical Properties
Perfect (010) cleavage. Uneven to subconchoidal fracture.
Hardness 4–4.5. Specific gravity 2.4.
Vitreous to adamantine luster. Transparent to translucent. Colorless to white or with tints of yellow or gray. Streak white.
Fusible (1.5) with exfoliation and crumbling.

Distinctive Properties and Tests
Cleavage. Evolves water in the closed tube. Tests for boron.

Association and Occurrence
Found in stratified deposits in ancient lake beds.

Confused with: Other borates.

Related Minerals
Other similar species: Inyoite, $Ca_2B_6O_{11} \cdot 13H_2O$; meyerhoffite, $Ca_2B_6O_{11} \cdot 7H_2O$; veatchite, $Ca_2B_6O_{11} \cdot 2H_2O$.

Sulfates

Sulfur is found in nature in a reduced state as a native element and in metalloidal compounds. In its oxidized state it is the central cation of a regular SO_4 tetrahedron. Only in very rare instances do these radicals share oxygens between them. Structurally, the sulfates are built up of alternating cations, which are usually bivalent, and sulfate radicals. The cation is commonly an alkaline earth or the metals Pb, Cu, or Fe. The water of the hydrous sulfates is very loosely bound and may be readily removed by low heating or dessication.

As a family, sulfates are characterized by softness, light color, and occasional ready solubility in water or high specific gravity. Sulfates are often confused with carbonates, but they may be distinguished from carbonates by the ready effervescence of the latter in warm HCl. The flame colors of the cations serve to distinguish between the different sulfate species.

Gypsum and anhydrite are rock-forming sulfates. Gypsum is the first mineral to precipitate in large amounts when sea water is evaporated and is followed by anhydrite. Limestones and rock salt are usually found with the gyprock formed in this environment.

The most useful sulfate is gypsum, which is used principally in the manufacture of plaster and plaster products but also finds use in statuary (alabaster), as an additive to Portland cement, and as a land plaster. Anglesite and some copper sulfates are minor ores. Celestite is used for pyrotechnics and in processing beet sugar. Barite is used to make heavy muds for oil-well drilling. The manufacture of sulfuric acid is an important potential use for anhydrite.

BARITE $Ba(SO_4)$

Crystallography, Structure, Habit

Orthorhombic. $\frac{2}{m}\frac{2}{m}\frac{2}{m}$. Thin to thick tabular crystals.

Barite structure, see Figure 6–10c.

Crystals, rosettes, massive, granular, and lamellar.

Physical Properties

Perfect (001) cleavage. Uneven fracture. Brittle.

Hardness 3–3.5. Specific gravity 4.5.

Vitreous to resinous luster. Transparent to translucent. Colorless to white with tints of yellow, brown, red, gray, green, or blue.

May be fluorescent, phosphorescent, or thermoluminescent. Melting point 1580°.

Distinctive Properties and Tests

Crystal form, cleavage, specific gravity. Tests for barium and sulfur. Insoluble in acids.

Association and Occurrence

Barite is the most common barium mineral. It is found (1) as a gangue mineral in hydrothermal veins, especially those of low to moderate temperature where it is associated with fluorite, calcite, siderite, dolomite, quartz, and galena; (2) disseminated in limestones and other sediments as veins, lenses, fillings, and replacements; (3) in sedimentary iron and manganese deposits; (4) filling cavities in lava; and (5) as a hot-spring deposit.

Alteration: Quite resistant, may change to witherite.

Confused with: Calcite, dolomite.

Variants

Chemical varieties: Strontian, calcian, plumbian.

Related Minerals

Isomorphs: Celestite.

Isotypes: Anglesite; avogadrite, KBF_4.

Polymorphs: Transforms at 1149° to a monoclinic (?) form.

CELESTITE

$Sr(SO_4)$

Crystallography, Structure, Habit

Orthorhombic. $\dfrac{2}{m}\dfrac{2}{m}\dfrac{2}{m}$. Crystals as thin to thick tablets, laths, and equant forms.

Isostructural with barite, see Figure 6–10c.

Crystal groups, fibrous, nodular, granular, and banded.

Physical Properties

Perfect (001) and good (010) cleavage. Uneven fracture. Brittle.

Hardness 3–3.5. Specific gravity 4.0.

Vitreous to pearly luster. Transparent to translucent. Colorless to pale blue, white, reddish, greenish, or brownish.

Occasionally fluorescent and thermoluminescent. Melting point 1605° and fuses to a white pearl.

Distinctive Properties and Tests

Crystal form, cleavage, specific gravity. Tests for strontium and sulfur.

Association and Occurrence

Found chiefly in sedimentary rocks: (1) bedded gypsum, anhydrite, or halite deposits often associated with native sulfur; (2) as cavity fillings and veins or disseminated in limestone and dolomite with strontianite, gypsum, calcite, dolomite, and fluorite; (3) disseminated in shale, marl, and sandstone; (4) in evaporite deposits with potassium salts and borates; and (5) as a gangue mineral in hydrothermal veins.

Alteration: To strontianite.

Confused with: Barite.

Variants

Chemical varieties: Barian, calcian.

Related Minerals

Isomorphs: Barite.

Isotypes: Anglesite.

Polymorphs: Transforms at 1152° to hexagonal α-$SrSO_4$.

ANGLESITE $\quad$ Pb(SO$_4$)

Crystallography, Structure, Habit

Orthorhombic. $\frac{2}{m}\frac{2}{m}\frac{2}{m}$. Crystal forms various, usually thin to thick tabular, prismatic, or equant.

Isostructural with barite, see Figure 6–10c.

Usually massive, also granular to compact, nodular, or banded.

Physical Properties

Good (001) cleavage. Conchoidal fracture. Brittle.

Hardness 2.5–3. Specific gravity 6.4.

Adamantine to resinous or vitreous luster. Transparent to opaque. Colorless to white or with tints of gray, yellow, green, blue.

Often fluorescent. Fusible (1.5) and yields a lead globule.

Distinctive Properties and Tests

Specific gravity, fusibility. Tests for lead and sulfur. Acquires a white coating (PbCO$_3$) in an ammonium carbonate solution and a black lustrous coating (PbS) in an ammonium sulfide solution.

Association and Occurrence

A common secondary mineral after galena. Associated with cerussite, pyromorphite, native sulfur, wulfenite, gypsum, and cerargyrite.

Alteration: From galena. To cerussite.

Confused with: Cerussite.

Variants

Chemical varieties: Barian.

Related Minerals

Isotypes: Barite, celestite.

Polymorphs: Transforms at 864° to a monoclinic form.

ANHYDRITE

$Ca(SO_4)$

Crystallography, Structure, Habit

Orthorhombic. $\frac{2}{m}\frac{2}{m}\frac{2}{m}$. Crystals rare, usually equant or thick tablets. Contact twins.

Anhydrite structure, Figure 6–10d. Tetrahedral $(SO_4)^{-2}$ groups are held together by calcium ions. Each Ca ion has eight nearly equally spaced oxygen neighbors.

Usually massive, also fine granular or fibrous.

Physical Properties

Perfect (010), nearly perfect (100), and good (001) cleavages yielding cubic or rectangular fragments. Uneven to splintery fracture. Brittle.

Hardness 3.5. Specific gravity 3.0.

Pearly, vitreous, or glassy luster. Transparent. Colorless to blue white, reddish, purplish, brown, or gray.

Melting point about 1450°, fuses to a white enamel.

Distinctive Properties and Tests

Cleavage. Soluble in HCl. Tests for Ca and S or $(SO_4)^{-2}$.

Association and Occurrence

Anhydrite is a rock-forming mineral and is often found in bedded deposits alone or with gypsum, limestone, dolomite, or halite. It is also found (1) as an accessory mineral in sedimentary rocks with celestite, dolomite, calcite, gypsum, and quartz; (2) as a gangue mineral in hydrothermal veins; (3) in cavities in lava with prehnite and zeolites; (4) as a component of caliche; and (5) as a deposit around fumaroles.

Alteration: Changes readily from and to gypsum.

Confused with: Gypsum, celestite.

Related Minerals

Isotypes: Ferrobrucite, $NaBF_4$.

Polymorphs: Transforms at 1193° to α-$CaSO_4$.

Other similar species: Gypsum; glaserite, $K_3Na(SO_4)_2$; glauberite, $CaNa_2(SO_4)_2$.

GYPSUM $Ca(SO_4) \cdot 2H_2O$

Crystallography, Structure, Habit

Monoclinic. $\frac{2}{m}$. Thick to thin tabular crystals, usually elongated; also prismatic and acicular forms. Often twinned on (100) yielding contact "swallowtail" twins.

Gypsum structure, see Figure 6–10g. Each calcium ion is surrounded by four sulfate radicals and two water molecules.

Massive, foliated, and as crystal aggregates or rosettes.

Physical Properties

Eminent (010), distinct (100), and good (001) cleavage yielding flattened rhombic fragments. Cleavage folia may be bent, but are not elastic.

Hardness 2. Specific gravity 2.3.

Subvitreous luster. Transparent to translucent. Colorless, white, gray, yellow, or brown.

Fusible (3).

Distinctive Properties and Tests

Softness, cleavage. Yields copious water in the closed tube. Soluble in hot dilute HCl. Tests for Ca, S, and $(SO_4)^{-2}$.

Association and Occurrence

Gypsum is the most common sulfate mineral. It is found (1) in bedded sedimentary deposits associated with limestone, red shale, sandstones, marl, and clay; (2) around fumaroles with native sulfur; (3) as an efflorescence from soils; and (4) in gossans.

Alteration: Changes readily from and to anhydrite.

Confused with: Anhydrite, calcite.

Variants

Form varieties: Selenite, crystallized; satin spar, fibrous; alabaster, massive.

Gypsum is one of the few minerals with no significant chemical variation. Traces of barium and strontium are sometimes present and admixed clay, sand, bitumens, etc., are common.

Related Minerals

Isotypes: Brushite, $CaH(PO_4) \cdot 2H_2O$; pharmacolite, $CaH(AsO_4) \cdot 2H_2O$.
Other similar species: Anhydrite; mirabilite, $Na_2(SO_4) \cdot 10H_2O$.

MELANTERITE $Fe(SO_4) \cdot 7H_2O$

Crystallography, Structure, Habit

Monoclinic. $\frac{2}{m}$. Equant to short prismatic crystals.

Usually stalactitic or concretionary, also fibrous, encrusting, and pulverulent.

Physical Properties

Perfect (001) and distinct (110) cleavage. Conchoidal fracture. Brittle. Hardness 2. Specific gravity 1.9.

Vitreous luster. Translucent. Color green, green blue, greenish white, or blue. Colored streak.

Sweetish astringent and metallic taste. Turns yellowish white and opaque on exposure to air.

Distinctive Properties and Tests

Taste, color. Tests for Fe, S, and the sulfate radical. Copious water in the closed tube.

Association and Occurrence

Melanterite is a secondary mineral formed by alteration of iron-bearing sulfides. It is found (1) typically as efflorescences in mines or pyritic deposits or in the oxidized zone of ore deposits and (2) in coals and lignites.

Alteration: From iron sulfides such as pyrite and marcasite. From and to other ferrous and ferric sulfates. Dehydrates readily to siderotil, $Fe(SO_4) \cdot 5H_2O$.

Variants

Chemical varieties: Cuprian, magnesian, zincian. May also contain small amounts of Co, Ni, or Mn.

Related Minerals

Isomorphs: Pisanite, $(CuFe)(SO_4) \cdot 7H_2O$; boothite, $Cu(SO_4) \cdot 7H_2O$; kirovite, $(FeMg)(SO_4) \cdot 7H_2O$.

Isotypes: Mallardite, $Mn(SO_4) \cdot 7H_2O$; bieberite, $Co(SO_4) \cdot 7H_2O$.

Other similar species: Siderotil, $Fe(SO_4) \cdot 5H_2O$.

EPSOMITE $Mg(SO_4) \cdot 7H_2O$

Crystallography, Structure, Habit
Orthorhombic. 222. Crystals rare.
Usually fibrous, wooly, or colloform.

Physical Properties
Perfect (010) and distinct (101) cleavage. Conchoidal fracture.
Hardness 2–2.5. Specific gravity 1.7.
Vitreous to silky luster. Transparent to translucent. Colorless to white or
tints of pink or green.
Bitter salt taste.

Distinctive Properties and Tests
Habit, low specific gravity, taste. Tests for S and sulfate radical. Melts in
its own water of crystallization in the closed tube.

Association and Occurrence
Found as (1) crusts or efflorescences in coal or metal mines, in limestone
caves, and in sheltered spots on outcrops of limestone, dolomite, gypsum, and
magnesia-rich igneous rocks; (2) in the oxidized zone of pyritic sulfide deposits
in arid regions; and (3) in mineral spring waters. Epsomite is usually associated with melanterite and other iron sulfates, gypsum, etc.

Alteration: From kieserite, $Mg(SO_4) \cdot H_2O$, serpentine, talc, magnesite. From
and to hexahydrite, $Mg(SO_4) \cdot 6H_2O$.

Confused with: Other hydrous sulfates.

Variants
Chemical varieties: Nickelian (green), manganoan (pink), zincian.

Related Minerals
Isomorphs: Goslarite, $Zn(SO_4) \cdot 7H_2O$; morenosite, $Ni(SO_4) \cdot 7H_2O$.

JAROSITE $KFe(SO_4)_3(OH)_6$

Crystallography, Structure, Habit

Hexagonal. $\frac{3}{m}$. Crystals minute and indistinct with the form of pseudo-cubes or tablets.

Found as crusts and coatings, also granular, fibrous, and nodular.

Physical Properties

Distinct (0001) cleavage. Uneven to conchoidal fracture. Brittle. Hardness 2.5–3.5. Specific gravity 3.

Adamantine to vitreous or resinous luster. Translucent. Color ocherous yellow to brown. Streak pale yellow.

Strongly pyroelectric.

Distinctive Properties and Tests

Color, habit, occurrence. Soluble in HCl. Evolves sulfur dioxide at red heat. Tests for Fe, S, $(SO_4)^{-2}$, and H_2O.

Association and Occurrence

Jarosite is a widespread secondary mineral and is found (1) as crusts and coatings on iron ores and (2) in veins in sedimentary rocks. It is commonly associated with limonite, barite, quartz, pyrite, and hematite.

Alteration: From iron sulfides. To iron oxides.

Confused with: Limonite, hematite.

Related Minerals

Isomorphs: Natrojarosite, $NaFe_3(SO_4)_2(OH)_6$.

Isotypes: Alunite, $KAl_3(SO_4)_2(OH)_6$; natroalunite, $NaAl_3(SO_4)_2(OH)_6$; ammoniojarosite, $NH_4Fe_3(SO_4)_2(OH)_6$; argentojarosite, $AgFe_3(SO_4)_2(OH)_6$; carphosiderite, $(H_2O)Fe_3(SO_4)_2(OH_3 \cdot H_2O)$; plumbojarosite, $PbFe_6(SO_4)_4(OH)_{12}$.

Phosphates

Arsenates

Vanadates

The phosphates, arsenates, and vanadates comprise a diverse group of minerals encompassing a great number of species. Although this group is very large, most of its members are so rare that they are seldom seen. Only apatite and possibly monazite can be considered common because of their wide distribution as accessory minerals in igneous rocks and their relatively high concentration in a few sediments.

In so far as is known, the minerals in these families do not share oxygen ions between their XO_4 tetrahedral radicals. Their structures, therefore, must be an alternation of cations and these tetrahedra. Isomorphism between phosphorus, arsenic, and vanadium is moderately common as, for example, in the pyromorphite series.

Apatite is the principal source of phosphorus for use in fertilizers. Crystalline apatite is used, but most production is from collophanite, a massive, cryptocrystalline variety of apatite. Monazite is the principal source of many of the rare earth metals and an important source of thorium which may be present in amounts up to 12 percent ThO_2. The pyromorphite series as a group forms a minor ore of lead, amblygonite is a potential source of lithium, and carnotite is exploited as an ore of both vanadium and uranium.

MONAZITE $(CeLaDy)(PO_4)$

Crystallography, Structure, Habit

Monoclinic. $\frac{2}{m}$. Crystals usually small, elongate, prismatic, and equant forms. Contact twins common.

Crystals, masses, and rounded grains.

Physical Properties

Distinct (100) cleavage. Parting often on (001), rarely on ($\bar{1}$11). Conchoidal to uneven fracture. Brittle.

Hardness 5–5.5. Specific gravity 5.1.

Luster variable, may be adamantine, resinous, waxy, or vitreous. Translucent. Color yellow or red brown; brown, yellow, green, or white. Streak white. Infusible.

Distinctive Properties and Tests

Color, habit, occurrence. Usually radioactive. Turns gray when strongly heated. Bluish-green flame color obtained when assay is moistened with H_2SO_4.

Association and Occurrence

Monazite is (1) widely disseminated as an accessory mineral in granitic or syenitic igneous rocks, pegmatites, and gneisses and (2) may be concentrated in beach or stream placers. It is associated with zircon, other rare-earth minerals, magnetite, apatite, columbite, and ilmenite.

Alteration: Resistant to change but usually acquires a yellow or red brown opaque coating on exposure to air.

Confused with: Zircon.

Variants

Chemical varieties: thorian (usually also silician), yttrian.

Related Minerals

Isotypes: Crocoite, $Pb(CrO_4)$.

Other similar species: Xenotime, YPO_4; pucherite, $BiVO_4$.

APATITE SERIES $\qquad$ $Ca_5(PO_4)_3F$

Crystallography, Structure, Habit

Hexagonal. $\dfrac{6}{m}$. Short to long prismatic crystals.

Apatite structure, see Figure 6–10e.

Usually in crystals, also massive, granular, or colloform.

Physical Properties

Imperfect (0001) cleavage. Conchoidal to uneven fracture. Brittle.

Hardness 5. Specific gravity 3.1.

Vitreous luster. Transparent to opaque. Color usually shades of green or red; green, blue green, violet blue, blue, pale green, dark red brown; also colorless, white. Streak white.

Most specimens fluoresce or phosphoresce. Thermoluminescent. Fuses with difficulty (4–4.5), purplish kinds lose color on heating.

Distinctive Properties and Tests

Crystal habit, color, lack of good cleavage. Soluble in HCl or HNO_3. A fragment moistened with H_2SO_4 and heated colors the flame pale bluish-green (phosphoric acid).

Association and Occurrence

Apatite is among the commonest and most widespread of minerals. It is found (1) as an accessory mineral in all igneous rocks; (2) as segregations from alkalic igneous rocks; (3) in pegmatites; (4) in magnetite deposits; (5) in hydrothermal veins; (6) in metamorphic rocks, especially marble with sphene, zircon, pyroxenes, amphiboles, spinel, vesuvianite, and phlogopite; (7) in talc and chlorite schists; (8) in bedded marine sediments; (9) as a replacement of limestone by guano; and (10) as a component of fossil bones, shells, and teeth.

Alteration: Resistant to change.

Confused with: Beryl, epidote.

Variants

Form varieties: Collophane, a massive cryptocrystalline apatite which makes up phosphate rocks.

Chemical varieties: Chlorian, hydroxylian, carbonatian (dahllite), manganoan (dark blue, in pegmatites only), strontian. S, Mg, Fe, As, Na, Y, and Si may be present in varying amounts.

Related Minerals

Isomorphs: The apatite series shows complete isomorphism between fluorapatite (the most common), chlor-apatite, and hydroxylian apatite. Further, Ca may be replaced in part by Sr, Mn, Mg, or Fe and (PO_4) by (AsO_4).

Isotypes: Svabite, $Ca_5(AsO_4)_3(OH)$; dahllite, $Ca_{10}(PO_4)_6(CO_3)$; ellestadite, $Ca_{10}[(SiS)O_4]_3(OH)_2$; pyromorphite series; vanadinite, $Pb_5(VO_4)_3Cl$.

PYROMORPHITE SERIES

Pyromorphite $Pb_3(PO_4)_3Cl$
Mimetite $Pb_3(AsO_4)_3Cl$

Crystallography, Structure, Habit

Hexagonal. $\frac{6}{m}$. Prismatic and equant crystals, often rounded and barrel-shaped.

Structure very similar to that of apatite, Figure 6–10e.

Crystals, granular, or colloform.

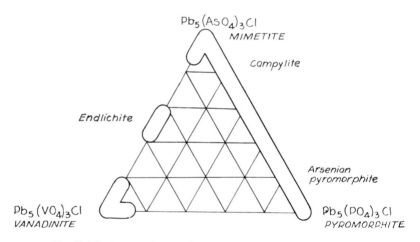

Fig. 7–10. Isomorphous relations in the pyromorphite series.

Physical Properties

No distinct cleavage. Uneven to subconchoidal fracture. Brittle.

Hardness 3.5–4. Specific gravity 7.

Resinous luster. Translucent. Color usually green, also yellow, brown, or reddish. Streak white.

Piezoelectric. Readily fusible (1.5) yielding a lead globule which assumes a polyhedral form on cooling.

Distinctive Properties and Tests

Crystal form, specific gravity, luster, color, fusibility and lead bead. Soluble in HNO_3. Tests for lead, $(PO_4)^{-3}$, or As.

Association and Occurrence

Secondary products in the oxidized zone of lead ore deposits with cerussite, limonite, smithsonite, hemimorphite, and wulfenite.

Alteration: From galena and cerussite.

Confused with: Apatite.

314

Pyromorphite Series (cont.)

Variants

Form varieties: Campylite, which has barrel-shaped crystals.

Chemical varieties: Calcian (brown, green, or white), vanadian (black), chromian (red or orange), arsenian (green to white).

Related Minerals

Isomorphs: A complete series exists between pyromorphite and mimetite, and a partial series connects mimetite with endlichite, $Pb_5(VAsO_4)_3Cl$, and vanadinite, $Pb_5(VO_4)_3Cl$. These relations are shown diagrammatically in Figure 7–10.

Isotypes: Apatite series.

AMBLYGONITE SERIES

Amblygonite $LiAl(PO_4)F$
Montebrasite $LiAl(PO_4)OH$

Crystallography, Structure, Habit

Triclinic. $\bar{1}$. Large, coarse, and poorly formed crystals. Repeated parallel twins are common.

Usually columnar to compact massive.

Physical Properties

Perfect (001), good (100), and sometimes distinct (0$\bar{2}$1) cleavage. Uneven to subconchoidal fracture. Brittle.

Hardness 5.5–6. Specific gravity 3.1.

Vitreous to greasy luster. Transparent to translucent. Color white with tints of yellow, pink, green, blue, or gray, also colorless.

Readily fusible (2) with bubbling.

Distinctive Properties and Tests

Crystals, cleavage, fusibility, association. Tests for Li and phosphate radical.

Association and Occurrence

Found only in (1) granite pegmatites rich in lithium and phosphorus associated with spodumene, apatite, lepidolite, and tourmaline, and (2) in high temperature tin veins and greisen with cassiterite, topaz, and mica.

Alteration: To kaolin plus mica, turquoise, $Al_2PO_4(OH)_3 \cdot H_2O + xCu$, wavellite, $Al_3(PO_4)_2(OH)_3 \cdot 5H_2O$, etc.

Confused with: Spodumene.

Variants

Chemical varieties: Sodian.

Related Minerals

Isomorphs: Complete isomorphism exists between amblygonite and montebrasite. The field of isomorphism extends toward a sodic end member fremontite, $(NaLi)Al(PO_4)(OHF)$.

Other similar species: Herderite, $CaBe(PO_4)(OHF)$.

CARNOTITE

$$K_2(UO_2)_2(VO_4)_2 \cdot nH_2O$$

Crystallography, Structure, Habit

Orthorhombic (?), monoclinic (?). Tiny platy crystals with six sides. Crystalline powder or pulverulent masses.

Physical Properties

Perfect (001) cleavage.
Hardness 1–2. Specific gravity 4–5.
Earthy to resinous luster. Color bright yellow.
Strongly radioactive.

Distinctive Properties and Tests

Color and habit. Radioactivity.

Association and Occurrence

Disseminated or localized in sandstones or conglomerates, especially near carbonized vegetable matter.

Confused with: Limonite, hydrated uranium oxides.

Related Minerals

Other similar species: Tyuyamunite, $Ca(UO_2)_2(VO_4)_2 \cdot nH_2O$; torbernite, $Cu(UO_2)_2(PO_4)_2 \cdot 8H_2O$; autunite, $Ca(UO_2)_2(PO_4)_2 \cdot 8H_2O$.

Tungstates, Molybdates

ANHYDROUS

  Wolframite group
   Wolframite series, $(FeMn)(WO_4)$
  Scheelite group
   Scheelite, $Ca(WO_4)$
   Wulfenite, $Pb(MoO_4)$

Tungsten * and molybdenum are poorly screened elements which co-ordinate four oxygen ions into a distorted XO_4 tetrahedron. Tungstate and molybdate structures are made up of alternating cations and tetrahedra. No instances of the formation of complex ions are known.

Both tungsten and molybdenum impart valuable and important properties to steel with which they are alloyed. Tungsten, obtained from the minerals wolframite and scheelite, is a steel-hardening metal and steels so alloyed keep their temper at high temperatures. Such steels are especially desirable for use in high-speed cutting tools. The extremely high melting point of tungsten ($3370°$ C) also makes this metal especially valuable for the manufacture of filaments for incandescent lamps, electrical contacts, spark plugs, and crucibles.

Molybdenum metal is principally obtained from the sulfide molybdenite, but the lead molybdate, wulfenite, is a minor ore of both lead and molybdenum. Molybdenum is used in both ferrous and nonferrous alloys intended for use in furnace windings, permanent magnets, rustless steels, and tough steels for railroad forgings and agricultural machinery.

Tungstates and molybdates are relatively rare minerals. Both wolframite and scheelite are formed at high temperatures in close association with salic igneous rocks. Scheelite is often closely associated with quartz, with which it is easily confused because of the very similar physical appearance of these two minerals. Fortunately, scheelite always fluoresces a characteristic electric blue color when irradiated with ultra-violet light, which greatly facilitates prospecting for and evaluation of scheelite deposits.

---

* The term *wolfram* has recently been adopted for this element. The use of the name tungsten is retained here to conform to mineral names which use tungsten as a root, for example, tungstite, WO_3.

WOLFRAMITE SERIES

Huebnerite $Mn(WO_4)$
Ferberite $Fe(WO_4)$

Crystallography, Structure, Habit

Monoclinic. $\frac{2}{m}$. Crystals as short to long prisms or tablets, usually striated vertically. Contact twins.

Structure, Figure 6–10f. Layers of discrete distorted WO_4 tetrahedra alternate with planes of (MnFe).

Subparallel crystal groups, granular.

Physical Properties

Perfect (010) cleavage. Parting on (100) and (102). Uneven fracture. Brittle.

Hardness 4–4.5. Specific gravity 7.3.

Submetallic luster. Transparent to opaque. Color black, brownish-black, or yellowish-black. Streak brown black to black.

Occasionally has an iridescent tarnish. Sometimes weakly magnetic. Fusible (2.5–3) to a magnetic globule with a polyhedral surface.

Distinctive Properties and Tests

Color, cleavage, luster, streak. Tests for Fe, Mn, and $(WO_4)^{-2}$. Partially dissolved in concentrated sulfuric acid, and metallic tin added to the solution causes it to turn intense blue.

Association and Occurrence

Found in (1) greisen, quartz-rich veins, or pegmatites immediately associated with granitic rocks; (2) in high-temperature hydrothermal veins with sulfides such as pyrrhotite, pyrite, chalcopyrite and arsenopyrite, scheelite, native bismuth, molybdenite, hematite, magnetite, tourmaline, topaz, albite, and apatite; (3) in mesothermal veins with sulfides, scheelite, native bismuth, quartz, siderite, barite, fluorite, and tourmaline; and (4) in placer deposits.

Alteration: Resistant to change but may alter to iron and manganese oxides.

Confused with: Hornblende.

Variants

May contain small amounts of Ca, Cb, or Ta.

Related Minerals

Isomorphs: A complete isomorphous series exists between huebnerite and ferberite. Most specimens have an intermediate composition.

Other similar species: Raspite, $Pb(WO_4)$.

Crystallography, Structure, Habit

Tetragonal. $\frac{4}{m}$. Pseudo-octahedral and tabular crystals. Contact and penetration twins.

Scheelite structure, Figure 7–11.

Found as crystals, massive, granular, and columnar.

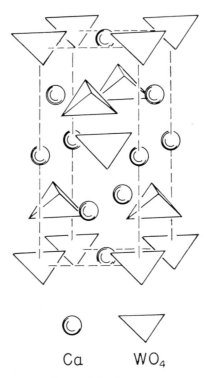

Ca WO_4

Fig. 7–11. Scheelite structure.

Physical Properties

Distinct (101) and interrupted (112) cleavage. Uneven to subconchoidal fracture. Brittle.

Hardness 4.5–5. Specific gravity 6.1.

Vitreous to adamantine luster. Transparent to translucent. Colorless to white or tints of yellow, brown, green, gray, or red. Streak white.

Fluoresces bluish white in X rays and shortwave ultraviolet light. Thermoluminescent. Fusible with difficulty (5).

Scheelite (cont.)

Distinctive Properties and Tests
Association, fluorescence. Decomposed by HCl or HNO_3, yielding a yellow powder which is soluble in NH_4OH. An HCl solution boiled with tin assumes a blue color which changes later to brown.

Association and Occurrence
Scheelite is typically a high-temperature mineral. It is found (1) in limestones metamorphosed at granite contacts with garnet, diopside, tremolite, hornblende, epidote, wolframite, vesuvianite, sphene, molybdenite, fluorite, pyrite, or chalcopyrite; (2) in quartzose hydrothermal veins and greisen; and (3) in pegmatites.

Alteration: To tungstite, WO_3, or hydrotungstite, $WO_3 \cdot nH_2O$, yellow or yellow-green powder.

Confused with: Quartz, feldspar.

Variants
Chemical varieties: Molybdian, cuprian.

Related Minerals
Isomorphs: Powellite, $Ca(MoO_4)$.
Isotypes: Cuprotungstite, $Cu(WO_4)$, cuproscheelite, $CaCu(WO_4)$, stolzite, $Pb(WO_4)$.

WULFENITE

$$Pb(MoO_4)$$

Crystallography, Structure, Habit

Tetragonal. $\bar{4}$. Crystals in square tablets.
Isostructural (?) with scheelite, Figure 7–11.
Usually in crystals, also granular or compact.

Physical Properties

Distinct (001) cleavage. Subconchoidal to uneven fracture. Not very brittle.
Hardness 2.75–3. Specific gravity 6.5–7.0.
Resinous to adamantine luster. Transparent. Color orange to yellow. Streak white.
Melting point 1065°. Easily fusible (2) to a lead globule.

Distinctive Properties and Tests

Crystals and color. Decomposed on evaporation with HCl yielding a residue of lead chloride and molybdic acid. This residue has an intense blue color when moistened with water in the presence of metallic zinc.

Association and Occurrence

Wulfenite is a secondary mineral found in the oxidized zone of lead deposits associated with pyromorphite, cerussite, limonite, calcite, galena, and manganese oxides.

Confused with: Native sulfur.

Variants

Chemical varieties: Calcian, vanadian, tungstenian. May also contain trace amounts of chromium and arsenic.

Related Minerals

Isomorphs: Stolzite, $Pb(WO_4)$.
Other similar species: Raspite $Pb(WO_4)$.

Silicates

NETWORKS

Silica group
    Quartz, SiO_2
    Opal, $SiO_2 \cdot nH_2O$
Monoclinic feldspar group
    Orthoclase series, $K(AlSi_3O_8)$
Triclinic feldspar group
    Microcline series
    Plagioclase series, $(CaNa)[(AlSi)_4O_8]$
Feldspathoid group
    Nepheline series
        Nepheline, $Na(AlSiO_4)$
    Sodalite series
        Sodalite, $Na_4(Al_3Si_3O_{12})Cl$
    Scapolite series, $(NaCa)_4[Al(AlSi)Si_2O_8]_3(Cl, CO_3)$
    Miscellaneous species
        Leucite, $K(AlSi_2O_6)$
        Cancrinite, $Na_3Ca(Al_3Si_3O_{12})CO_3(OH)_2$
        Analcite, $Na(AlSi_2O_6) \cdot H_2O$
Zeolite family
    Stilbite, $(CaNaK)_3[Al_5(AlSi)Si_{14}O_{40}] \cdot 15H_2O$
    Chabazite, $(CaNaK)_7[Al_{12}(AlSi)_2Si_{26}O_{80}] \cdot 40H_2O$
    Natrolite, $Na_2(Al_2Si_3O_{10}) \cdot 2H_2O$

SHEETS

Clay group
    Kaolinite, $Al_2(Si_2O_5)(OH)_4$
    Montmorillonite series, $x(AlMg)_2[(AlSi)_4O_{10}](OH)_2$
Talc group
    Pyrophyllite, $Al_2(Si_4O_{10})(OH)_2$
    Talc, $Mg_3(Si_4O_{10})(OH)_2$
Chlorite group, $(MgFeAl)_6[(AlSi)_4O_{10}](OH)_8$
Vermiculite group
Brittle mica group
    Margarite, $CaAl_2(Al_2Si_2O_{10})(OH)_2$
    Prehnite, $Ca_2Al(AlSi_3O_{10})(OH)_2$
Elastic mica group
    Muscovite series
        Muscovite, $KAl_2(AlSi_3O_{10})(OH)_2$
    Biotite series
        Biotite, $K(MgFe)_3(AlSi_3O_{10})(OH)_2$
        Phlogopite, $KMg_3(AlSi_3O_{10})(OH)_2$
    Lepidolite series, $K_2Li_2Al_3(AlSi_7O_{20})(OH, F)_4$
Miscellaneous species
    Serpentine, $Mg_6(Si_4O_{10})(OH)_8$
    Glauconite, $K_2(MgFe)_2Al_6(Si_4O_{10})_3(OH)_{12}$

Silicates (cont.)

CHAINS AND RINGS
DOUBLE CHAINS
  Amphibole group
    Anthophyllite series, $(MgFeAl)_7[(SiAl)_8O_{22}](OH)_2$
    Cummingtonite series
    Tremolite series, $Ca_2(MgFe)_5(Si_8O_{22})(OH)_2$
    Hornblende series
SINGLE CHAINS
  Pyroxene group
    Enstatite series, $(MgFe)_2(Si_2O_6)$
    Pigeonite series
    Diopside series, $Ca(MgFe)(Si_2O_6)$
    Acmite series
  Miscellaneous species
    Spodumene, $LiAl(Si_2O_6)$
    Rhodonite, $Mn(SiO_3)$
    Chrysocolla, $Cu(SiO_3) \cdot nH_2O$
    Garnierite, $(NiMg)(SiO_3) \cdot nH_2O$
    Wollastonite, $Ca(SiO_3)$
    Pectolite, $Ca_2NaH(SiO_3)_2$
RINGS
  Tourmaline series, $(NaCaLi)(MgFe)_3B_3Al_3(Al_3Si_6O_{27})(OH, F)_4$
  Miscellaneous species
    Beryl, $Be_3Al_2(SiO_3)_6$
    Cordierite, $Mg_2Al_3(AlSi_5O_{18})$

PAIRS
  Melilite series, $Ca_2(MgAl)[(AlSi)_2O_7]$
  Miscellaneous species
    Hemimorphite, $Zn_4(Si_2O_7)(OH)_2 \cdot H_2O$
COMBINED PAIRS AND UNITS
  Vesuvianite, $Ca_{10}(MgFe)_2Al_4(Si_2O_7)_2(SiO_4)_5(OH)_4$

UNITS
  Chrysolite group
    Olivine series, $(MgFe)_2(SiO_4)$
  Phenakite group
  Garnet group
    Almandite series, $R_3{}^{+2}Al_2(SiO_4)_3$
    Andradite series, $Ca_3R_2{}^{+3}(SiO_4)_3$
  Zircon group
    Zircon, $Zr(SiO_4)$
  Humite group, $xMg_2(SiO_4) \cdot Mg(OH, F)_2$
  Epidote group
    Epidote series, $Ca_2(AlFeMn)_3(SiO_4)_3(OH)$
  Miscellaneous species
    Topaz, $Al_2(SiO_4)(OH, F)_2$

Silicates (cont.)

SUBSATURATES

Aluminum group
    Andalusite, $AlAl(SiO_4)O$
    Sillimanite, $AlAl(SiO_4)O$
    Kyanite, $Al_2(SiO_4)O$
Titanium group
    Sphene, $CaTi(SiO_4)O$
Magnesium group
Miscellaneous species
    Staurolite, $FeAl_4(SiO_4)_2O_2(OH)_2$

Chemical and Blowpipe Tests for the Silicates

Mineral	Reaction with HCl			Water in Closed Tube	Fusibility (3)	Miscellaneous
	Insoluble	Soluble (1)	Gel (2)			
Analcite		x		x	3.5	
Andalusite	x				Infusible	
Anthophyllite	x			x	5*	
Augite	x				4–4.5*	
Beryl	x				5.5	
Biotite	x			x	5*	Decomposes in boiling H_2SO_4 giving a milky solution
Cancrinite			x	x	2	Effervesces
Chabazite		x		x	3	
Chlorite	x			x	5.5*	As biotite
Chondrodite			x	x	Infusible	
Chrysocolla		x		x	Infusible	Cu tests
Cordierite	x				5.5*	
Diopside	x				4	
Enstatite series						Solubility and
Enstatite	x				Infusible	fusibility increase with
Hypersthene	x				5*	increasing iron
Epidote	x			x	3–4(*)	Gelatinizes if previously ignited
Garnet	x			x	3–3.5(*)	As epidote
Garnierite		x		x	Infusible	

(1) Yields free silica when boiled in HCl.
(2) Dissolves in boiling HCl and yields first a jelly and then granular silica on evaporation.
(3) An asterisk * indicates the fused mineral is magnetic. An asterisk within parentheses indicates the fused mineral is sometimes magnetic.

Silicates (cont.)

Chemical and Blowpipe Tests for the Silicates (cont.)

Mineral	Reaction with HCl			Water in Closed Tube	Fusibility (3)	Miscellaneous
	Insoluble	Soluble (1)	Gel (2)			
Glauconite		x		x	Easy*	
Hemimorphite			x	x	6	
Hornblende	x			x	4*	
Kaolinite	x			x	Infusible	
Kyanite	x				Infusible	
Lepidolite	x			x	2	
Leucite		x			Infusible	
Margarite	x			x	4–4.5	Slowly decomposed
Melilite			x		3	
Montmorillonite	x			x	Infusible	
Muscovite	x			x	5	
Natrolite			x	x	2.5	
Nepheline			x		4	
Olivine			x		Infusible	Slow reaction
Opal	x			x	Infusible	
Orthoclase	x				5	
Pectolite		x		x	2.5–3	
Phlogopite	x			x	4.5–5	As biotite
Plagioclase series						
Albite	x				4–4.5	
Anorthite		x			5	
Prehnite	x			x	2.5	Gelatinizes after being fused
Pyrophyllite	x			x	Infusible	
Quartz	x				Infusible	
Rhodonite	x				3	
Scapolite		x			3	Imperfectly decomposed
Serpentine		x		x	Infusible	
Sillimanite	x				Infusible	
Sodalite			x		3.5–4	
Sphene	x				4	
Spodumene	x				3.5	
Staurolite	x			x	Infusible	
Stilbite		x		x	3	
Talc	x			x	5	
Topaz	x				Infusible	
Tourmaline	x				Varies with composition from 3 to infusible	
Tremolite	x			x	3–4	
Vesuvianite	x			x	3	Gelatinizes after being fused
Wollastonite		x			4	
Zircon	x				Infusible	

Silicates (cont.)

Silicate minerals are a very large and diverse mineral class. No generalizations hold for all silicates, but as a rule they are translucent to transparent, of moderate specific gravity, have a vitreous luster, and are chemically inert.

The different species have markedly different physical characteristics, and this wide range of hardness, color, cleavage, and luster coupled with habit and association will usually suffice for identification.

Some blowpipe and wet chemical tests are useful for the identification or confirmation of silicates. The most generally applicable chemical test is the manner of solution of the mineral in boiling hydrochloric acid. Some silicates are insoluble, some yield a granular siliceous product, and still others first dissolve and on evaporation yield first a jelly and then granular silica. The most generally applicable blowpipe tests are fusibility coupled with a test of the assay for magnetism and the closed-tube test for water. These chemical and blowpipe tests are tabulated on pages 325–326.

A discussion of the details of structure and modifications of the various silicates will be found preceding the description of species of each of the major divisions: networks, sheets, chains, pairs, units, and subsaturates.

Silicates (cont.)

Silica Group. SiO_4 tetrahedra sharing all four oxygens with adjacent tetrahedra may be arranged in at least four distinctively different ways, each of which may have several minor modifications. These possibilities give rise to an extensive group of SiO_2 polymorphs. Figure 3–6, page 106, illustrates the structures of the various polymorphs under conditions of normal pressure. A high-pressure member of the group, coesite, is not shown but has a structure analagous to a feldspar and different from those illustrated.

The temperature relations between the polymorphs of silica were figured and described on p. 108 ff. Transformations (inversions) between forms of the same name, e.g., high quartz and low quartz, are displacive transformations which are reversible and take place instantaneously at the transformation temperature. Transformations between different mineral species, e.g., quartz and tridymite, are reconstructive transformations which are nonreversible and very sluggish.

The minerals of the silica group are structurally related to a number of other mineral species through replacement of Si^{+4} with geologically common Al^{+3} and concomitant admittance of an alkali metal of appropriate size in order to maintain electrical neutrality. Examples of minerals isotypic with the silica group are:

High cristobalite, SiO_2—high carnegieite, $Na(AlSiO_4)$

High tridymite, SiO_2—$\begin{cases} \text{kaliophyllite, } K(AlSiO_4) \\ \text{nepheline, } Na(AlSiO_4) \end{cases}$

Low quartz, SiO_2—eucryptite, $Li(AlSiO_4)$

In each case alternate Si ions in the basic structure are replaced by Al ions, thus requiring an enlarged unit cell. The charge deficiency of -1 per interchange is made up by the addition of one alkali metal atom (charge $+1$) per interchange. The alkali is located in interstices of the basic structure and the size of this hole largely controls the kind of alkali metal which may enter.

Another isotypic relationship of a somewhat different nature is that which connects cristobalite and opal. Opal is an example of the link between amorphous and crystalline substances in that it is composed of minute crystalline patches arranged in a random manner. X-ray study shows the crystalline patches to have the structure of cristobalite with water molecules occupying the structural holes.

The only common representative of the silica group is low quartz. This species is, however, one of the most ubiquitous of minerals, being formed and found over a very wide range of geological environments.

LOW QUARTZ

Crystallography, Structure, Habit

Hexagonal. 32. Hexagonal prisms with pyramoidal termination. Left- and right-handed forms. Prism faces often horizontally striated. Crystals often distorted. Penetration and contact twins.

Quartz structure, see Figure 7–12.

Found massive, as crystals, and rarely in many other habits.

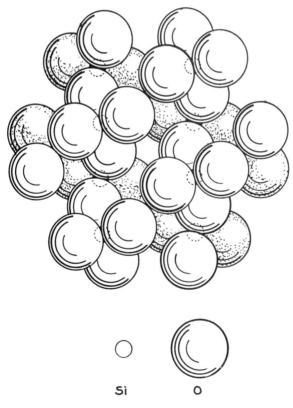

Si   O

Fig. 7–12. Quartz structure.

Low Quartz (cont.)

Physical Properties

No cleavage. No parting. Conchoidal fracture. Brittle.

Hardness 7. Specific gravity 2.65.

Vitreous luster. Transparent to translucent. Colorless, white, and less commonly purple, pink, or black.

Strong piezo- and pyroelectric properties. May be colored by radiation. Some varieties luminescent. Melting point 1410°.

Distinctive Properties and Tests

Hardness, lack of cleavage, luster. Infusible, insoluble.

Association and Occurrence

Quartz is among the most common of minerals, being found almost everywhere. It is (1) an important constituent in many igneous, metamorphic, and sedimentary rocks and largely comprises some, e.g., sandstone, quartzite, novaculite; (2) the most common mineral in veins, either as a gangue or sole constituent; and (3) an almost universal residual and detrital mineral found in soils, sediments, and on beaches.

Alteration: Resistant to change.

Confused with: Beryl, calcite, cordierite, scheelite.

Variants

Form varieties.

Coarsely crystalline varieties: Amethyst (purple), rose quartz (pink), smoky quartz (yellow brown to black), milky quartz, rock crystal (clear), citrine (yellow).

Fibrous cryptocrystalline varieties: Chalcedony, including carnelian (red), chrysoprase (apple green), bloodstone (red-flecked green), agate (banded and variegated), onyx.

Granular cryptocrystalline varieties: Flint (dull to dark in color), chert (light in color), jasper (red), prase (dull green).

With inclusions: Rutilated quartz, aventurine (scaly inclusions of hematite or mica).

Related Minerals

Isotypes: Eucryptite, $Li(AlSiO_4)$.

Polymorphs: High quartz; high, middle, and low tridymite; high and low cristobalite; lechatelierite (silica glass); coesite.

Other similar species: Opal.

Crystallography, Structure, Habit

Isometric. Never in crystals.

Composed of crystalline patches identical to cristobalite joined in a random glasslike way.

Massive, often stalactitic or encrusting. Commonly banded.

Physical Properties

No cleavage. Conchoidal fracture. Brittle.

Hardness 5–6. Specific gravity 1.9–2.2.

Vitreous to resinous luster. Transparent to translucent. Colorless, white, and various tints.

Often milky or opalescent. May display a brilliant play of colors.

Distinctive Properties and Tests

Luster, habit. Yields water in the closed tube.

Association and Occurrence

Found (1) lining cavities in rocks, (2) replacing wood or other organic matter, and (3) as accumulations of diatom tests (diatomaceous earth).

Confused with: Chalcedony.

Variants

Form varieties

Common opal: Without internal reflections.

Precious opal: Internal play of colors.

Hyalite: Colorless globular form.

Geyserite: Hot-spring deposit.

Wood opal: Wood replaced by opal.

Diatomite: Fine-grained sedimentary deposit similar to chalk in appearance.

Related Minerals

Similar species: Quartz, tridymite, cristobalite.

331

Silicates (cont.)

Feldspars. Feldspars constitute nearly 60 per cent of igneous rocks which in turn make up over 90 per cent of the earth's crust. The importance of feldspars to the geologist is evident from these figures, and the complex mineralogical relations within the family make their understanding a challenge to the mineralogist.

Feldspars crystallize in the monoclinic and triclinic systems, but because the angular differences are less than 5° the crystals resemble each other closely. All feldspars exhibit two directions of excellent cleavage at about 90° to each other, have a hardness of 6, and similar luster, color, streak, etc. Distinguishing features are usually twinning, habit, association, and sometimes color.

Chemically, feldspars are alumino-silicates of potassium, sodium, calcium, or, rarely, barium with a considerable degree of isomorphism. The formulae of the end members may be written as:

Alkali feldspars $\begin{cases} K(AlSi_3O_8) \\ Na(AlSi_3O_8) \end{cases}$

Plagioclase feldspars $\begin{cases} Na(AlSi_3O_8) \\ Ca(Al_2Si_2O_8) \end{cases}$

Celsian $\qquad Ba(Al_2Si_2O_8)$

The distinction between alkali and plagioclase feldspars is not always clear-cut because of isomorphism, but the alkali feldspars are monoclinic or, if triclinic, have more K than Ca, while the plagioclases are triclinic with less K than Na or Ca.

The structure of all feldspars is very similar. These minerals are networks in which one-quarter to one-half of the tetrahedrally coordinated silicon ions are replaced by aluminum ions. The charge discrepancy resulting from this substitution is compensated by the entry into the structure of Na^{+1}, K^{+1}, Ca^{+2}, and rarely other alkali metals or alkaline earths. Figure 7–13 illustrates the structure of orthoclase, $K(AlSi_3O_8)$. In orthoclase the potassium ion just fits the indicated site fixing the angle between the a and b axes and the cleavage at 90°. In the plagioclase series the alkali site is occupied by varying proportions of sodium and calcium ions which, being smaller than potassium, allow a small slumping of the network of linked tetrahedra. The angle between the a and b axes and the two directions of cleavage are then close to, but not exactly, 90°.

Potash feldspar, $K(AlSi_3O_8)$, has at least two polymorphic modifications represented by triclinic microcline and monoclinic sanidine. The mechanism of transformation from sanidine to microcline with falling temperature is believed to be an ordering of Al and Si by diffusion. Such a process should be continuous, accelerate with increasing temperature (below the ordering temperature), and be nonreversible, as is indeed

332

Silicates (cont.)

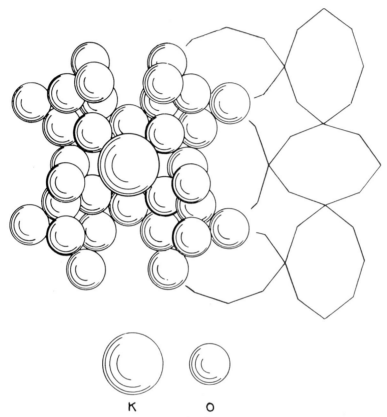

K   O

Fig. 7–13. Orthoclase structure.

indicated by field and laboratory observations. The relationship of orthoclase to ordered microcline and disordered sanidine is uncertain. Orthoclase is monoclinic (like sanidine) but has an ordered arrangement of
Al-Si (like microcline) and must be considered as somehow intermediate.
Sodium feldspar, $Na(AlSi_3O_8)$, also has two different modifications (albite and high albite or analbite) related by a diffusive transformation
analogous to that between the potash feldspars.

Virtually continuous isomorphous series exist at high temperatures between potash and soda feldspars and between the plagioclase feldspars.
Both series, however, show more or less exsolution on cooling. The sani-
dine-high albite series, $K(AlSi_3O_8)$-$Na(AlSi_3O_8)$, exsolves into K- and
Na-rich domains in the $AlSi_3O_8$ network below about 560°. Growth of
these domains with time and under favorable temperature conditions
leads to truly exsolved regions of potash and soda feldspar as distinct
phases. This two-phase material is called *perthite* and appears as sub-

333

Silicates (cont.)

oriented threads or lenses of slightly different color or luster. The isomorphous series among the plagioclases is much more complete at low temperatures. Two gaps of miscibility at about 10 and 50 atom per cent sodium are believed to exist. The optical evidence for the gaps is a characteristic schiller or internal reflection exhibited by plagioclases of these compositions. No perthitic textures are found in plagioclases, probably because the segregation of Na- and Ca-rich phases requires concomitant transport of Al and Si ions.

The polymorphic and isomorphic relations of feldspars are summarized by Figure 7–14,* which shows the fields of stability of these minerals.

The proportions of K, Na, and Ca which can enter the feldspar structure are dependent upon the temperature at the time of crystallization. Figure 7–14 shows the proportions of these elements which can coexist in feldspars at various temperature levels.

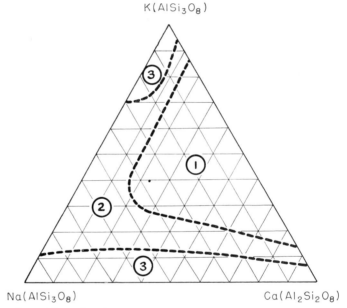

1. Crystals unstable at all temperatures.
2. Crystals stable at high and unstable at low temperatures.
3. Crystals stable at low temperatures.

Fig. 7–14. Stability of feldspars (after A. N. Winchell).

MONOCLINIC FELDSPAR GROUP. The orthoclase series of the monoclinic feldspar group is principally potassic feldspars, but sodium is usually present and sometimes becomes the predominant alkali.

* Modified by permission from *Descriptions of Minerals* by A. N. Winchell and Horace Winchell. Copyright, 1951, by John Wiley & Sons, Inc., New York.

Silicates (cont.)

TRICLINIC FELDSPAR GROUP. The microcline series is much like the orthoclase series in all respects. The common representatives are potassic, but sodium may predominate as in anorthoclase, $(NaK)(AlSi_3O_8)$.

Hand-specimen distinction between orthoclase and microcline is usually impossible unless a variety with special characteristics is being examined, and it is common practice to combine the two series under the term *potash feldspar*. It is probable that much of the potash feldspar commonly classed as orthoclase is really microcline. However, since the distinction cannot be made in hand specimens, it is recommended that students follow the accepted practice and use the term *orthoclase* for all the potassic feldspars.

PLAGIOCLASE SERIES. The plagioclase series is an isomorphous sequence whose end members are albite, $Na(AlSi_3O_8)$, and anorthite, $Ca(Al_2Si_2O_8)$. This series may be arbitrarily divided into species as follows:

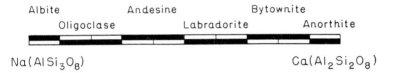

The individual species are difficult to distinguish without petrographic, X-ray, chemical, or similar studies, and it is preferable for hand-specimen determination to use the series name, *plagioclase*.

Certain of the plagioclase species may sometimes be distinguished on the basis of the width of the polysynthetic twin lamellae, play of colors, color, and association. Plagioclase may usually be distinguished from the potash feldspars by twinning.

ORTHOCLASE

$$K(AlSi_3O_8)$$

Crystallography, Structure, Habit

Monoclinic. $\frac{2}{m}$. Crystals as stubby to elongate prisms, often flattened and doubly terminated. Twinning common as simple penetration or contact twins.

Feldspar structure, see Figure 7–13.

Commonly found as more or less well developed crystals, also massive and in formless grains.

Physical Properties

Perfect (001) and (010) cleavage yielding square prismatic fragments. Parting parallel to (100) and also at a small angle to (100) giving rise to schiller. Conchoidal to uneven fracture. Brittle.

Hardness 6. Specific gravity 2.6.

Vitreous luster. Transparent to translucent. Colorless, white, or flesh red in color for most specimens. Streak white.

Fusible with difficulty (5).

Distinctive Properties and Tests

Cleavage, crystal habit, twinning, hardness, color. Insoluble in acids.

Association and Occurrence

Orthoclase is among the most common of minerals. It is (1) a principal constituent of igneous rocks such as granite and syenite, (2) a major constituent of the sedimentary rock arkose, (3) common in many kinds of metamorphic rocks, found (4) in pegmatities, and (5) in veins. It is usually associated with quartz and muscovite.

Alteration: To sericite (muscovite), kaolin.

Confused with: Calcite, corundum, plagioclase series.

Variants

Form varieties: Moonstone, usually transparent crystals in cavities in schists and veins.

Chemical varieties: Sodian; barian (hyalophane). May contain small amounts of Cs, Rb, or Ca.

Related Minerals

Isomorphs: Soda orthoclase, $(KNa)(AlSi_3O_8)$; anorthoclase, (KNa)-$(AlSi_3O_8)$.

Isotypes: Celsian, $Ba(Al_2Si_2O_8)$.

Polymorphs: Adularia, sanidine, microcline.

Other similar species: Kaliophyllite, $K(AlSiO_4)$; leucite.

PLAGIOCLASE SERIES

Albite $Na(AlSi_3O_8)$

Anorthite $Ca(Al_2Si_2O_8)$

Crystallography, Structure, Habit

Triclinic. $\bar{1}$. Crystals usually tabular to bladed. Frequently twinned, often with both contact and polysynthetic twins.

Structure essentially that of orthoclase, Figure 7–14, with a small distortion.

Rarely in distinct crystals, usually found as cleavable masses or as irregular embedded grains.

Physical Properties

Perfect (001) and (010) cleavage intersecting at about 86°. Uneven to conchoidal fracture. Brittle.

Hardness 6–6.5. Specific gravity 2.6(albite)–2.75(anorthite).

Vitreous luster. Transparent to translucent. Color white, gray, and occasionally reddish. Streak white.

Melting point 1100° (albite) to 1550° (anorthite). A play of colors is often observed in labradorite ($Ab_{40}An_{60}$) and less often in andesine and albite.

Distinctive Properties and Tests

Cleavage, polysynthetic twinning, hardness. Albite is insoluble in acids but anorthite is decomposed with HCl and yields gelatinous silica.

Association and Occurrence

Plagioclase is probably the most abundant mineral in the earth's crust. It is the principal constituent of many igneous rocks with intermediate members being the most common.

Albite is found in (1) igneous rocks such as granite, syenite, rhyolite, and trachyte associated with orthoclase and quartz and (2) in pegmatites.

Intermediate members of the plagioclase series are found principally in igneous rocks with the more calcic members being found in less siliceous rock types.

Anorthite is a relatively rare plagioclase found in very mafic igneous rocks, in contact metamorphosed marble, and in meteorites.

Alteration: to sericite (muscovite), kaolin, calcite.

Confused with: Potash feldspars, quartz, calcite.

Variants

Form varieties: Albite—peristerite (iridescent), aventurine (reddish reflections), moonstone, pericline (opaque white crystals), cleavelandite (lamellar masses in pegmatites).

Related Minerals

Isomorphs: The plagioclase series is a continuous isomorphous series. Intermediate compounds have been accorded species names as given below.

337

Plagioclase Series (cont.)

Species	Albite:Anorthite
Albite	100:0 to 90:10
Oligoclase	90:10 to 70:30
Andesine	70:30 to 50:50
Labradorite	50:50 to 30:70
Bytownite	30:70 to 10:90
Anorthite	10:90 to 0:100

Isotypes: Other feldspars.
Other similar species: Nepheline.

Feldspathoid Group. Feldspathoids, as implied by their name, are feldspar-like in general composition. They are interesting composition-ally in that several of the species contain chlorine, sulfur, or the carbonate radical, which are unusual constituents in silicate minerals.

Feldspathoids serve as useful geological indicators since they crystallize from silica-poor magmas in lieu of feldspars.

The feldspathoid group is composed of three isomorphous series and several miscellaneous species. Most fuse readily, and are decomposed or gelatinize when treated with hydrochloric acid.

NEPHELINE $Na(AlSiO_4)$

Crystallography, Structure, Habit

Hexagonal. 6. Short prismatic to tabular crystals.

Isostructural with tridymite, see Figure 3–6, page 106. Alternate Si ions of tridymite are replaced with Al ions. Na occupies the large holes in the tridymite structure.

Massive, compact, or embedded grains.

Physical Properties

Distinct ($10\bar{1}0$) cleavage. Subconchoidal fracture. Brittle.

Hardness 5–6. Specific gravity 2.6.

Vitreous luster, greasy on cleaved surfaces. Transparent to opaque. Usually colorless, white, or yellowish, also greenish, grayish, or reddish.

Fusible (3.5).

Distinctive Properties and Tests

Greasy luster, association. Yields gelatinous silica when boiled with HCl and evaporated.

Association and Occurrence

Typically found in silica-poor igneous rocks such as syenites or basalts. Associated with feldspars, cancrinite, biotite, sodalite, corundum, and zircon.

Alteration: To zeolites, sodalite, cancrinite, and kaolinite.

Confused with: Feldspar, quartz, and apatite.

Variants

Form varieties: Glassy; elæolite, massive nepheline with a greasy luster.

Chemical varieties: Potassian (all natural nepheline contains about one K for every three Na ions). May also contain Li and an excess of Si or Al.

Related Minerals

Isomorphs: Kaliophyllite, $K(AlSiO_4)$ at high temperatures only.

Isotypes: Tridymite, SiO_2.

Polymorphs: Isometric $Na(AlSiO_4)$.

Other similar species: Albite; eucryptite, $Li(AlSiO_4)$.

SODALITE

$Na_4(Al_3Si_3O_{12})Cl$

Crystallography, Structure, Habit
Isometric. $\bar{4}3m$. Rare rhombic dodecahedral crystals. Contact twins. Compact, cleavable, nodular, or disseminated masses.

Physical Properties
Distinct dodecahedral (011) cleavage. Uneven to conchoidal fracture. Brittle.

Hardness 5.5–6. Specific gravity 2.1–2.4.

Luster vitreous on faces and greasy on cleavages. Transparent to opaque. Usually blue in color, also white, green, reddish, or gray. Streak colorless.

Colored varieties turn white on heating. Fusible (3.5) with intumescence to a colorless glass.

Distinctive Properties and Tests
Color, association, color loss on heating. Gelatinizes with HCl. Tests for chlorine after solution in HNO_3.

Association and Occurrence
Associated with nepheline, cancrinite, leucite, feldspar, and zircon in silica-poor igneous rocks.

Confused with: Leucite, analcite.

Variants
Chemical varieties: Sulfurian (hackmanite), potassian.

Related Minerals
Isotypes: Haüynite, $Na_3Ca(AlSiO_4)_3(SO_4)$; noselite, $Na_8(AlSiO_4)_6(SO_4)$; lazurite, $Na_5(AlSiO_4)_3S$.

SCAPOLITE SERIES   Marialite $Na_4(AlSi_3O_8)_3Cl$

Meionite $Ca_4(Al_2Si_2O_8)_3(CO_3)$

Crystallography, Structure, Habit

Tetragonal. $\frac{4}{m}$. Coarse prismatic crystals, often woody looking.

Structure illustrated in Figure 7–15.

In crystals, massive, and granular.

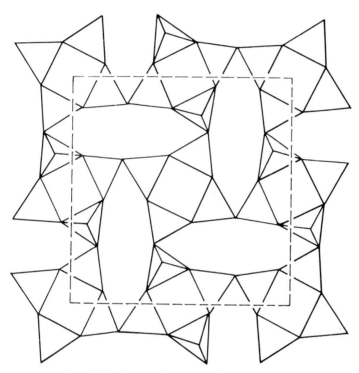

Fig. 7–15. Tetrahedral network of scapolite.

Physical Properties.

Distinct but interrupted (100) and (110) cleavage. Subconchoidal fracture. Brittle.

Hardness 5–6.5. Specific gravity 2.6–2.8.

Vitreous to pearly luster. Transparent to translucent. Color white or gray, also greenish, bluish, or reddish. Streak white.

Fuses (3) with intumescence to a white blebby glass. Sometimes luminescent.

Scapolite Series (cont.)

Distinctive Properties and Tests

Square prismatic crystals with a woody surface, cleavages intersecting at 45°, association. Imperfectly decomposed by HCl and yields granular silica but not a jelly.

Association and Occurrence

Typically found in metamorphic rocks, especially those rich in calcium such as marble. Associated with pyroxenes, amphiboles, garnets, apatite, sphene, zircon, and biotite.

Alteration: Readily to mica, epidote, talc, kaolin, zeolites, etc.

Confused with: Feldspar, pyroxene.

Variants

K may replace Na, and (OH), F, or (SO_4) may replace Cl and (CO_3).

Related Minerals

Isomorphs: The pure end members of this series are not found in nature. The only common member is of intermediate composition and is called *wernerite*.

LEUCITE

$$K(AlSi_2O_6)$$

Crystallography, Structure, Habit

Orthorhombic. $\frac{4}{m}$ (?). Commonly in pseudotrapezohedra. Faces often show fine striations as a result of repeated twinning.

Usually in well-formed crystals, rarely in disseminated grains or massive.

Physical Properties

Poor (110) cleavage. Conchoidal fracture. Brittle.

Hardness 5.5–6. Specific gravity 2.5.

Vitreous to dull luster. Translucent to opaque. Color white or gray. Streak uncolored.

Infusible.

Distinctive Properties and Tests

Crystal form, color, association. Decomposed by HCl without gelatinization.

Association and Occurrence

Found only in silica-poor igneous rocks, and especially in recent lavas.

Alteration: To analcite, kaolin.

Confused with: Analcite, garnet, melilite.

Variants

Chemical varieties: Sodian. Traces of Li, Rb, and Cs may be present.

Related Minerals

Polymorphs: Isometric above 600°.

Other similar species: Pollucite, $Cs_4(Al_4Si_9O_{26}) \cdot H_2O$; orthoclase; kali-ophilite $K(AlSiO_4)$; analcite.

$$Na_3Ca(Al_3Si_3O_{12})CO_3(OH)_2$$

Crystallography, Structure, Habit

Hexagonal. $\dfrac{6}{m}\dfrac{2}{m}\dfrac{2}{m}$. Rare prismatic crystals.

Structurally similar to sodalite.

In compact, lamellar, or disseminated masses.

Physical Properties

Perfect $(10\bar{1}0)$ and distinct $(11\bar{2}0)$ cleavage. Uneven fracture.

Hardness 5–6. Specific gravity 2.5.

Subvitreous to greasy luster. Transparent to translucent. Color yellow, white, gray, green, blue, reddish. Streak colorless.

Fusible (2) with intumescence to a white blebby glass. Colored varieties lose color on heating.

Distinctive Properties and Tests

Color, association, loss of color on heating. Evolves water in the closed tube. Effervesces with HCl and forms a jelly on heating.

Association and Occurrence

Found in silica-poor igneous rocks (e.g., nepheline syenite). Associated with nepheline, sodalite, biotite, feldspar, sphene, and apatite.

Alteration: From nepheline.

Confused with: Other feldspathoids.

Variants

Chemical varieties: Sulfatic, chlorian, potassian, calcian.

Related minerals

Other similar species: Sodalite.

Crystallography, Structure, Habit

Isometric. $\frac{4}{m}\bar{3}\frac{2}{m}$. Usually in trapezohedra and sometimes in cubes.
As crystals and crystal crusts, also granular and compact.

Physical Properties

No cleavage. Subconchoidal fracture. Brittle.
Hardness 5–5.5. Specific gravity 2.5.
Vitreous luster. Transparent to nearly opaque. Colorless to white and occasionally gray, green, yellowish, or reddish.
Fuses easily (2.5) to a colorless glass.

Distinctive Properties and Tests

Crystal form, association. Gelatinizes when treated with HCl and evaporated. Yields water in the closed tube.

Association and Occurrence

Found (1) in cavities and as a primary mineral in the groundmass of mafic igneous rocks and especially lavas and (2) in lake sediments. Associated with other zeolites and calcite.

Confused with: Garnet, leucite.

Variants

Usually contains a little K and Na. Adsorbed ions are always present.

Related Minerals

Similar species: Leucite; pollucite, $Cs(AlSi_2O_6) \cdot H_2O$.

Zeolite Family. The members of the zeolite family are usually found as fillings and coatings of cavities in mafic lavas such as basalt. All of the zeolites are hydrated silicates in which the water of hydration is continuously driven off when they are heated rather than being evolved at some fixed temperature.

Zeolites exhibit the property of base or ion exchange which is the phenomenon of adsorbing nonformulary ions and holding them rather tightly on the grain surface.

Zeolites are commonly found in well-formed crystals, all are quite soft with hardnesses less than that of a knife, have low specific gravity (2–2.4), and are generally colorless or pale colored. All of the zeolites are readily decomposed by hot HCl and usually gelatinize when the solution is evaporated. Their characteristic intumescence, when heated, gives the name to the group from the Greek "boil stone."

STILBITE $(CaNaK)_3[Al_5(AlSi)Si_{14}O_{40}] \cdot 15H_2O$

Crystallography, Structure, Habit

Monoclinic. $\frac{2}{m}$. Simple crystals are unknown, all crystals are cruciform penetration twins.

Crystals aggregated in sheaf-like groups, also radiate, or globular.

Physical Properties

Perfect (010) cleavage. Uneven fracture. Brittle.

Hardness 3.5–4. Specific gravity 2.2.

Luster vitreous, pearly on cleavage. Transparent to translucent. Color white, also yellowish, brownish, or reddish.

Fuses easily (2–2.5) with swelling and exfoliation to a white enamel.

Distinctive Properties and Tests

Sheaf-like habit, manner of fusion. Decomposed by HCl without gelatinization. Evolves water in the closed tube.

Association and Occurrence

Typically found in cavities in basalt and related rocks associated with other zeolites and calcite. Rarely found in hydrothermal veins or in granite or gneiss.

Confused with: Other fibrous or tabular zeolites.

Variants

Chemical varieties: Sodian, potassian. Adsorbed ions are always present.

Related Minerals

Similar species: Phillipsite and harmotone are monoclinic zeolites with a complex and variable composition analogous to that of stilbite; laumontite, $(CaNa_2)(AlSi_2O_6)_2 \cdot 4H_2O$; and heulandite, $Ca(Al_2Si_6O_{16}) \cdot 5H_2O$.

CHABAZITE

$$(CaNaK)_7Al_{12}[(AlSi)_2Si_{26}O_{80}] \cdot 40H_2O$$

Crystallography, Structure, Habit

Hexagonal. $\bar{3}\frac{2}{m}$. Crystals usually simple rhombohedra close to cubes in angle. Penetration twins common.

Found as crystals and crystal crusts.

Physical Properties

Distinct $(10\bar{1}1)$ cleavage. Uneven fracture. Brittle.

Hardness 4–5. Specific gravity 2.1.

Vitreous luster. Transparent to translucent. Color flesh red to white. Streak colorless.

Readily fusible (3) with swelling to a nearly opaque blebby glass.

Distinctive Properties and Tests

Crystal form, color, association. Decomposed by HCl with the separation of slimy silica but without gelatinization. Evolves abundant water in the closed tube.

Association and Occurrence

Found in cavities in lavas near basalt in composition and rarely in cavities in other rocks. Associated with other zeolites and calcite.

Confused with: Calcite.

Variants

The composition is variable and adsorbed ions are always present.

Related Minerals

Isomorphs: Chabazite shows continuous variation from Ca-rich to (Na,K)-rich forms.

Isotypes: Gmelinite, $(NaCa)_6Al_6[(AlSi)Si_{13}O_{40}] \cdot 2OH_2O$.

NATROLITE

$Na_2(Al_2Si_3O_{10}) \cdot 2H_2O$

Crystallography, Structure, Habit
Monoclinic. $2mm$. Pseudo-orthorhombic crystals with a square cross-section, thin prisms or acicular. Vertically striated. Cruciform twins.

Usually in radiating crystal groups, also massive, granular.

Physical Properties
Perfect (110) cleavage. Uneven fracture.

Hardness 5–5.5. Specific gravity 2.2.

Vitreous to silky or pearly luster. Transparent to translucent. Colorless or white, also greenish, yellowish, or reddish.

Easily fusible (2) to a colorless glass.

Distinctive Properties and Tests
Habit, cleavage, association. Evolves water, whitens, and becomes opaque in the closed tube. Soluble in HCl and yields gelatinous silica on evaporation.

Association and Occurrence
A secondary mineral found filling cavities in basaltic lavas. It is associated with other zeolites and calcite.

Alteration: From nepheline, sodalite, plagioclase.

Confused with: Aragonite, pectolite.

Variants
May contain minor amounts of K or Ca. Adsorbed ions are always present.

Related Minerals
Isotype: Scolecite, $Ca(Al_2Si_3O_{10}) \cdot 3H_2O$.

Other similar species: Mesolite, $Na_2Ca_2(Al_2Si_3O_{10})_3 \cdot 8H_2O$; thomsonite, $NaCa_2[(AlSi)_5O_{10}]_2 \cdot 5H_2O$; edingtonite, $Ba(Al_2Si_3O_{10}) \cdot 3H_2O$.

Silicates (cont.)

Clay Group. The term "clay" is variously applied to mean a particle size, a group of physical properties, or a related group of minerals. The clay minerals usually have a very fine grain size and, in bulk, often exhibit such clay properties as plasticity.

The structure of all clay minerals is based upon a sheet of linked silicon-oxygen tetrahedra. The octahedrally coordinated cation is predominately

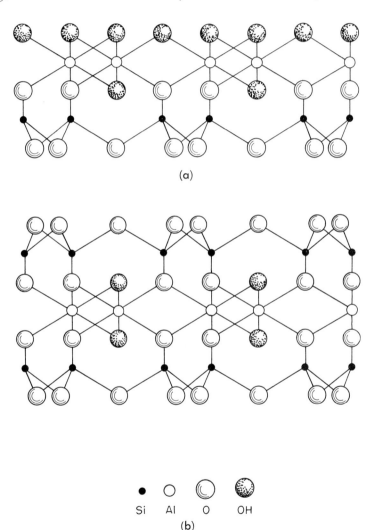

(a)

(b)

Fig. 7–16. Comparison of the bonding for one-layer clay minerals (above) and two-layer clay minerals (below).

Silicates (cont.)

Al^{+3} but may be Mg^{+2} or Fe^{+2}. Both $(OH)^{-1}$ and H_2O are always present, and alkali metals or alkaline earths are absent except as adsorbed ions.

The structural complexity of the clay group arises from the different ways in which the various components may be arranged in space, i.e., the clays, broadly speaking, are polymorphs. One fundamental difference between the species is whether one or two Si-O sheets are involved in a repeating unit. Figure 7–16 shows the bonding for the two arrangements. A second structural difference between the various clay minerals is the manner in which the sheets are stacked. Successive layers may be displaced by different amounts or in different directions in different species, and, further, the stacking may be either ordered or disordered. Figure 7–17 compares two such displacements diagrammatically. The hexagons represent the ring of SiO_4 tetrahedra which is repeated infinitely to form the sheet.

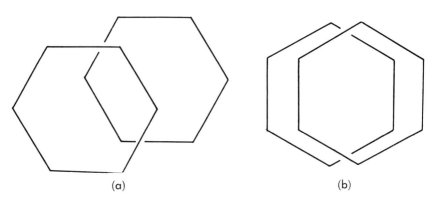

Fig. 7–17. Displacement of adjacent sheets (a) in kaolinite, and (b) in dickite.

Intersheet bonding in a single-sheet structure such as kaolinite may be accomplished by hydrogen atoms in the hydroxyl groups, one-half of such atoms forming bonds in the sheet itself while the other half form hydrogen bonds with oxygens in the base of the adjacent sheet. These hydrogen bonds are very weak and their ready rupture is responsible for the easy deformation and excellent cleavage of such a clay.

Intersheet bonding in double-sheet structures such as montmorillonite requires some replacement of tetrahedrally coordinated Si^{+4} by Al^{+3} or more probably the replacement of octahedrally coordinated Al^{+3} by Mg^{+2}. Such substitution causes a net negative charge on the sheet which would attract cations or water molecules and provide for a weak intersheet bond. Such cations or water molecules would not have structural

Silicates (cont.)

sites and hence not be fixed in quantity. Ready substitution in this inter-layer position explains the ion exchange and swelling properties of such clays.

The clay minerals may be divided in the following manner:

Single-sheet Clays	Double-sheet Clays
Kaolinite group	Montmorillonite group
Kaolinite	Montmorillonite series
Anauxite	
	Hectorite
Nacrite	
	Nontronite
Dickite	
	Saponite
Halloysite-endellite series	
	Illite group
	Members not well established. Includes clays that are similar but not identical with the white micas.
	Polygorskite group
	Attapulgite series

The clay minerals are typically found as very fine-grained hydrous aggregates, often as alteration products from the decomposition of aluminous silicates.

KAOLINITE $\qquad$ $Al_2(Si_2O_5)(OH)_4$

Crystallography, Structure, Habit

Monoclinic. $\frac{2}{m}$. Pseudo-hexagonal tabular crystals.

Structure illustrated in Figure 7–17a.

Usually found as earthy masses, also in folia, granular.

Physical Properties

Perfect (001) cleavage yielding flexible but inelastic folia.

Hardness 2–2.5. Specific gravity 2.6.

Luster pearly for crystals and dull and earthy for massive specimens. Transparent to translucent. Color white, but often stained grayish, brownish, bluish, or reddish.

Usually unctuous and plastic or if dry adheres to the tongue. Earthy smell when dampened. Infusible.

Distinctive Properties and Tests

Habit, feel, and smell. Insoluble in acids. Yields water in the closed tube. Tests for Al.

Association and Occurrence

A very common mineral and widespread in occurrence. It is secondary in origin, usually forming through the decomposition of aluminous silicates with which it is associated. It is found (1) in rocks undergoing weathering, (2) in extensive beds, and (3) as a constituent of soils.

Alteration: From aluminous silicates.

Confused with: Chalk, other clay minerals.

Variants

The Al:Si ratio may vary, usually favoring Si.

Related Minerals

Polymorphs: Dickite, nacrite, halloysite.

$$\text{Montmorillonite} \quad X(AlMg)_2(Si_4O_{10})(OH)_2$$
$$\text{Beidellite} \quad XAl_2[(AlSi)_4O_{10}](OH)_2$$
$$X = \text{exchangeable cation}$$

Crystallography, Structure, Habit

Monoclinic. Minute pseudo-hexagonal plates.
Structure illustrated in Figure 7-17b. See also mica.
Earthy masses.

Physical Properties

Perfect (001) cleavage into flexible inelastic folia. Tender.
Very soft. Specific gravity 2.
White or gray in color or stained bluish, reddish, or greenish.
Unctuous feel and earthy smell when wet. Swells and disaggregates when dried and rewet.

Distinctive Properties and Tests

Unctuous feel, slaking. Infusible. Yields abundant water in the closed tube. Insoluble in acids. Tests for Al.

Association and Occurrence

A secondary mineral formed by alteration of aluminous silicates.

Alteration: From aluminous silicates.

Confused with: Chalk, kaolin.

Variants

Form varieties: Bentonite, montmorillonite derived from alteration of volcanic ash or tuff.

Related Minerals

Isomorphs: Montmorillonite, beidellite, nontronite, $X(FeMg)_2(Si_4O_{10})$-$(OH)_2$.
Isotypes: Pyrophyllite.

Talc Group. The isotypic minerals pyrophyllite, $Al_2(Si_4O_{10})(OH)_2$, and talc, $Mg_3(Si_4O_{10})(OH)_2$, are the only important species in this group. Structurally, these minerals are built up from paired Si-O sheets bound together by Al^{+3} or Mg^{+2} in octahedral coordination with oxygen ions. The manner in which these structures are built up is illustrated by Figure 7–16b.

Pyrophyllite and talc are very soft (hardness of 1), have a platy or micaceous habit, a greasy feel, and a perfect basal cleavage which supplies flexible but inelastic folia.

PYROPHYLLITE $Al_2(Si_4O_{10})(OH)_2$

Crystallography, Structure, Habit

Monoclinic. $\frac{2}{m}$ (?). Crystals not known.

Isostructural with talc, see Figures 7–16b and 7–18 for general structural arrangement.

Foliated, massive, or radiate.

Physical Properties

Perfect (001) cleavage yielding flexible inelastic folia. Hackly fracture. Sectile.

Hardness 1–2. Specific gravity 2.8.

Luster pearly to dull. Translucent. Color white, greenish, or yellowish.

Greasy feel. Infusible.

Distinctive Properties and Tests

Greasy feel, cleavage, association. May exfoliate on heating. Partially broken down with H_2SO_4. Yields water with difficulty in the closed tube. Tests for Al.

Association and Occurrence

Pyrophyllite is a relatively rare mineral found in metamorphic rocks and frequently associated with kyanite.

Confused with: Talc.

Variants

Form varieties: Agalmatolite—impure compact pyrophyllite.

May contain a little Fe.

Related Minerals

Isotype: Talc.

TALC $Mg_3(Si_4O_{10})(OH)_2$

Crystallography, Structure, Habit

Monoclinic. $\frac{2}{m}$. Rare pseudohexagonal tabular crystals.

Talc structure, see Figures 7–16b and 7–18 for general structural arrangement.

Compact or foliated massive, sometimes in globular or radiating groups.

Physical Properties

Perfect (001) cleavage yielding flexible inelastic folia. Hackly fracture. Sectile.

Hardness 1–1.5. Specific gravity 2.7.

Luster greasy to pearly. Translucent. Color apple green to white. Colorless streak.

Greasy feel. Fusible with difficulty (5).

Distinctive Properties and Tests

Greasy feel, cleavage. Insoluble in acids. Yields water in the closed tube with intense heating.

Association and Occurrence

Found in igneous and metamorphic rocks as an alteration product of magnesian silicates. Associated with serpentine, chlorite, dolomite, magnetite, magnesite, apatite, tourmaline, pyrite, and actinolite.

Alteration: From aluminous magnesian silicates such as pyroxene, olivine, or amphibole.

Confused with: Pyrophyllite, chlorite, serpentine.

Variants

Form varieties: Soapstone, steatite, or french chalk—impure massive talc often forming large rock masses.

May contain small amounts of Ni or Mn and variable quantities of (OH).

Related Minerals

Isotypes: Pyrophyllite.

Chlorite Group. The numerous members of the chlorite group have closely similar chemical, crystallographic, and physical properties. It is extremely difficult to distinguish between the various species without recourse to quantitative chemical analysis, petrographic examination, or X-ray studies.

The chlorites are structurally based on a sheet of linked SiO_4 tetrahedra in which some replacement of Si^{+4} by Al^{+3} has taken place. Charge de-

Silicates (cont.)

ficiencies of the sheets are neutralized by such cations as Al^{+3}, Fe^{+3}, Fe^{+2}, Mg^{+2}, and, more rarely, by chromium or manganese. Alkali metals and alkaline earths are absent.

Chlorites are characterized by their dark green color, perfect basal cleavage yielding flexible inelastic folia, and by their association with primary ferromagnesian silicates as alteration products.

CHLORITE GROUP

$$X_m(Y_4O_{10})(OH)_8$$

X = octahedral cation,
usually Mg + Al, Fe, Cr, or Mn
Y = tetrahedral cation, Si + Al
m = 4 to 6

Crystallography, Structure, Habit

Monoclinic. $\frac{2}{m}$. Rare pseudohexagonal tablets.

Alternating double sheets, as in mica, and sheets of octahedrally coordinated Mg, Al, Fe, etc. Random stacking common.

Foliated masses, scaly aggregates, and disseminated flakes.

Physical Properties

Perfect (001) cleavage yielding flexible inelastic folia.

Hardness 2–2.5. Specific gravity 2.7.

Vitreous to pearly or dull luster. Transparent to translucent. Color dark green or rarely yellow, white, or rose.

Fusible with difficulty (5–5.5). Sometimes has a slightly soapy feel.

Distinctive Properties and Tests

Color, habit, cleavage. Yields water in the closed tube. Insoluble in HCl but decomposed by boiling H_2SO_4 to yield a milky solution.

Association and Occurrence

Chlorite is very widespread. It is usually secondary and is found (1) as the alteration product of ferromagnesian silicates, (2) as the main component of some schists, and (3) in schists and serpentines with garnet, diopside, magnesite, magnetite, and apatite.

Alteration: From ferromagnesian silicates such as pyroxene, amphibole, biotite, or garnet.

Confused with: Talc.

Variants

Chlorites vary widely in composition, especially in Mg:Fe. Essentially iron-free varieties are called *orthochlorites* and iron-bearing varieties are called *leptochlorites*.

Chemical varieties: Manganoan, nickelian, and ferrian (chamosite, thuringite).

The Brittle Micas. The brittle micas are intermediate between the chlorites and the elastic micas in their structure and properties.

357

MARGARITE

$$CaAl_2(Al_2Si_2O_{10})(OH)_2$$

Crystallography, Structure, Habit
Monoclinic. Crystals are very rare.

Modified mica structure with intersheet bonding by Ca^{+2}, intrasheet bonding by Al^{+3}, and 50 per cent proxy of Al^{+3} for Si^{+4} in tetrahedral coordination. Usually found in foliated aggregates.

Physical Properties
Perfect (001) cleavage yielding brittle folia.

Hardness 3.5–5. Specific gravity 3.0.

Luster vitreous to pearly. Translucent. Color pink, white, or gray.

Fusible (4–4.5).

Distinctive Properties and Tests
Brittle cleavage folia, color, association. Slowly and incompletely decomposed by boiling HCl.

Association and Occurrence
Usually found associated with corundum and rarely as a component of chlorite schists.

Alteration: From corundum.

Confused with: Lepidolite.

Variants
Chemical varieties: Sodian, potassian.

Related Minerals
Similar species: Chloritoid, $Fe_2Al_2(Al_2Si_2O_{10})(OH_4)$; ottrelite, $Fe^{+2}Fe^{+3}Al$ silicate with (OH); stilpnomelane, $Fe^{+2}Fe^{+3}Mg$ Al silicate with H_2O; chalcodite, $Fe^{+2}Mg$ Al silicate with 10 H_2O; ephesite, $NaLiAl_2(Al_2Si_2O_{10})(H_2O)$.

358

PREHNITE $Ca_2Al(AlSi_3O_{10})(OH)_2$

Crystallography, Structure, Habit

Orthorhombic. $2mm$. Rare tabular crystals.

Barrel-shaped, colloform, or stalactitic, with a crystalline surface. Often in rounded aggregates of tabular crystals.

Physical Properties

Distinct (001) cleavage. Uneven fracture. Brittle.
Hardness 6–6.5. Specific gravity 2.9.
Vitreous luster. Translucent. Color light green to white.
Fuses (2.5) with intumescence to a white enamel.

Distinctive Properties and Tests

Habit, color, association. Slowly reacted on by HCl, but is readily dissolved and yields gelatinous silica on evaporation after simple fusion.

Association and Occurrence

Prehnite is a secondary mineral found as crusts and cavity fillings in silica-poor igneous rocks, usually lavas. Associated with zeolites, pectolite, calcite, and native copper.

Confused with: Smithsonite, hemimorphite, beryl, chalcedony.

Variants

Chemical varieties: Ferrian.

The Elastic Micas. The elastic micas are an isotypic and partially isomorphous mineral group. They are characterized by such features as pseudohexagonal crystals or "mica books," perfect basal cleavage, flexible cleavage folia, and similar hardness.

The structure of all the elastic micas is based on two opposed silica sheets in which from none to one-fourth of the silicon ions have been replaced by aluminum ions. The intrasheet bonding is accomplished by octahedrally coordinated Al^{+3} ions in the muscovite series, octahedrally coordinated Mg^{+2} or Mg^{+2} and Fe^{+2} ions in the biotite series, and Li^{+1} and Al^{+3} ions in the lepidolite series. The net negative charge on the double sheet occasioned by the substitution of aluminum for silicon in the tetrahedral sites is neutralized by K^{+1} ions located between the double-sheet units. The packing and bond distribution of one of the elastic micas is shown in Figure 7–18.

The elastic mica group is divided into three series, each of which shows some isomorphism within the series but no isomorphism with the other series. The series are (1) the muscovite series including muscovite, paragonite, picrophengite, and others, (2) the biotite series including biotite, phlogopite, and others, and (3) the lepidolite series.

Silicates (cont.)

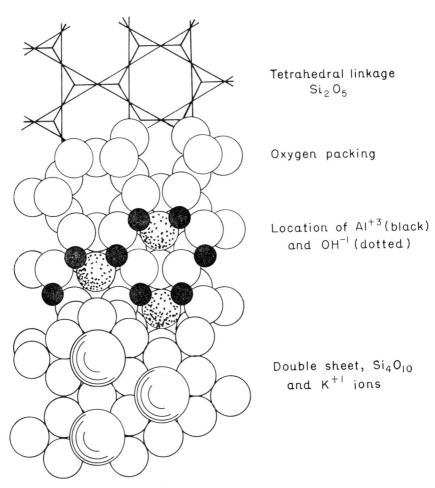

Tetrahedral linkage
Si_2O_5

Oxygen packing

Location of Al^{+3} (black) and OH^{-1} (dotted)

Double sheet, Si_4O_{10} and K^{+1} ions

Fig. 7–18. Muscovite structure.

MUSCOVITE

$$KAl_2(AlSi_3O_{10})(OH)_2$$

Crystallography, Structure, Habit

Monoclinic. $\frac{2}{m}$. Distinct crystals are rare, usually in the form of tabular rhombs or pseudohexagonal prisms. Contact twins united on (001) are fairly common.

Mica structure, see Figure 7–18.

Tabular or foliated (micaceous) habits predominate. Discrete flakes, foliated masses, plumose, stellate, or globular.

Physical Properties

Very perfect (001) cleavage, yielding elastic folia. Ragged fracture. Tough. Hardness 2.5–3. Specific gravity 2.75–3.0.

Vitreous to silky luster. Transparent to translucent. Colorless, often tinted gray, brown, pale green, violet, yellow, olive green, or rose.

Whitens and fuses (5) when heated.

Distinctive Properties and Tests

Cleavage, habit, color. Insoluble in acids. Yields a small amount of water in the closed tube.

Association and Occurrence

Muscovite is the most common of the micas. It is a primary constituent of potash and alumina-rich igneous rocks (i.e., granites and pegmatites) and is an essential mineral in many schists and gneisses. Muscovite is also found as detrital flakes in sedimentary rocks. Usually associated with such minerals as orthoclase, quartz, albite, beryl, tourmaline, or garnet.

Alteration: From topaz, kyanite, feldspars.

Confused with: Other micas.

Variants

Form varieties: Sericite, fine scaly muscovite; ruby mica, red; pinite, pseudomorphs after cordierite.

Chemical varieties: Sodian; chromian (fuchsite), green; vanadian (roscoelite), green brown; ferrian; magnesio-ferroan (phengite); fluorian; barian.

Related Minerals

Isomorphs: Paragonite, $NaAl_2(AlSi_3O_{10})(OH)_2$.

Polymorphs: 1M and 2M, muscovite (sheet-stacking polymorphs).

Isotypes: Biotite, phlogopite, lepidolite.

BIOTITE

$$K(MgFe)_3(AlSi_3O_{10})(OH)_2$$

Crystallography, Structure, Habit

Monoclinic. $\frac{2}{m}$. Rare tabular pseudohexagonal or pseudorhombohedral crystals. Contact twins joined on (001).

Isostructural with muscovite, see Figure 7–18. In biotite all of the inter-sheet octahedral sites are filled with Mg^{+2} or Fe^{+2} while in muscovite some of these sites (occupied by Al^{+3}) are vacant.

Commonly in disseminated scales or irregular foliated masses.

Physical Properties

Very perfect (001) cleavage yielding flexible folia. Ragged fracture. Tough. Hardness 2.5–3. Specific gravity 2.7–3.1.

Splendent luster. Transparent to opaque. Color black, greenish-black, or brownish-black.

Whitens and fuses (5) when heated. Becomes weakly magnetic after heating in the reducing flame.

Distinctive Properties and Tests

Cleavage, habit, color, post-heating magnetism. Completely decomposed by boiling H_2SO_4, yielding a milky solution. Yields water in the closed tube.

Association and Occurrence

Biotite is an important constituent of many igneous rocks, especially those rich in potassium and aluminum. It is also a common mineral in metamorphic rocks. Associated with muscovite, orthoclase, amphiboles.

Alteration: From augite, hornblende, scapolite, garnet, etc. To chlorite, epidote, quartz, iron oxides, and vermiculite.

Confused with: Other micas, especially phlogopite, chlorite.

Variants

Chemical varieties: Ferrian (lepidomelane), black; manganoan, bronze to copper red; titanian; calcian, brown to colorless; magnesio-aluminian (easton-ite); ferroan (annite); ferro-aluminian (siderophyllite); fluorian. Biotite may also contain small amounts of Na and Rb.

Related Minerals

Isomorphs: Phlogopite (?).

Isotypes: Other micas.

Polymorphs: 1M and 3T biotite (sheet-stacking polymorphs).

Other similar species: Vermiculite, an altered biotite or chlorite depleted in K and hydrated. Glauconite.

$$KMg_3(AlSi_3O_{10})(OH)_2$$

Crystallography, Structure, Habit

Monoclinic. $\frac{2}{m}$. Rare tapering or pseudohexagonal platy crystals.

Mica structure, see biotite and Figure 7–18.

Found in disseminated scales and plates.

Physical Properties

Very perfect basal cleavage yielding elastic folia. Ragged fracture. Tough. Hardness 2.5–3. Specific gravity 2.8.

Pearly to submetallic luster. Transparent to translucent. Color reddish brown, yellowish brown.

Asterism often displayed when viewed in transmitted light. Fusible (4.5–5).

Distinctive Properties and Tests.

Cleavage, color, occurrence. Decomposed by boiling H_2SO_4, and yields a milky solution. Yields small amounts of water in the closed tube.

Association and Occurrence

Commonly found in marble asociated with pyroxenes, amphiboles, and serpentine. Rarely a constituent of igneous rocks.

Confused with: Other micas.

Variants

Chemical varieties: Fluorian, ferroan, manganoan.

Related Minerals

Isomorphs: Biotite (?).

Isotypes: Other micas.

Polymorphs: 1M and 3T phlogopite (sheet-stacking polymorphs).

Crystallography, Structure, Habit

Monoclinic. $\frac{2}{m}$. Very rare short prismatic crystals. Contact twins with (001) as composition plane.

Mica structure, see Figure 7–18.

Coarse- to fine-grained scaly or granular aggregates.

Physical Properties

Very perfect (001) cleavage yielding elastic folia. Ragged fracture. Tough. Hardness 2.5–4. Specific gravity 2.9.

Pearly luster. Translucent. Color rose red to lilac and less commonly yellowish or grayish to white.

Fuses easily (2) with intumescence and colors the flame red.

Distinctive Properties and Tests

Color, occurrence. Flame test for Li. Test for F. Some water in the closed tube. Attacked by acids after fusion.

Association and Occurrence

Found in granitic pegmatites with tourmaline, spodumene, muscovite, cassiterite, albite, quartz, and topaz.

Confused with: Rose muscovite, margarite.

Variants

Chemical varieties: Ferrian (zinnwaldite). Lepidolite may contain Rb, Cs, and Mg.

Related Minerals

Isomorphs: The lepidolite series is a complex group of isomorphs including polylithianite, $K_4Li_8Al_4(Si_{16}O_{40})(OH, F)_8$; lepidolite, $K_4Li_4Al_6[(AlSi)_{16}O_{40}]$-$(OH, F)_8$; protolithionite, $K_4(FeAl)_8(Si_{16}O_{40})(OH, F)_8$; cryophyllite, K_4Li_4-$(FeAl)_8(Si_{16}O_{40})(OH, F)_8$; and zinnwaldite, an intermediate between lepidolite and protolithionite. These minerals are plotted in Figure 7–19.

Polymorphs: 1M, 2M, $2M_2$, 3T, and 6M lepidolite (sheet-stacking polymorphs).

Isotypes: Other micas.

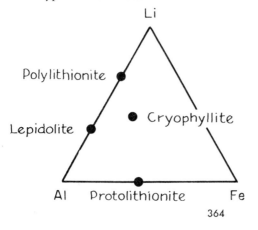

Fig. 7–19. End members of the lepidolite series.

SERPENTINE (antigorite) $Mg_6(Si_4O_{10})(OH)_8$

Crystallography, Structure, Habit
Monoclinic. Crystals unknown.
Structure similar to mica, but strain causes sheets to curl.
Usually massive, platy, or foliated.

Physical Properties
Poor (010) cleavage. Conchoidal to splintery fracture.
Hardness 2.5–5.5. Specific gravity 2.6.
Greasy or waxy luster. Translucent. Color various shades of green.
Smooth to greasy feel. Infusible.

Distinctive Properties and Tests
Color, luster, feel. Decomposed by HCl, yielding silica but not a jelly. Yields water in the closed tube.

Association and Occurrence
Serpentine is a common and widespread secondary mineral, often forming large rock masses. It is associated with magnesite, chromite, spinel, garnet, etc.

Alteration: From magnesia-rich silicates, especially olivine, pyroxene, and amphibole.

Confused with: Epidote, chlorite.

Variants
Form varieties: Antigorite—common serpentine (compact masses); verd antique—a rock composed of antigorite and carbonates; asbestos—fibrous serpentine (chrysotile).
Iron and nickel may be present in small amounts.

Related Minerals
Polymorphs: Clinochrysotile, orthochrysotile, lizardite.

GLAUCONITE $K_2(MgFe)_2Al_6(Si_4O_{10})_3(OH)_{12}$

Crystallography, Structure, Habit
Monoclinic. No crystals.

Sheet structure analogous to muscovite.

Resembles earthy chlorite, usually found in small pellets.

Physical Properties
(010) cleavage.

Hardness 2. Specific gravity approximately 2.3.

Color dull green.

Distinctive Properties and Tests
Color, habit, occurrence. Evolves water in the closed tube.

Association and Occurrence
Found typically in sedimentary rocks ("green sands") deposited near a continental shore. May be a major component of such rocks. Associated with chalk, fragmental calcite, and quartz.

Alteration: Perhaps from ferromagnesian silicates such as pyroxene, amphibole, and biotite.

Confused with: Chlorite.

Variants
May be mixed layer structure with montmorillonite, etc.

Celadonite—well crystallized, Mg-rich.

Related Minerals
Similar species: Greenalite, a mineral resembling glauconite but without potash.

Silicates (cont.)

Double Chains. The skeleton of an Si-O double chain is utilized in the structure of one large mineral group—the amphiboles, and possibly in the mineral garnierite.

Amphiboles may be separated into an orthorhombic anthophyllite series and monoclinic cummingtonite, tremolite, and hornblende series, each of which shows some isomorphism within the series. All of the amphiboles are characterized by a prismatic to fibrous habit and two cleavages intersecting at 56° and 124°.

Tetrahedral linkage Si_4O_{11}

Oxygen packing

Location of Mg^{+2} and Fe^{+2} (small dotted) and $(OH)^{-1}$ (large dotted) ions

Fig. 7–20. Double chain.

Silicates (cont.)

In the structure of an amphibole, two facing double chains have their apical oxygens coordinated by iron or magnesium ions. This results in a strong serrated rod about four oxygen diameters square. These rods are cross-linked by sodium or calcium ions coordinating the unsatisfied oxygen ions on the edge of the chains and neutralizing the residual charge of the basal oxygens resulting from aluminum proxy for silicon. The make-up and stacking of the rods are as shown in Figures 7–20 and 7–21. (OH) groups are positioned in the center of the ring of apical oxygens as in the sheet structures.

The bond density between adjacent rods is less than that within the rods, and mechanical rupture will therefore take place between the rods. (See the cleavage of pyroxene in Figure 4–1, page 126). The steplike character of these planes cannot be directly observed, and the macroscopic effect is that of two smooth cleavage planes intersecting at about 60° and 120°.

Amphiboles are widespread as principal and accessory minerals in igneous and metamorphic rocks. Hornblende and riebeckite are chiefly igneous species, whereas the other amphiboles are typically metamorphic minerals.

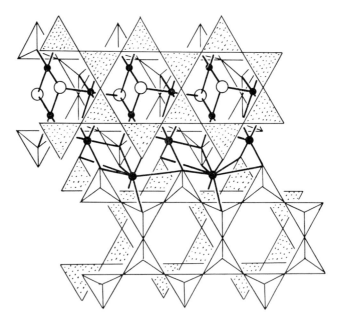

Fig. 7–21. Stacking of double chains.

ANTHOPHYLLITE SERIES

Anthophyllite $(MgFe)_7(Si_8O_{22})(OH)_2$

Gedrite $(MgFeAl)_7[(SiAl)_8O_{22}](OH)_2$

Crystallography, Structure, Habit

Orthorhombic. $\frac{2}{m}\frac{2}{m}\frac{2}{m}$. Rare prismatic crystals.

Amphibole structure, see Figures 7–20 and 7–21.

Lamellar or fibrous.

Physical Properties

Perfect (110) cleavage at 56° and 124°. Subconchoidal fracture. Brittle.

Hardness 5.5–6. Specific gravity 2.8–3.2.

Vitreous luster. Translucent. Color shades of brown to green. Streak uncolored or grayish.

Fusible (5) to a black magnetic enamel.

Distinctive Properties and Tests

Habit, clove brown color. Yields water in the closed tube.

Association and Occurrence

Found in crystalline schists.

Alteration: From olivine (?) by metamorphism.

Confused with: Other amphiboles.

Variants

Form varieties: Asbestiform (amosite).

Chemical varieties: Sodian.

Related Minerals

Polymorphs: Cummingtonite.

Other similar species: Other amphiboles.

TREMOLITE SERIES

Tremolite $\quad Ca_2Mg_5(Si_8O_{22})(OH)_2$

Actinolite $\quad Ca_2(MgFe)_5(Si_8O_{22})(OH)_2$

Crystallography, Structure, Habit

Monoclinic. $\frac{2}{m}$. Prismatic crystals, often flattened or columnar.

Amphibole structure, see Figures 7–20 and 7–21.

Fibrous, felted, and asbestiform aggregates, compact or columnar masses.

Physical Properties

Perfect (110) cleavage intersecting at 56° and 124°. Subconchoidal fracture. Brittle.

Hardness 5–6. Specific gravity 3.0–3.3.

Vitreous luster. Transparent to translucent. Color white or gray (tremolite) to dark green (actinolite).

Fusible (3–4).

Distinctive Properties and Tests

Habit, color. Yields a little water in the closed tube.

Association and Occurrence

Tremolite is typically found as a contact metamorphic mineral in impure limestones and dolomites and also in talc schists. Associated with garnet, diopside, pyrite, and calcite.

Actinolite is found in green-colored schists and greenstones.

Alteration

Tremolite—to talc.

Actinolite—from pyroxene; to chlorite, epidote, serpentine, and calcite.

Confused with: Epidote, vesuvianite, wollastonite.

Variants

Form varieties: Fibrous (asbestos), or matted (mountain leather); nephrite (jade), tough and compact, in part jadeite.

Chemical varieties: Manganoan (hexagonite), lavender.

Related Minerals

Isotypes: Hornblende series

Other similar species: anthophyllite series.

370

HORNBLENDE SERIES

Crystallography, Structure, Habit
Monoclinic. $\frac{2}{m}$. Prismatic crystals with a pseudohexagonal outline, usually terminated with a low dome. Contact twins.
Amphibole structure, see Figures 7–20 and 7–21.
Columnar, bladed, fibrous, also granular massive.

Physical Properties
Perfect prismatic (110) cleavage at 56° and 124°. Parting on (001). Subconchoidal to uneven fracture. Brittle.
Hardness 5–6. Specific gravity 2.9–3.3.
Vitreous luster. Translucent. Color black to dark green.
Hornblende is fusible with difficulty (4); soda-rich varieties fuse more easily (2) with intumescence and yield a black, magnetic globule.

Distinctive Properties and Tests
Crystal habit, cleavage. Yields a small amount of water in the closed tube.

Association and Occurrence
Hornblende and riebeckite are widely distributed minerals in igneous rocks and are associated with quartz, feldspar, pyroxene, and chlorite.
Other members of the series are rare components of metamorphic rocks.

Alteration: From pyroxene. To chlorite, epidote, calcite, siderite, quartz, and biotite.

Confused with: Augite.

Variants
Form varieties: Uralite, a pseudomorph of hornblende after pyroxene.
Titanium and fluorine are commonly present.

Related Minerals
Isomorphs: The various distinct species in the isomorphous hornblende series are: pargasite, $Ca_4Na_2Mg_9Al(Al_3Si_{13}O_{44})(OH, F)_4$; hornblende, $Ca_4Na_2(MgFe)_8(AlFe)_2(Al_4Si_{12}O_{44})(OH, F)_4$; arfvedsonite, $Na_6Mg_8Al_2(Si_{16}O_{44})(OH, F)_4$; glaucophane, $Na_4Mg_6Al_4(Si_{16}O_{44})(OH, F)_4$; riebeckite, $Na_4Fe_6Fe_4(Si_{16}O_{44})(OH)_4$.
Isotypes: Tremolite series.
Other similar species: Anthophyllite series.

Single Chains. Nearly all of the minerals based on Si-O single chains are members of the pyroxene group. This group is analogous to the amphiboles both chemically and in general structure, and members of the two groups are often confused in hand specimens. Some distinguishing characteristics are given in the following table.

371

Silicates (cont.)

Properties of Pyroxenes and Amphiboles

Property	Pyroxene	Amphibole
Structure	Single (SiO_3) chains	Double (Si_4O_{11}) chains
Composition	Anhydrous (may alter to hydrous minerals)	Contains hydroxyl groups and yields water in the closed tube
Crystal habit........	Short, complex, four- or eight-sided prisms (pseudotetragonal)	Long, simple, six-sided crystals (pseudohexagonal)
Cleavage	Two directions at ∼90°	Two directions at ∼60° and 120°
Parting	(001) often prominent	Parting not common
Mineral habit.......	Lamellar or granular masses	Columnar or fibrous masses
Occurrence	In more mafic igneous rocks	In more salic igneous rocks

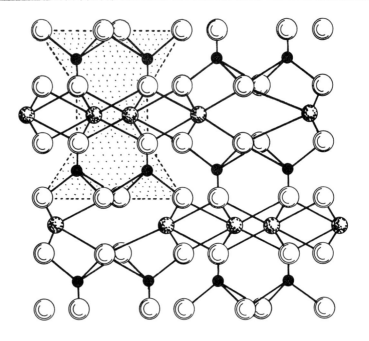

Mg Si O

Fig. 7–22. Enstatite structure.

Silicates (cont.)

The structure of a pyroxene (see Figure 7–22), like that of an amphibole, is based on rods consisting of two facing single chains bound together by octahedrally coordinated ions like Mg^{+2} or Fe^{+2}. These rods are stacked and cross-linked in a manner analogous to those in the amphiboles (see Figure 7–21) but because of the different cross-sectional shape of the rod the intercleavage angle is different. The angle is 87° and 93° in pyroxene and 56° and 124° in amphibole.

The pyroxene group is divisible into an orthorhombic enstatite series (orthopyroxenes) and monoclinic pigeonite, diopside, and acmite series (clinopyroxenes). Complete isomorphism exists within each series, but interseries isomorphism is at best partial.

Enstatite $Mg_2(Si_2O_6)$
                                       Hypersthene $(MgFe)_2(Si_2O_6)$

Crystallography, Structure, Habit

Orthorhombic. $\dfrac{2}{m}\dfrac{2}{m}\dfrac{2}{m}$. Rare prismatic or tabular crystals.

Pyroxene structure, see Figure 7–22.
Usually massive, fibrous, or lamellar.

Physical Properties

Good (110) cleavage, two directions intersecting at 87° and 93°. Good (010) and rare (100) parting. Uneven fracture. Brittle.

Hardness 5–6. Specific gravity 3.1–3.5.

Vitreous to pearly luster. Translucent. Color grayish, yellowish or greenish white to olive green and brown. Sometimes a metalloidal luster or "schiller" because of oriented opaque inclusions.

Enstatite is almost infusible, hypersthene fuses to a magnetic black enamel.

Distinctive Properties and Tests

Color, cleavage. Enstatite is insoluble in HCl, hypersthene is decomposed.

Association and Occurrence

Enstatite is a common constituent of calcium-poor mafic and ultramafic igneous rocks. Hypersthene is found in mafic igneous rocks, especially lavas, of a more calcic nature associated with calcic plagioclase. Both species are found in stony meteorites.

Alteration: To chlorite, hornblende (uralite), etc.

Confused with: Other pyroxenes, anthophyllite.

Variants

Chemical varieties: Ferroan enstatite (bronzite).

Related Minerals

Isomorphs: The isomorphism of the enstatite series is shown in Figure 3–3, page 100.

Polymorphs: Clinoenstatite (unknown in nature).

Other similar species: Other pyroxenes.

DIOPSIDE SERIES

Diopside $CaMg(Si_2O_6)$
Hedenbergite $CaFe(Si_2O_6)$
Augite $Ca(MgFeAl)[(SiAl)_2O_6]$

Crystallography, Structure, Habit

Monoclinic. $\frac{2}{m}$. Stubby prismatic crystals with a square, rectangular, or eight-sided cross section. Common contact and rare polysynthetic twins.
Pyroxene structure, see Figure 7–22.
Granular, lamellar, or columnar masses. Discrete grains or crystals.

Physical Properties

Imperfect (110) cleavage, two directions intersecting at 87° and 93°. (100) parting often prominent (diallage). Uneven to conchoidal fracture. Brittle.
Hardness 5–6. Specific gravity 3.2–3.6.
Vitreous luster. Transparent to translucent. Color white (diopside), green (hedenbergite), black (augite).
Fusible (4) to a glass insoluble in acids.

Distinctive Properties and Tests

Crystal form, cleavage, parting, color.

Association and Occurrence

Diopside is found (1) in contact metamorphosed limestones with tremolite, scapolite, vesuvianite, garnet, and sphene; (2) in mafic and ultramafic igneous rocks and their altered equivalents; and (3) in gneiss and schist.
Hedenbergite is a constituent of mafic and ultramafic igneous rocks.
Augite is the most common pyroxene. It is found chiefly in igneous rocks rich in iron, calcium, and magnesium and lacking quartz. Associated with orthoclase, plagioclase, nepheline, olivine, leucite, magnetite, and hornblende.

Alteration

Augite alters to hornblende (uralite), and to serpentine.
Diopside alters to serpentine, talc, chlorite, limonite, and hedenbergite.

Confused with: Amphiboles, scapolite, spodumene.

Variants

Form varieties: Diallage—lamellar greenish diopside found in igneous rocks; omphacite—the pyroxene of the garnet-bearing rock eclogite.
Chemical varieties: Manganoan (schefferite); manganoan-zincian (jeffersonite); manganoan-sodian (blanfordite); sodian, (aegerine-augite); chromian; vanadian.
Titanium is commonly present in small amounts in augite.

Related Minerals

Isomorphs: See Figure 3–3, page 100, illustrating the isomorphous relations of this series.
Isotypes: Acmite (aegirite), $NaFe(Si_2O_6)$; jadeite $NaAl(Si_2O_6)$; johannsenite, $CaMn(Si_2O_6)$; pigeonite, which has a composition between enstatite and diopside.

SPODUMENE

$$LiAl(Si_2O_6)$$

Crystallography, Structure, Habit

Monoclinic. $\frac{2}{m}$. Prismatic crystals, often flattened and deeply striated parallel to the c axis. Crystals may be very large (tens of feet in length). Polysynthetic twins common.

Related to pyroxene structure, see Figure 7–22.

Cleavable masses, crystals.

Physical Properties

Perfect (110) cleavages intersecting at 87° and 93°. Good (100) parting. Uneven to splintery or subconchoidal fracture. Brittle.

Hardness 6.5–7. Specific gravity 3.2.

Vitreous luster. Translucent to transparent. Color white or tinted green, gray, yellow green, yellow, purple, or pink. Streak white.

Fusible (3) with branching and yields a clear or white glassy globule. Swells and colors the flame crimson before the blowpipe.

Distinctive Properties and Tests

Cleavage and parting, hardness, color, manner of fusion, association. Insoluble in acids. Flame test for Li.

Association and Occurrence

Found in granitic pegmatites associated with tourmaline, beryl, garnet, lepidolite, feldspars, micas, and quartz.

Alteration: To eucryptite, $Li(AlSiO_4)$ and albite, or to muscovite and albite (cymatolite).

Confused with: Feldspar, scapolite, amblygonite, and tremolite.

Variants

Form varieties: Hiddenite (emerald green), kunzite (lilac).

Chemical varieties: Sodian. Spodumene commonly contains small amounts of Fe and Ca.

Related Minerals

Polymorphs: β-spodumene above 690°.

Other similar species: Pyroxene family.

RHODONITE $\qquad$ Mn(SiO_3)

Crystallography, Structure, Habit
Triclinic. $\bar{1}$. Large and rough tabular crystals. Polysynthetic twins. Cleavable masses, compact, discrete grains.

Physical Properties
Perfect (110) cleavage intersecting at 88° and 92°. Conchoidal to uneven fracture. Tough.

Hardness 5.5–6.5. Specific gravity 3.4–3.7.

Vitreous to pearly luster. Translucent to transparent. Color pink or red, sometimes masked by black or brown surface oxidation. Streak white.

Fuses (2.5) and blackens.

Distinctive Properties and Tests
Color, hardness. Tests for Mn. Insoluble in HCl.

Association and Occurrence
Found with iron and zinc ores associated with other manganese minerals (pyrolusite, tephroite, rhodochrosite, zincite, willemite), calcite, and quartz.

Alteration: To pyrolusite.

Confused with: Rhodochrosite.

Variants
Chemical varieties: Zincian (fowlerite); calcian; ferroan.

Related Minerals
Other similar species: Pyroxene family; babingtonite, $(CaFeFe)(SiO_3)$; pyroxmangite, $(MnFe)(SiO_3)$.

CHRYSOCOLLA

$$Cu(SiO_3) \cdot nH_2O$$

Crystallography, Structure, Habit
Cryptocrystalline.
Encrustations and fillings of enamel-like or earthy texture, colloform.

Physical Properties
Conchoidal fracture. Sectile to brittle.
Hardness 2–4. Specific gravity 2.3.
Vitreous, shining or earthy luster. Translucent to opaque. Color green to green blue or brown to black when impure.
Decrepitates and colors the flame green before the blowpipe. Infusible.

Distinctive Properties and Tests
Habit, color. Decomposed by HCl without gelatinization. Blackens and yields water in the closed tube. Tests for Cu.

Association and Occurrence
Chrysocolla is a secondary copper mineral usually associated with other secondary copper minerals such as malachite, cuprite, and native copper.

Alteration: From primary copper minerals, e.g., chalcopyrite.

Confused with: Opal, turquoise, malachite, chalcanthite, and garnierite.

Variants
Chrysocolla is typically impure, and the formula given is only an approximation.

Related Minerals
Similar species: Bisbeeite, $Cu(SiO_3) \cdot H_2O$; shattuckite, $2Cu(SiO_3) \cdot H_2O$.

GARNIERITE

$(NiMg)(SiO_3) \cdot nH_2O$

Crystallography, Structure, Habit

Monoclinic (?). Never found in crystals.
Rounded pellets, encrustations, or earthy masses.

Physical Properties

Conchoidal fracture or friable.
Hardness 2–3. Specific gravity 2.5. Dull or earthy luster (pellets may have a varnish-like surface). Color apple green to white.
Sometimes unctuous and adheres to the tongue. Infusible, but becomes magnetic on heating.

Distinctive Properties and Tests

Habit, color, feel. Blackens and yields water in the closed tube. Soluble with difficulty in HCl and yields silica but does not gelatinize. Tests for Ni.

Association and Occurrence

Found in serpentine rocks associated with olivine, talc, and chromite.

Confused with: Chrysocolla, malachite.

Variants

The composition varies widely.

Related Minerals

Similar species: Serpentine.

WOLLASTONITE $\qquad$ $Ca(SiO_3)$

Crystallography, Structure, Habit

Triclinic. $\bar{1}$. Short prismatic or tabular crystals.

SiO_3 chains composed of tetrahedral pairs linked by a differently oriented tetrahedron run parallel to the b axis. Ca ions are surrounded by six oxygen ions, and the Ca-O octahedra share faces to form a sheet parallel to (010). Cleavable masses to fibrous aggregates, also compact.

Physical Properties

Perfect (001) and (100) cleavage intersecting at 84° and 96°. Uneven fracture. Brittle.

Hardness 4.5–5. Specific gravity 2.8.

Vitreous to silky luster. Translucent. White tending towards grayish, yellowish, reddish, or brownish. Streak white.

Fusible (4) to a subglassy globule. Often phosphorescent.

Distinctive Properties and Tests

Cleavage, habit, occurrence. Decomposed by HCl with separation of silica.

Association and Occurrence

Found in contact metamorphosed limestones with lime garnets, diopside, tremolite, calcic plagioclase, vesuvianite, epidote, and calcite.

Confused with: Tremolite.

Variants

May contain Fe, Sr, Mg, or Mn.

Related Minerals

Isotypes: Bustamite, $CaMn(SiO_3)_2$; pectolite.

Polymorphs: pseudowollastonite.

Other similar species: Alamosite, $Pb(SiO_3)$; rhodonite.

PECTOLITE $Ca_2NaH(SiO_3)_2$

Crystallography, Structure, Habit
Triclinic. $\bar{1}$. Acicular crystals.
Isostructural with wollastonite.
Fibrous radiated masses.

Physical Properties
Perfect (100) and (001) cleavage yielding needle-like fragments. Uneven fracture. Brittle.
Hardness 5. Specific gravity 2.8.
Vitreous to silky luster. Opaque. Color and streak white.
Readily fusible (2.5–3) to a glass. Sometimes phosphoresces when crushed.

Distinctive Properties and Tests
Habit, cleavage, opacity, occurrence. Yields water in the closed tube. Decomposed by HCl with the separation of silica but without gelatinization.

Association and Occurrence
Found as crusts and fillings in mafic lavas. Associated with zeolites, prehnite, calcite.

Confused with: Wollastonite, fibrous zeolites.

Variants
Chemical varieties: Magnesian, manganoan. May contain a little Fe or K.

Related Minerals
Isotypes: Wollastonite.

Rings. Rings of Si-O tetrahedra can be built up from three, four, or six linked tetrahedra as illustrated in Figure 7–23. Minerals containing three- and four-membered rings are rare in nature, but species whose structure is based on a six-membered ring are relatively common and widespread. These minerals will usually show the crystal form and habit of a hexagonal prism.

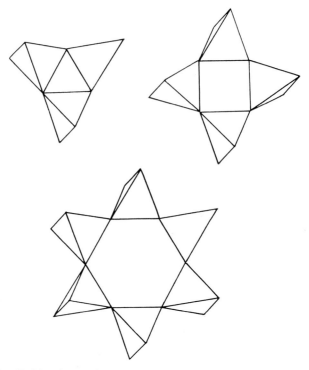

Fig. 7–23. Three-, four-, and six-membered tetrahedral rings.

TOURMALINE SERIES

$$XY_3B_3Al_3(Al_3Si_6O_{27})(OH, F)_4$$
$$\text{Where } X = \text{Na, Ca, Li}$$
$$Y = \text{Mg, Fe}$$

Crystallography, Structure, Habit

Hexagonal. $3m$. Usually slender columnar crystals with prism faces showing strong vertical striations. The cross section is either hexagonal or has the form of a spherical triangle.

Tourmaline structure, Figure 7–24. SiO_4 tetrahedra, MgO_6 octahedra, and BO_3 triangles in rodlike aggregates are cross-linked by Al^{+3}. Alkali metals are centered in the rings of tetrahedra.

Parallel or radiating crystal groups, massive and compact.

Physical Properties

No cleavage. Subconchoidal to uneven fracture. Brittle, sometimes friable. Hardness 7–7.5. Specific gravity 3.0–3.2.

Vitreous to resinous luster. Transparent to opaque. Color various—black, blue, green, red, colorless. Colors may be zoned. Streak uncolored.

Pyroelectric. Electrified by friction. Fusibility varies with composition, iron-rich varieties are fused with difficulty, magnesia-rich varieties at 3, and lithia-rich varieties are infusible.

Distinctive Properties and Tests

Crystal habit, hardness, lack of cleavage, association.

Association and Occurrence

Tourmaline is one of the more common minerals formed by the action of hot high-pressure vapors. It is an accessory mineral in pegmatites and at granitic contacts and, less commonly, in gneisses and schists. Associated with orthoclase, quartz, micas including lepidolite, beryl, apatite, fluorite, topaz, and cassiterite.

Alteration: To muscovite, biotite, chlorite.

Confused with: Hornblende, staurolite.

Variants

Form varieties: Uvite (brown), Ca and Mg rich; schorlite (black), Na and Fe rich; rubellite (red), Li rich; indicolite (blue); chrysolite or peridot (green); dravite (brown), Na and Mg rich.

Chemical varieties: Potassian; chromian.

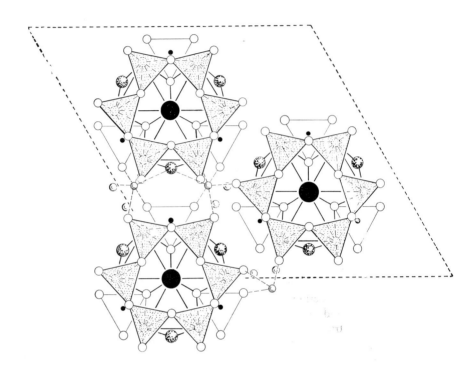

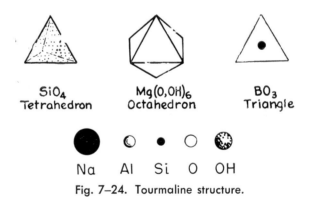

SiO₄
Tetrahedron

Mg(O,OH)₆
Octahedron

BO₃
Triangle

Na   Al   Si   O   OH

Fig. 7–24. Tourmaline structure.

BERYL

$$Be_3Al_2(SiO_3)_6$$

Crystallography, Structure, Habit

Hexagonal. $\frac{6}{m}\frac{2}{m}\frac{2}{m}$. Simple hexagonal prisms, often large. Vertically striated faces. Pinacoidal termination.

Beryl structure, see Figure 7–25. Hexagonal rods made up of six-membered tetrahedral rings and cross-linked by Be and Al.

Found as distinct crystals, columnar aggregates, and massive.

Physical Properties

No cleavage. Conchoidal to uneven fracture. Brittle.

Hardness 7.5–8. Specific gravity 2.8.

Vitreous to resinous luster. Transparent to translucent. Color blue green, green, blue, yellow, white.

Fusible with difficulty (5.5), whitens on heating.

Distinctive Properties and Tests

Crystal form, lack of cleavage, color, hardness, association.

Association and Occurrence

Found in granitic rocks, especially pegmatites. Also in mica schist. Associated with feldspar, mica, tourmaline, spodumene, and garnet.

Alteration: To mica and kaolin.

Confused with: Quartz, apatite, green tourmaline.

Variants

Form varieties: Emerald, bright green due to traces of Cr; aquamarine, pale greenish blue; morganite (rose beryl), rose; golden beryl, yellow from included Cs.

Chemical varieties: Sodian; lithian; cesian.

Related Minerals

Isotypes: Cordierite.

Beryl (cont.)

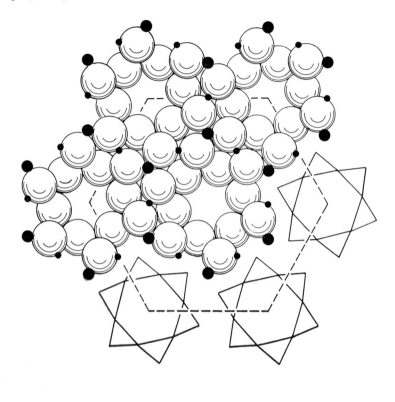

Be   Al   O

Fig. 7–25. Beryl structure.

CORDIERITE (iolite) $Mg_2Al_3(AlSi_5O_{18})$

Crystallography, Structure, Habit

Orthorhombic. $\dfrac{2}{m}\dfrac{2}{m}\dfrac{2}{m}$. Short prismatic crystals, usually twinned into pseudohexagonal forms.

Structure closely related to that of beryl.

As grains, massive, and compact.

Physical Properties

Poor (010) cleavage. Good (001) parting when slightly altered. Sub-conchoidal fracture. Brittle.

Hardness 7–7.5. Specific gravity 2.6.

Vitreous to greasy luster. Transparent to translucent. Color shades of blue (fresh) to shades of green (altered).

Fusible with difficulty (5–5.5).

Distinctive Properties and Tests

Cleavage, color, association.

Association and Occurrence

An accessory mineral in metamorphic rocks, gneisses, schists, and in contact zones. Rare as an accessory in granite and salic lavas. Associated with garnet, mica, quartz, andalusite, sillimanite, staurolite, and spinel.

Alteration: Alters readily, first developing a basal parting and a gray-green color later changing to mica, chlorite, or talc.

Confused with: Quartz, corundum.

Variants

Chemical varieties: Ferroan (all natural cordierite is ferroan), calcian, hydroxylian.

Related Minerals

Isotypes: Beryl.

Silicates (cont.)

Very few minerals have paired Si-O tetrahedra in their structures. Included here is the mineral vesuvianite, an exceptional silicate mineral which incorporates two kinds of tetrahedral silica groups in its structure. This mineral contains both pairs and individual tetrahedral units.

Silica tetrahedra sharing a single oxygen ion to form paired tetrahedra comprise a relatively unstable type of silicate articulation. Both tetrahedral units, which share no oxygen ions, and tetrahedral chains, in which two oxygen ions per tetrahedron are shared, provide a more stable linkage for a silicate structure. The formation of minerals whose structure incorporates tetrahedral pairs therefore requires rather special conditions. These conditions must either be chemical restrictions or high temperatures. The melilite series is an example of minerals for which both of these conditions are met, since melilites form only in silica-deficient environments under high-temperature conditions.

Hemimorphite represents an interesting problem in mineral classification. In its usual formularization, $Zn_4Si_2O_7(OH)_2 \cdot H_2O$, zinc appears as a normal cation coordinating the Si_2O_7-complex ions. However, the structure of this mineral shows zinc to coordinate four oxygen ions into a regular ZnO_4 tetrahedral group. Each of these groups, in turn, shares oxygen ions with adjacent ZnO_4 or SiO_4 tetrahedra. In sum, the structure of hemimorphite is a network of XO_4 tetrahedra where X is either Zn or Si.

Hemimorphite is here classed as a tetrahedral pair structure, but future studies of the complete range of structures in which some other ion occupies the silicon site will probably require reclassification of this and other minerals. Aluminum proxy for silicon is generally recognized as not affecting the structural type, but substitution of other ions in the same way is not accorded the same treatment.

MELILITE SERIES

Gehlenite $Ca_2Al(AlSiO_7)$
Åkermanite $Ca_2Mg(Si_2O_7)$

Crystallography, Structure, Habit
Tetragonal. $\bar{4}\,2m$. Short square or octagonal prisms.
Found as crystals and embedded grains.

Physical Properties
Distinct (001) cleavage. Conchoidal to uneven fracture. Brittle.
Hardness 5. Specific gravity 3.0.
Vitreous to resinous luster. Color white, yellowish, often tinted yellow, green, red, or brown.
Fusible (3) to a yellow or green glass.

Distinctive Properties and Tests
Melilites are found in mafic extrusives poor in silica and alkalies and rich in lime and alumina. They are associated with nepheline, leucite, augite, and hornblende.
Gehlenite is formed in limestone by contact metamorphism.

Confused with: Leucite.

Variants
Chemical varieties: Ferroan. May also contain small amounts of Na, Zn, and Mn.

Related Minerals
Isomorphs: Soda-melilite, $CaNaAl(Si_2O_7)$.
Isotypes: Hardystonite, $Ca_2Zn(Si_2O_7)$.

HEMIMORPHITE   (calamine) $Zn_4(Si_2O_7)(OH)_2 \cdot H_2O$

Crystallography, Structure, Habit

Orthorhombic. $2mm$. Tabular or prismatic crystals with vertical striations. (Si_2O_7) and $[Zn_2(O, OH)_7]$ pairs are articulated into a network of shared tetrahedra. See Figure 7–26.

Usually in rounded forms; divergent crystal groups, stalactitic, or colloform, also massive or earthy, encrusting.

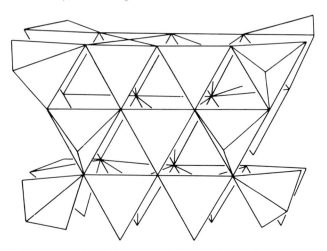

Fig. 7–26. Network of Si-O and Zn-O tetrahedra in hemimorphite.

Physical Properties

Perfect (110) cleavage. Uneven fracture. Brittle.

Hardness 4.5–5. Specific gravity 3.5.

Vitreous luster. Transparent to translucent. Color white with tints of blue or green, also yellowish to brown. Streak white.

Decrepitates and whitens in the closed tube, yields water. Fusible with difficulty (5–6). Strongly pyroelectric.

Distinctive Properties and Tests

Habit, color, fusibility. Decomposed by boiling HCl and gelatinizes on evaporation of the solution. Tests for Zn.

Association and Occurrence

A secondary mineral found in the oxidized portion of zinc deposits where it is associated with smithsonite, sphalerite, cerussite, anglesite, and galena.

Alteration: From other zinc minerals.

Confused with: Smithsonite, prehnite.

Variants

Small amounts of Al, Fe, and Pb may be present.

VESUVIANITE (idocrase)

$$Ca_{10}(MgFe)_2Al_4(Si_2O_7)_2(SiO_4)_5(OH)_4$$

Crystallography, Structure, Habit

Tetragonal. $\frac{4}{m}\frac{2}{m}\frac{2}{m}$. Prisms or pyramids, often vertically striated. Striated columnar aggregates, massive, granular.

Physical Properties

No cleavage. Subconchoidal to uneven fracture. Brittle.
Hardness 6.5. Specific gravity 3.4.
Vitreous to resinous luster. Translucent. Color brown to green.
Fusible (3) with intumescence to a greenish brown glass.

Distinctive Properties and Tests

Habit, color, association. Gelatinizes with HCl after simple fusion.

Association and Occurrence

Never found in igneous rocks. Found (1) in contact metamorphosed limestones associated with garnet (grossularite), phlogopite, diopside, wollastonite, epidote, tourmaline, and (2) in serpentines, chlorite schists, and gneisses.

Confused with: Epidote, tourmaline, garnet.

Variants

Form varieties: Cyprine (blue); californite (compact green).
Chemical varieties: Borian; beryllian. The composition is quite variable and the presence of F, Ti, Cu, Fe, Mg, Mn, Na, K, and Li has been noted.

Silicates (cont.)

Minerals utilizing individual Si-O tetrahedra as their structural basis embrace several cohesive mineral groups and many miscellaneous species.

The chrysolite group includes the olivine series which shows complete isomorphism between Fe_2SiO_4, Mg_2SiO_4, Mn_2SiO_4 (see Figure 3–2, page 99), and several Ca or CaMg species. The type species is the common mineral olivine, which contains Fe and Mg in various proportions. All members of the chrysolite group crystallize in the orthorhombic system. Structurally, the cations lie between opposed faces of individual tetrahedra, coordinating three oxygens in each tetrahedron. The structure of olivine is illustrated in Figure 7–27.

The garnet group includes two series, each of which show fairly complete isomorphism within the series, but there is only slight isomorphism between the series. The general formula for a garnet is $R_3^{+2}R_2^{+3}(SiO_4)_3$. R^{+2} is always Ca^{+2} in the andradite series, while R^{+3} may be Cr^{+3}, Al^{+3}, Fe^{+3}, etc. R^{+3} is always Al^{+3} in the almandite series while R^{+2} may be Fe^{+2}, Mg^{+2}, or Mn^{+2}. The principal minerals of the garnet group are:

Andradite Series		Almandite Series	
Uvarovite	$Ca_3Cr_2(SiO_4)_3$	Pyrope	$Mg_2Al_3(SiO_4)_3$
Crossularite	$Ca_3Al_2(SiO_4)_3$	Almandite	$Fe_2Al_3(SiO_4)_3$
Andradite	$Ca_3Fe_2(SiO_4)_3$	Spessartite	$Mn_2Al_3(SiO_4)_3$

All garnets crystallize in the isometric system and have the dodecahedron and the trapezohedron as common forms. Garnets are usually some shade of red, although grossularite is often cinnamon brown and uvarovite is emerald green as a consequence of its chromium content. The physical characteristics of garnets are so similar, and the intraseries isomorphism so extensive, that chemical analysis or measurement of specific gravity or refractive index must be used to distinguish them.

Garnets are found in both igneous and metamorphic rocks. Almandite and spessartite are common as accessory minerals in schists and gneisses. The garnet found in metamorphosed limestone is usually grossularite. Pyrope is a common accessory mineral in ultramafic rocks such as peridotite and is also found in the derived serpentines. Uvarovite also has a peridotitic association where it frequently occurs with chromite. Spessartite is sometimes found in siliceous lavas.

Minerals of the humite group have the formula $xMg_2(SiO_4) \cdot Mg(OH, F)_2$, where x may be 1, 2, 3, or 4. The structure of the various members of this group is essentially one or more $Mg_2(SiO_4)$ layers separated by an $Mg(OH, F)_2$ layer. The packing is such that when x is odd the mineral is orthorhombic, and when x is even the mineral is monoclinic.

OLIVINE SERIES

Forsterite Fe$_2$(SiO$_4$)
Fayalite   Mg$_2$(SiO$_4$)

Crystallography, Structure, Habit

Orthorhombic. $\dfrac{2}{m}\dfrac{2}{m}\dfrac{2}{m}$. Flattened prisms. Rare contact twins.

Olivine structure, see Figure 7–27.

Granular masses and embedded formless grains.

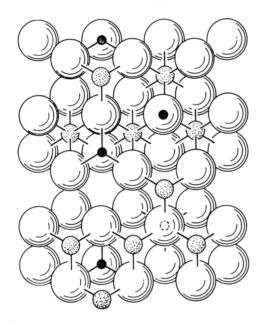

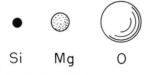

Si   Mg   O

Fig. 7–27. Olivine structure.

Physical Properties

No distinct cleavage. Conchoidal fracture. Brittle.

Hardness 6.5–7. Specific gravity 3.3–3.4.

Glassy to vitreous luster. Transparent to translucent. Color olive green, sometimes brownish or reddish. May turn yellow brown or red on oxidation of iron.

Infusible unless iron rich. Whitens when heated.

393

Olivine Series (cont.)

Color, lack of cleavage, association. Slowly dissolved in boiling HCl, and gelatinizes on evaporation of the solution.

Association and Occurrence
A necessary constituent of certain mafic and ultramafic rocks (the sole constituent of dunite). Usually associated with calcic plagioclase, augite, chromite, spinel, and garnet. Also found in metamorphosed limestones associated with dolomite and magnesite.

Alteration: Readily to serpentine, magnesite, iron oxides.

Confused with: Quartz, epidote.

Variants
Form varieties: Precious olivine (peridot), pale yellow-green, and transparent.

Chemical varieties: Titanian (proxy for silica). Sn, Zn, Ca, and Ni may be present in minute amounts.

Related Minerals
Isomorphs: Complete series among forsterite, fayalite, and tephroite, $Mn_2(SiO_4)$ end members. See page 99.

Isotypes: Larnite, $Ca_2(SiO_4)$; merwinite, $Ca_3Mg(SiO_4)_2$; monticellite, $CaMg(SiO_4)$; chrysoberyl, Al_2BeO_4; triphylite, $LiMn(PO_4)$.

GARNET GROUP

$$R_3^{+2}R_2^{+3}(SiO_4)_3$$
$$\text{Where } R^{+2} = \text{Mg, Fe, Mn, or Ca}$$
$$R^{+3} = \text{Cr, Al, Fe}$$

Crystallography, Structure, Habit

Isometric. $\frac{4}{m}\bar{3}\frac{2}{m}$. Well-formed dodecahedra or trapezohedra.

Usually in well-formed crystals, also embedded grains, massive.

Physical Properties

No cleavage. Fair (110) parting. Subconchoidal to uneven fracture. Brittle.

Hardness 6.5–7.5. Specific gravity 3.5–4.3, varying with composition (see below).

Vitreous to resinous luster. Transparent to translucent. Color usually red, also brown, yellow, white, green, and black.

Fusible (3–3.5) to a light brown or black glass. (Uvarovite fuses at 6.)

Distinctive Properties and Tests

Crystal form, color association. All species, except uvarovite, are dissolved in boiling HCl after fusion and gelatinize on evaporation of the solution.

Association and Occurrence

Garnets are common and widely distributed.

Uvarovite is found in gneiss, serpentine, and metamorphosed limestone associated with chromite.

Grossularite is found in metamorphosed calcareous rocks with wollastonite, vesuvianite, diopside, and scapolite.

Andradite is an accessory in syenite and is found in serpentine, chlorite schist, and marble associated with feldspar, nepheline, leucite, epidote, and magnetite.

Pyrope is a constituent of mafic igneous rocks where it is associated with olivine, pyroxene, spinel, and diamond.

Almandite is found in schists with andalusite, sillimanite, and kyanite.

Spessartite is found in granitic and rhyolitic igneous rocks in association with orthoclase, quartz, tourmaline, and topaz.

Alteration: To chlorite, serpentine, talc.

Confused with: Vesuvianite, apatite.

Garnet Group (cont.)

Species

	Color	Specific Gravity
Andradite Series		
Uvarovite .... $Ca_3Cr_2(SiO_4)_3$	Emerald green	3.5
Grossularite .... $Ca_3Al_2(SiO_4)_3$	Cinnamon brown	3.5
Andradite .... $Ca_3Fe_2(SiO_4)_3$	Various	3.8
Almandite Series		
Pyrope .... $Mg_3Al_2(SiO_4)_3$	Deep red	3.5
Almandite .... $Fe_3Al_2(SiO_4)_3$	Deep red	4.3
Spessartite .... $Mn_3Al_2(SiO_4)_3$	Dark red	4.2

Variants

Chemical varieties: Titanian; yttrian (in spessartite). Zinc and scandium may be present in pyrope.

Related Minerals

Isotypes: Schorlomite, $Ca_3(AlFeTi)_2[(TiSi)O_4]_3$; berzeliite, $Ca_2NaMg_2(AsO_4)_3$.

Crystallography, Structure, Habit

Tetragonal. $\dfrac{4}{m}\dfrac{2}{m}\dfrac{2}{m}$. Simple square prisms with a pyramidal termination. Cyclic twins.

Isostructural with rutile, Figure 6–6d. The structure of zircon is illustrated in Figure 7–28.

Found as distinct crystals and embedded grains.

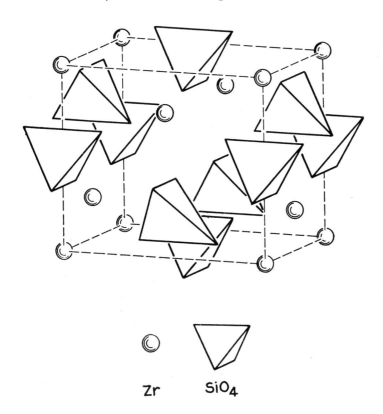

Zr   SiO$_4$

Fig 7–28. Zircon structure.

Physical Properties

Imperfect (110) cleavage. Conchoidal fracture. Brittle.

Hardness 7.5. Specific gravity 4.7.

Adamantine luster. Transparent to opaque. Color usually shades of brown, also colorless, gray, green, or red.

Infusible. Colored varieties lose color on heating. Often weakly radioactive

Distinctive Properties and Tests

Crystals, luster, color. Insoluble in acids.

Zircon (cont.)

Association and Occurrence

Zircon is a common accessory mineral in igneous rocks, especially syenite, granite, and diorite. It is also found in schists, in iron formations, and in beach sands and placers.

Alteration: Resistant to change.

Confused with: Diamond, topaz, spinel.

Variants

Form varieties: Hyacinth, orange, reddish, or brownish and transparent; jargon, colorless or smoky; malacon, altered zircon.

Chemical varieties: Hafnian (cyrtolite). Rare earths and phosphorus are usually present, but may be as xenotime. Fe, U, and Th are present in small amounts.

Related Minerals

Isotypes: Thorite, $Th(SiO_4)$, xenotime, YPO_4.
Other similar species: Baddelyite, ZrO_2.

HUMITE GROUP

Norbergite	$Mg_2(SiO_4) \cdot Mg(OH, F)_2$
Chondrodite	$2Mg_2(SiO_4) \cdot Mg(OH, F)_2$
Humite	$3Mg_2(SiO_4) \cdot Mg(OH, F)_2$
Clinohumite	$4Mg_2(SiO_4) \cdot Mg(OH, F)_2$

Crystallography, Structure, Habit

Norbergite and humite are orthorhombic. $\frac{2}{m}\frac{2}{m}\frac{2}{m}$. Chondrodite and clino-humite are monoclinic. $\frac{2}{m}$. Highly modified orthorhombic or pseudo-orthorhombic crystals. Repeated twins common, both cyclic and polysynthetic. Embedded formless grains, crystals, and massive.

Physical Properties

Sometimes distinct (001) cleavage. Subconchoidal to uneven fracture. Brittle.

Hardness 6–6.5. Specific gravity 3.1–3.3.

Vitreous to resinous luster. Translucent. Color yellow, brown, or red, also white.

Infusible, some varieties blacken and then turn white on heating.

Distinctive Properties and Tests

Color, association. Yields water in the closed tube. Dissolved by boiling HCl and gelatinizes on evaporation of the solution.

Association and Occurrence

Found typically in ancient dolomitic marbles associated with phlogopite, spinel, pyroxene, olivine, magnetite, pyrrhotite, and graphite.

Alteration: To serpentine, brucite.

Confused with: Olivine, garnet.

Variants

Chemical varieties: Titanian; ferroan.

EPIDOTE SERIES

Clinozoisite	$Ca_2Al_3(SiO_4)_3(OH)$
Epidote	$Ca_2(AlFe)_3(SiO_4)_3(OH)$
Piedmontite	$Ca_2(AlFeMn)_3(SiO_4)_3(OH)$

Crystallography, Structure, Habit

Monoclinic. $\frac{2}{m}$. Prismatic to acicular crystals, striated. Common polysynthetic twins.

Granular, fibrous, crystals.

Physical Properties

Perfect (001) cleavage. Uneven fracture. Brittle.

Hardness 6–7. Specific gravity 3.2–3.5.

Vitreous to resinous luster. Transparent to opaque. Color pistachio green, brownish-green, greenish-black, black, also red to gray.

Fusible (3–3.5) with intumescence.

Distinctive Properties and Tests

Color, habit. Will gelatinize with HCl when previously ignited.

Association and Occurrence

Epidote is formed by metamorphism of calcium-rich rocks. It is a common and widespread mineral associated with iron oxides, quartz, feldspar, actinolite, chlorite, etc.

Alteration: From garnet, hornblende, augite, biotite, scapolite, plagioclase, and olivine.

Variants

Chemical varieties: chromian, magnesian.

Related Minerals

Polymorphs: Zoisite, $Ca_2Al_3(SiO_4)_3(OH)$.

Other similar species: Allanite, $R_2^{+2}R_3^{+3}(SiO_4)_3(OH)$, where $R^{+2} = Ca$, Ce, La, Na and $R^{+3} = Al$, Fe, Mn, Be, Mg.

TOPAZ $\qquad$ $Al_2(SiO_4)(F)_2$

Crystallography, Structure, Habit
Orthorhombic. $\frac{2}{m}\frac{2}{m}\frac{2}{m}$. Prisms, often highly modified, with vertically striated faces.

Found as crystals and granular.

Physical Properties
Highly perfect (001) cleavage. Subconchoidal to uneven fracture. Brittle. Hardness 8. Specific gravity 3.5.

Vitreous luster. Transparent to translucent. Colorless, light yellow, white, or tinted greenish, bluish, or reddish.

Infusible. Yellow varieties turn pink on heating.

Distinctive Properties and Tests
Hardness, crystals, cleavage, color. Insoluble in acids.

Association and Occurrence
Topaz is found (1) as an accessory mineral in highly siliceous rocks such as granite, rhyolite, or granitic pegmatite, and (2) in veins and cavities in schists near granite contacts. Associated with fluorite, cassiterite, tourmaline, and also with apatite, beryl, quartz, mica, and feldspar.

Alteration: To muscovite plus kaolin.

Confused with: Quartz.

Variants
Chemical varieties: Hydroxylian.

Subsaturates are silicate minerals in which some portion of the oxygen present is not coordinated by silicon into Si-O tetrahedra. The structure thus contains both anionic $(SiO_4)^{-4}$ groups and O^{-2} anions. With increasing proportions of simple oxygen anions, these minerals provide a link between silicates and oxides.

Subsaturates are divided into an Aluminum Group containing andalusite, sillimanite, and kyanite; a Titanium Group represented by sphene; and some miscellaneous species.

Andalusite, sillimanite, and kyanite are polymorphs of $Al_2(SiO_4)O$ with rather similar structures. In all three minerals chains of Al-O octahedra parallel the c axis. Each octahedral group shares two oxygens with the group above and two oxygens with the group below, thus giving the Al-O chains the composition AlO_4. The chains are cross-linked by the remaining Al and Si ions. The variations in structure between the polymorphs result from different cross-linking and chain positioning. In all cases, silicon is tetrahedrally surrounded by oxygen ions, resulting in discrete SiO_4 structural units. The remaining Al ion is presumed to lie between six oxygens in kyanite, five in andalusite, and four in sillimanite.

Subsaturates are characteristically formed at high temperatures and are occasionally major constituents of metamorphic rocks derived from aluminous sediments.

Andalusite and kyanite provide a ceramic source for the manufacture of high-grade porcelain capable of withstanding extreme temperatures. Spark plugs, laboratory ware, and thermocouple tubing are some typical products made with this high-temperature porcelain. Sphene is a minor source for titanium. Andalusite and staurolite have a minor use as gemstones.

ANDALUSITE $AlAl(SiO_4)O$

Crystallography, Structure, Habit

Orthorhombic. $\dfrac{2}{m}\dfrac{2}{m}\dfrac{2}{m}$. Square prisms.

Andalusite structure, see Figure 7–29.

Rough rounded or elongate crystals, massive, granular.

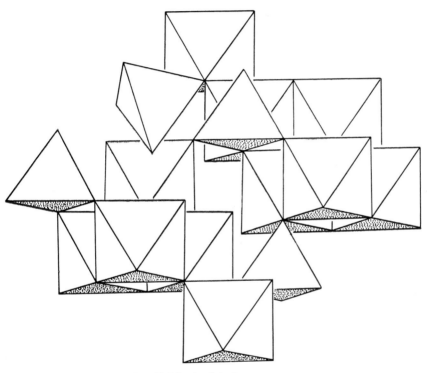

Fig. 7–29. Andalusite structure.

Physical Properties

Distinct (110) cleavage. Uneven fracture. Brittle.

Hardness 7.5. Specific gravity 3.2.

Vitreous to dull luster. Transparent to opaque. Color white, rose red, violet, pearl gray, olive green.

Infusible.

Distinctive Properties and Tests

Crystal form, hardness association. Insoluble in acids. Maltese cross on (001) sections of the variety chiastolite.

Andalusite (cont.)

Association and Occurrence
Commonly found in aluminous rocks near intrusive igneous bodies. Associated with sillimanite, kyanite, cordierite, garnet, corundum, tourmaline.

Alteration: To muscovite (sericite), kyanite, kaolinite.

Confused with: Scapolite.

Variants
Form varieties: Chiastolite, carbonaceous impurities pushed aside during growth form a maltese cross on a (001) section.

Chemical varieties: Manganoan, ferrian.

Related Minerals
Polymorphs: Sillimanite; kyanite.

SILLIMANITE $\qquad$ AlAl$(SiO_4)O$

Crystallography, Structure, Habit

Orthorhombic. $\dfrac{2}{m}\dfrac{2}{m}\dfrac{2}{m}$. Slender to acicular prisms with striated faces. Usually in parallel fibrous crystal groups, also columnar.

Physical Properties

Very perfect (010) cleavage. Uneven fracture. Brittle.

Hardness 6–7. Specific gravity 3.2.

Vitreous to adamantine luster. Transparent to translucent. Color brown, gray green, or white.

Infusible.

Distinctive Properties and Tests

Habit, cleavage, association. Insoluble in acids.

Association and Occurrence

Found in metamorphic rocks (gneiss, schist, etc.) associated with corundum, andalusite, and zircon.

Alteration: To muscovite, kaolin.

Confused with: Anthophyllite.

Variants

May contain a little Fe.

Related Minerals

Polymorphs: Andalusite; kyanite.

KYANITE $Al_2(SiO_4)O$

Crystallography, Structure, Habit
Triclinic. $\bar{1}$. Bladed crystals, rarely terminated.
Aggregates of bladed crystals, usually subparallel.

Physical Properties
Perfect (010) cleavage. Sometimes (001) parting. Uneven fracture. Brittle.

Hardness 4.5 parallel to the c axis, 6.5 normal to the c axis. Specific gravity 3.6.

Vitreous to pearly luster. Translucent to transparent. Color blue, white, also gray, green, or black. Color may be patchy.

Infusible.

Distinctive Properties and Tests
Habit, color, differential hardness. Insoluble in acids.

Association and Occurrence
Found in gneiss and schist associated with garnet, staurolite, rutile, and corundum.

Alteration: To kaolin.

Variants
May contain a little Fe.

Related Minerals
Polymorphs: Andalusite; sillimanite.

Crystallography, Structure, Habit

Monoclinic. $\frac{2}{m}$. Varied habit, often wedge-shaped and flattened or stout prismatic. Contact and cruciform penetration twins common.

Structure illustrated in Figure 6–7b.

Usually as distinct crystals, also lamellar, compact, or massive.

Physical Properties

Good (110) cleavage. (221) parting sometimes present. Conchoidal fracture. Brittle.

Hardness 5–5.5. Specific gravity 3.5.

Adamantine to resinous luster. Transparent to opaque. Color brown, gray, green, red, or black.

Some specimens when heated change color to yellow and fuse (3–4) with intumescence to a yellow, brown, or black glass.

Distinctive Properties and Tests

Sphenoidal crystals, luster, color. Imperfectly soluble in HCl, but decomposed by H_2SO_4. Tests for Ti.

Association and Occurrence

Sphene is a widespread accessory mineral, especially in coarse-grained igneous rocks of intermediate composition. It is also common in metamorphic rocks. Associated with pyroxene, amphibole, chlorite, scapolite, zircon, apatite, magnetite, and ilmenite.

Alteration: To rutile, ilmenite.

Confused with: Staurolite, sphalerite, zircon.

Variants

Chemical varieties: Manganoan; cerian; yttrian. May contain Fe, Al.

Crystallography, Structure, Habit

Orthorhombic. $\dfrac{2}{m}\dfrac{2}{m}\dfrac{2}{m}$. Prismatic crystals, often flattened and having a rough surface. Penetration twins very common.

Structure illustrated in Figure 7–30.

Usually found in distinct crystals.

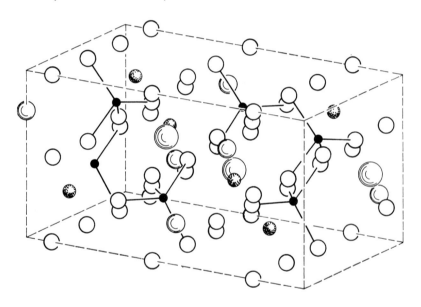

Fe Al Si O OH

Fig. 7–30. Staurolite structure.

Staurolite (cont.)

Physical Properties
Interrupted (010) cleavage. Subconchoidal fracture. Brittle.
Hardness 7–7.5. Specific gravity 3.7.
Resinous to dull luster. Translucent to opaque. Color dark reddish-brown to brown black. Streak uncolored to grayish.
Infusible.

Distinctive Properties and Tests
Crystal form and twinning, hardness, color, association. Yields a little water in the closed tube. Insoluble in acids.

Association and Occurrence
Found in metamorphic rocks (gneiss, schist, slate) associated with garnet, sillimanite, kyanite, and tourmaline.

Alteration: To kaolin and iron oxides.

Confused with: Andalusite, pyroxene, amphibole, tourmaline.

Variants
Chemical varieties: Manganoan; cobaltian.
Often quite impure and containing Mg, Zn, Co, etc.

APPENDIX I

Table of Atomic Parameters

Symbol	Element	Atomic Number	Atomic [*] Weight	Usual Valence	Ionic [†] Radius, Å	First Ionization [*] Potential, ev
A	Argon	18	39.944	0	–	15.68
Ac	Actinium	89	(227)	+3	1.18	–
Ag	Silver	47	107.880	+1, +2	1.26, 0.89	7.542
Al	Aluminum	13	26.97	+3	0.51	5.96
As	Arsenic	33	74.91	+3	0.69	10.5
At	Astatine	85	(221)	–	–	–
Au	Gold	79	197.2	+1	1.37	9.18
B	Boron	5	10.82	+3	0.23	8.257
Ba	Barium	56	137.36	+2	1.34	5.19
Be	Beryllium	4	9.02	+4	0.35	9.28
Bi	Bismuth	83	209.00	+3	0.96	8.0
Br	Bromine	35	79.916	−1	1.96	11.80
C	Carbon	6	12.01	+4	0.16	11.217
Ca	Calcium	20	40.08	+2	0.99	6.09
Cb	Columbium	41	92.91	+5	0.69	–
Cd	Cadmium	48	112.41	+2	0.97	8.96
Ce	Cerium	58	140.13	+3	1.07	6.54
Cl	Chlorine	17	35.457	−1	1.81	12.952
Co	Cobalt	27	58.94	+2, +3	0.72, 0.63	7.81
Cr	Chromium	24	52.01	+3	0.63	6.74
Cs	Cesium	55	132.91	+1	1.67	3.87
Cu	Copper	29	63.57	+1, +2	0.96, 0.72	7.68
Dy	Dysprosium	66	162.46	+3	0.92	6.8
Er	Erbium	68	167.2	+3	0.89	–
Eu	Europium	63	152.0	+3	0.98	5.64
F	Fluorine	9	19.000	−1	1.33	17.34
Fe	Iron	26	55.85	+2, +3	0.74, 0.64	7.83
Fr	Francium	87	(224)	+1	–	–
Ga	Gallium	31	69.72	+3	0.62	5.97
Gd	Gadolinium	64	156.9	+3	0.97	6.7
Ge	Germanium	32	72.60	+4	0.53	8.09
H	Hydrogen	1	1.0080	+1	–	13.527

NOTE: Figures in parenthesis in atomic weight column are approximate only and have not been adopted.

[*] M. S. Hodgman, Robert C. Weast, and Samuel M. Selby, *Handbook of Chemistry and Physics* (Cleveland: Chemical Rubber Publishing Co., 1958).

[†] L. H. Ahrens, "The Use of Ionic Potentials, Part I: Ionic Radii of the Elements," *Geochimica & Cosmochimica Acta*, 1952, Vol. II, pp. 155–169 (London: Pergamon Press).

411

Table of Atomic Parameters (Continued)

Symbol	Element	Atomic Number	Atomic * Weight	Usual Valence	Ionic † Radius, Å	First Ionization * Potential, ev
He	Helium	2	4.003	0	–	24.46
Hf	Hafnium	72	178.6	+4	0.78	–
Hg	Mercury	80	200.61	+2	1.10	10.39
Ho	Holmium	67	164.94	+3	0.91	–
I	Iodine	53	126.92	−1	2.19	10.6
In	Indium	49	114.76	+3	0.81	5.76
Ir	Iridium	77	193.1	+4	0.68	–
K	Potassium	19	39.096	+1	1.33	4.318
Kr	Krypton	36	83.7	0	–	13.93
La	Lanthanum	57	138.92	+3	1.14	5.6
Li	Lithium	3	6.940	+1	0.68	5.363
Lu	Lutecium	71	174.99	+3	0.85	–
Mg	Magnesium	12	24.32	+2	0.66	7.61
Mn	Manganese	25	54.93	+3, +4	0.80, 0.66	7.41
Mo	Molybdenum	42	95.95	+4	0.70	7.35
N	Nitrogen	7	14.008	+5	0.13	14.48
Na	Sodium	11	22.997	+1	0.97	5.12
Nb	Niobium (see Columbium, Cb)					
Nd	Neodymium	60	144.27	+3	1.04	6.3
Ne	Neon	10	20.183	0	–	21.47
Ni	Nickel	28	58.69	+2	0.69	7.61
O	Oxygen	8	16.000	−2	1.41	13.550
Os	Osmium	76	190.2	+6	0.69	8.7
P	Phosphorus	15	30.98	+5	0.13	10.9
Pa	Protactinium	91	231	+4	0.98	–
Pb	Lead	82	207.21	+4	0.84	7.38
Pd	Palladium	46	106.7	+2	0.80	8.3
Pm	Prometheum	61	(146)	+3	1.06	–
Po	Polonium	84	(210)	–	–	–
Pr	Praesodymium	59	140.92	+3	1.06	5.8
Pt	Platinum	78	195.23	+2	0.80	8.88
Ra	Radium	88	226.05	+2	1.43	5.252
Rb	Rubidium	37	85.48	+1	1.47	4.159
Re	Rhenium	75	186.31	+4	0.72	–
Rh	Rhodium	45	102.91	+3	0.68	7.7
Rn	Radon	86	222	0	–	10.698
Ru	Ruthenium	44	101.7	+4	0.67	7.7
S	Sulfur	16	32.06	−2	1.81	10.30
Sb	Antimony	51	121.76	+3	0.76	8.5
Sc	Scandium	21	45.10	+3	0.81	6.7
Se	Selenium	34	78.96	−2	1.95	9.70
Si	Silicon	14	28.06	+4	0.42	8.12
Sm	Samarium	62	150.43	+3	1.00	6.6
Sn	Tin	50	118.70	+4	0.71	7.30
Sr	Strontium	38	87.63	+2	1.12	5.667
Ta	Tantalum	73	180.88	+5	0.68	–
Tb	Terbium	65	159.2	+3	0.93	6.7
Te	Tellurium	52	127.61	−2	0.85	8.96

Table of Atomic Parameters (Continued)

Symbol	Element	Atomic Number	Atomic ° Weight	Usual Valence	Ionic † Radius, Å	First Ionization ° Potential, ev
Th	Thorium	90	232.12	+4	1.02	–
Ti	Titanium	22	47.90	+4	0.68	6.81
Tl	Thallium	81	204.39	+1, +3	1.47, 0.95	6.07
Tm	Thulium	69	169.4	+3	0.87	–
U	Uranium	92	238.07	+4, +6	0.97, 0.80	–
V	Vanadium	23	50.95	+5	0.59	6.71
W	Tungsten (Wolfram)	74	183.92	+4	0.70	8.1
Xe	Xenon	54	131.3	0	–	12.08
Y	Yttrium	39	88.92	+3	0.92	6.5
Yb	Ytterbium	70	173.04	+3	0.86	7.1
Zn	Zinc	30	65.38	+2	0.74	9.36
Zr	Zirconium	40	91.22	+4	0.79	6.92

APPENDIX II

DETERMINATIVE TABLES

The inherent difficulties of mineral identification may be decreased by grouping together minerals which have closely similar physical character-istics in order to limit the number of minerals to choose between. This procedure will lead to small groups of minerals, and final identification may then be made either by a simple chemical test, some distinctive property, the mineral occurrence, or by recognition of associated minerals.

For a number of reasons, it is difficult both to construct and to use determinative tables on a completely logical and objective basis. Mineral determination is, to a large degree, accomplished by a subjective summa-tion of all of the mineral characteristics and is ordinarily not a step-by-step process. Physical properties show relatively large variations, and unless the mineral under study is an average specimen, its classification may be impossible without recourse to chemical, optical, or X ray testing. Small grain size, incipient alteration, pseudomorphism, staining, and many other phenomena may make the determination of critical properties difficult or impossible. It is recommended that small mineral grains be separated from their matrix and examined against a white paper back-ground with a good lens or binocular microscope in order to judge luster, cleavage, and color. Hardness may be tested on fine-grained material in matrix by the use of a needle.

Two listings and a set of determinative tables are given on the follow-ing pages as aids to the determination of the minerals described in this book. A number of other minerals are also included in the tabulations and will be found under the entries "Related Minerals" in Part II of the text.

Table I lists those minerals which may be found in some of the more common geological environments. In general, the minerals in any column may be found together, but associations should be checked by reference to the mineral descriptions. The order in the columns follows the order of the mineral families in Part II of the text, i.e., from native elements to silicates.

Table II groups those minerals which display some relatively striking physical properties. Again, the order in the columns is that of the min-eral families.

Table III is a determinative table in which the minerals are grouped into sections according to their luster, cleavage, hardness, and color. The table is divided into two principal parts in which minerals with metallic and nonmetallic lusters are listed. Each of these parts is further divided into sections based on cleavage and color, in accordance with the following outline:

PART I

Minerals with a Metallic Luster

(Opaque on thinnest edge and having a dark-colored streak)
Section A: No cleavage
Section B: Distinct cleavage

PART II

Minerals with a Nonmetallic Luster

(Transparent on thinnest edge and having a colorless or light-colored streak)
Section A: No cleavage
Section B: One cleavage yielding tabular or micaceous fragments
Section C: Cleavage fragments are polyhedral
Section D: Distinct cleavage, but not yielding fragments classified in Sections B and C above
Colorless, white, or lightly tinted minerals
Section E: Distinct cleavage, but not yielding fragments classified in Sections B and C above
Black, brown, or red minerals
Section F: Distinct cleavage, but not yielding fragments classified in Sections B and C above
Orange, yellow, green, blue, or violet minerals

The minerals in each section are arranged in the order of their increasing hardness, which is shown graphically in the left-hand column. Vertical bars represent the hardnesses respectively of a copper penny, a knife blade or window glass, and an unglazed porcelain streak plate.

The mineral formulae will provide clues to critical chemical spot tests, as described in Chapter 5, which may be used to distinguish otherwise similar species. Specific gravity may be a useful criterion, especially if its value has been determined or the contrast of specific gravity of two possibilities is large. Color, and especially streak, may be essential clues in the identification of a particular species, but color must be used with caution. Particular features of determinative value are given in the remarks column, and the page number provides a cross reference to the mineral description, which should be checked before final identification is made.

Multiple entries of minerals have been made for those species in which confusion might arise because the critical parameters are difficult to assess or because the variations in physical properties are large enough to warrant more listings. For example, sphalerite will be found under both metallic and nonmetallic luster, gypsum in Sections B, C, and D of Part II, and orthoclase under both uncolored and red cleavable minerals.

The use of the tables may be illustrated by a few examples:

1. OBSERVATIONS: The mineral is nonmetallic, blue-green, shows cleavage, is softer than 3, and is water soluble.

   DETERMINATION: The mineral will be found in Part II, Section F. The only minerals fitting the observations are melanterite and chalcanthite. A test for copper or iron will readily distinguish these two species.

2. OBSERVATIONS: The mineral has a metallic luster, no cleavage, hardness between 3 and 5.5, yellowish color, and black streak.

   DETERMINATION: The mineral will be found between pyrolusite and magnetite, inclusive, in Part I, Section A. The mineral is gold, chalcopyrite, or pyrrhotite, based on color, and chalcopyrite or pyrrhotite based on streak. These two minerals can be readily distinguished by a test for copper (chalcopyrite, if positive) or magnetism (pyrrhotite, if positive).

3. OBSERVATIONS: The mineral is nonmetallic, has a micaceous cleavage yielding flexible folia, can be scratched by a copper penny, and is sectile. Further, the mineral does not have an unctuous or greasy feel nor an earthy smell when wet.

   DETERMINATION: The mineral will be found between montmorillonite and barite, inclusive, in Part II, Section B. Color and streak somewhat limit the choice, and feel and smell further reduce the possibilities. The mineral must be gypsum, vivianite, sericite, brucite, muscovite, lepidolite, or barite. The occurrence of the mineral in a vein in serpentine rock together with the evolution of copious water when heated, low specific gravity, and sectility identify the mineral as brucite.

4. OBSERVATIONS: The mineral is metallic and shows distinct cleavage. The hardness is about 3, and the color and streak are black.

   DETERMINATION: The mineral will be found in Part I, Section B. The black color and streak coupled with the hardness make jamesonite, bournonite, and enargite the only possibilities. The distinctive habits of these minerals may serve to distinguish them, or combinations of tests for Cu, Pb, and Fe can be used.

5. OBSERVATIONS: The mineral is nonmetallic, yields rhombic cleavage fragments, has a hardness of about 3.5, and is pink in color.

   DETERMINATION: The mineral will be found in Part II, Section C. Only one pink mineral, rhodochrosite, is listed, but a confirmatory test with cold, dilute HCl is negative because strong effervescence is observed. The mineral must therefore be a carbonate, and only calcite satisfies the observations.

TABLE I

Occurrence of Minerals

	Igneous Rocks			Metamorphic Rocks	
Silica-rich	Silica-poor	Mafic Volcanics	Crystalline Schists and Gneisses	Calcareous Metamorphics	Contact Metamorphic Rocks
Molybdenite	Platinum	Copper	Graphite	Graphite	Sphalerite
Fluorite	Chalcopyrite	Diamond	Pyrrhotite	Arsenopyrite	Chalcopyrite
	Pyrrhotite		Arsenopyrite		Arsenopyrite
Cassiterite	Niccolite	Anhydrite		Calcite	Molybdenite
Magnetite			Rutile	Dolomite	
	Corundum	Chalcedony	Corundum		Corundum
Monazite	Ilmenite	Opal	Spinel	Scapolite	Hematite
Apatite	Rutile	Leucite		Phlogopite	Cassiterite
	Spinel	Analcite	Diaspore	Olivine	Spinel
Quartz	Magnetite	Plagioclase		Tremolite	Magnetite
Tridymite	Chromite	Stilbite	Rhodochrosite	Garnet	
Orthoclase		Heulandite		Humite	Gibbsite
Sanidine	Apatite	Chabazite	Monazite	Epidote	
Microcline	Zoisite	Thomsonite	Apatite		Scheelite
Plagioclase		Natrolite	Pyromorphite		
Muscovite	Plagioclase	Apophyllite			Tremolite
Garnet	Nepheline	Prehnite	Quartz		Diopside
Allanite	Sodalite	Pectolite	Orthoclase		Wollastonite
Hornblende	Leucite	Melilite	Plagioclase		Tourmaline
Zircon	Cancrinite	Datolite	Chlorite		Cordierite
Topaz	Chrysotile		Margarite		Melilite
Sphene	Enstatite		Muscovite		Vesuvianite
	Diopside		Biotite		Axinite
	Augite		Anthophyllite		Staurolite
	Olivine		Hornblende		Lazurite
	Garnet		Diopside		
	Sphene		Vesuvianite		
			Garnet		
			Zircon		

TABLE I (Continued)

Sedimentary Rocks	Veins	Oxidized Zone	Volcanic Sublimates
Sulfur	Gold, Silver, Arsenic	Copper	Sulfur
Bornite, Chalcopyrite, Marcasite	All Sulfides	Chalcocite, Bornite, Covellite	Realgar, Orpiment
	All Sulfosalts	Pyrargyrite, Cerargyrite	
Halite, Sylvite, Fluorite, Carnallite	Fluorite		Halite, Fluorite
Hematite, Uraninite	Hematite, Ilmenite, Rutile, Cassiterite, Uraninite, Magnetite	Cuprite, Hematite, Cassiterite	
		Psilomelane	
Gibbsite, Diaspore, Bauxite	Brucite, Manganite		
Magnesite, Siderite, Aragonite, Strontianite	Calcite, Magnesite, Siderite, Rhodochrosite	Smithsonite, Aragonite, Cerussite, Malachite, Azurite	
	Witherite, Strontianite, Dolomite		
Borax, Colemanite			
Barite, Celestite, Anhydrite, Melanterite, Polyhalite	Barite, Celestite, Anhydrite, Jarosite	Anglesite, Gypsum, Melanterite, Epsomite	Anhydrite, Gypsum
Apatite, Collophane, Carnotite	Apatite, Amblygonite	Pyromorphite, Vanadinite	
	Wolframite, Scheelite	Wulfenite	
Quartz, Orthoclase	Quartz, Orthoclase, Rhodonite, Topaz	Chrysocolla, Hemimorphite	
Analcite, Kaolinite, Montmorillonite, Muscovite, Glauconite			

TABLE II

Minerals Showing Some Distinctive Physical Properties

Sectile Minerals	Magnetic Minerals	Radioactive Minerals	Luminescent or Fluorescent Minerals	Piezo-, Pyro-, Thermo-, and Triboelectric Minerals	Minerals Whose Fusibility Is 1 or Less
Gold	Platinum	Uraninite	Diamond	Diamond	Sulfur
Silver	Pyrrhotite	Monazite	Sphalerite	Graphite	
Platinum		Carnotite			Realgar
Graphite	Ilmenite†	Autunite	Fluorite	Arsenopyrite	Orpiment
Sulfur	Hematite†	Torbernite	Carnallite	Sphalerite	Stibnite
	Magnetite				Bismuthinite
Argentite	Franklinite	Zircon	Corundum	Alunite	Skutterudite
Chalcocite*	Chromite	Sphene		Jarosite	
Cinnabar			Calcite	Pyromorphite	Pyrargyrite
Realgar	Wolframite		Aragonite		Proustite
Orpiment			Witherite		Enargite
Stibnite*			Strontianite	Quartz	Bournonite
Bismuthinite*			Cerussite	Thomsonite	
Molybdenite			Dolomite	Tourmaline	Carnallite
			Magnesite	Hemimorphite	Cerargyrite
Cerargyrite					
			Barite		Ice
Brucite			Celestite		
			Anglesite		
Wulfenite*					
Soda niter*			Apatite		
			Scheelite		
Pyrophyllite					
Talc			Quartz		
Chrysocolla*			Scapolite		
Garnierite*			Wollastonite		
			Pectolite		
			Willemite		

* Subsectile.   † Included magnetite.

Minerals Whose Color May Change on Heating

Rutile
Corundum
Spinel

Apatite
Lazulite
Turquois
Vivianite
Crocoite

Sodalite
Cancrinite
Muscovite
Biotite
Rhodonite
Beryl
Olivine
Zircon
Humite
Topaz
Sphene

Water-soluble Minerals

Sylvite
Halite
Carnallite
Soda niter

Borax
Kernite
Mirabilite

Melanterite
Epsomite
Polyhalite
Chalcanthite

Minerals Whose Specific Gravity Is Greater Than 3.5 but Less Than 5.0

Diamond

Sphalerite
Greenockite
Chalcopyrite
Pyrrhotite
Covellite
Realgar
Orpiment
Stibnite
Marcasite
Molybdenite

Tetrahedrite
Enargite

Corundum
Ilmenite
Spinel
Chrysoberyl
Chromite

Goethite
Limonite
Psilomelane

Siderite
Rhodochrosite
Smithsonite

Witherite
Strontianite
Malachite
Azurite

Barite
Celestite
Carnotite

Wolframite

Enstatite
Acmite
Diopside
Jadeite
Rhodonite
Hemimorphite
Garnet
Zircon
Willemite
Epidote
Allanite
Topaz
Humite
Sphene

Minerals Whose Specific Gravity Is Greater Than 5.0

Gold
Silver
Platinum
Arsenic

Argentite
Chalcocite
Bornite
Galena
Niccolite
Cinnabar
Pyrite
Cobaltite
Arsenopyrite
Skutterudite
Bismuthinite

Pyrargyrite
Proustite
Tetrahedrite
Bournonite
Jamesonite

Cerargyrite

Cuprite
Hematite
Pyrolusite
Cassiterite
Uraninite
Magnetite
Columbite-tantalite

Cerussite

Anglesite
Monazite
Pyromorphite
Vanadinite
Carnotite

Scheelite
Wulfenite
Crocoite

Hardness 1 2 3 4 5 6 7 8 9 10	Hardness Range	Mineral Name	Formula	Speci Grav
·· | | |	2–2.5	Argentite	Ag_2S	7.3
··········	2–6.5	Pyrolusite	MnO_2	5.0
··	2.5–3	Gold	Au	19.3
··	2.5–3	Silver	Ag	10.5
··	2.5–3	Copper	Cu	8.9
··	2.5–3	Chalcocite	Cu_2S	5.7
··	2.5–3	Bournonite	$PbCuSbS_3$	5.8
·	3	Bornite	Cu_5FeS_4	5.1
····	3–4.5	Tetrahedrite series	$Cu_{12}(SbAs)_4S_{13}$	4.6–5
··	3.5–4	Chalcopyrite	$CuFeS_2$	4.2
···	3.5–4.5	Pyrrhotite	$Fe_{1-x}S$	4.6
··	4–4.5	Platinum	Pt	14–1
··	5–5.5	Niccolite	$NiAs$	7.8
···	5–6	Psilomelane	$BaMnMn_8O_{16}(OH)_4$	4.7
···	5–6	Hematite	Fe_2O_3	5.2
···	5–6	Ilmenite	$FeTiO_3$	4.7
···	5–6	Uraninite	UO_2	10.8 less
·	5.5	Chromite	$FeCr_2O_4$	4.6
··	5.5–6	Allanite	$R_2{}^{+2}R_3{}^{+3}(SiO_4)_3(OH)$	3.0–4
···	5.5–6.5	Magnetite	$FeFe_2O_4$	5.2
···	5.5–6.5	Franklinite	$(FeZnMn)Fe_2O_4$	5.1–
··	6–6.5	Pyrite	FeS_2	5.0
··	6–6.5	Marcasite	FeS_2	4.9

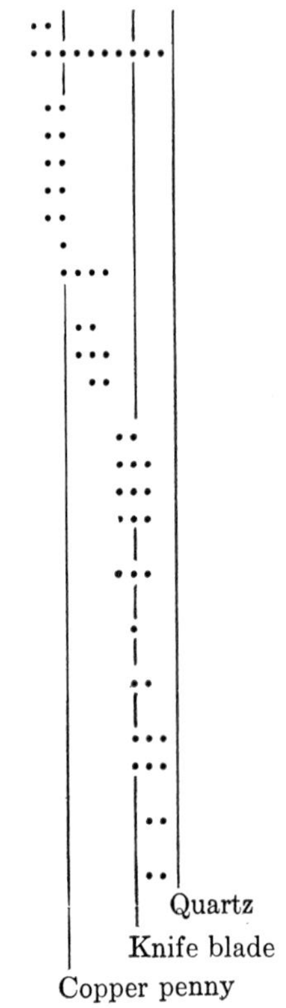

Quartz
Knife blade
Copper penny

Color	Streak	Remarks	Page
rk lead gray	Black and shining	Sectile, darkens on exposure to light	230
el gray	Black	Pulvurent forms may soil fingers, crystals hard	270
llow	Yellow	Sectile, does not tarnish	220
ver white	Silver white	Sectile, black tarnish	221
pper red	Copper red	Sectile, brown tarnish	222
rk lead gray	Dark lead gray	Subsectile, massive	231
ay to black	Gray to black	Wheel-like twins, easily fused	254
pper red	Gray black	"Peacock" tarnish	232
ay to black	Black to red	Very thin splinters red in transmitted light	252
ass yellow	Green black	Common sulfide	235
onze yellow	Black	Weakly magnetic	236
ay	Gray	Sectile, may be weakly magnetic, in mafic rocks	223
le copper red	Brownish black	Green alteration "bloom"	237
ack to gray	Black and shining	Colloform or earthy	283
d brown to black	Brick red	Common mineral	267
ack	Black	Common mineral, may be weakly magnetic	268
ack	Brownish black	Radioactive, usually massive or colloform	272
ack	Brown	May be weakly magnetic, in mafic rocks	275
own to black	Grayish brown	Accessory in granitic rocks, usually radioactive	400
ack	Black	Common mineral, strongly magnetic	274
ack	Brown	With willemite and zincite, weakly magnetic	274
le brass yellow	Black	Common mineral, crystals as cubes or pyritohedra	243
hite to pale yellow	Black	Tarnishes to brass yellow, "coxcomb" crystals	245

Hardness 1 2 3 4 5 6 7 8 9 10	Hardness Range	Mineral Name	Formula	Speci Gravi
··	1–1.5	Molybdenite	MoS_2	4.7
···	1–2	Graphite	C	2.2
··	1.5–2	Covellite	CuS	4.7
·	2	Stibnite	Sb_2S_2	4.6
·	2	Bismuthinite	Bi_2S_3	6.8
··	2–2.5	Argentite	Ag_2S	7.3
··	2–2.5	Cinnabar	HgS	8.1
·	2.5	Galena	PbS	7.6
·	2.5	Pyrargyrite	Ag_3SbS_3	5.8
·	2.5	Jamesonite	$Pb_4FeSb_6S_{14}$	5.6
··	2.5–3	Bournonite	$PbCuSbS_3$	5.8
·	3	Bornite	Cu_5FeS_4	5.1
·	3	Enargite	Cu_3AsS_4	4.4
··	3–3.5	Millerite	NiS	5.3–5
·	3.5	Arsenic	As	5.7
··	3.5–4	Sphalerite	ZnS	3.9–4
··	3.5–4	Pentlandite	$(FeNi)_9S_8$	4.6–5
··	3.5–4	Cuprite	Cu_2O	6.1
···	3.5–4.5	Pyrrhotite	$Fe_{1-x}S$	4.6
·	4	Manganite	$MnO(OH)$	4.2–4
··	4–4.5	Wolframite series	$(FeMn)(WO_4)$	7.3
··	5–5.5	Goethite	$FeO(OH)$	3.3–4
···	5–6	Ilmenite series	$(FeMgMn)TiO_3$	4.7
·	5.5	Cobaltite	CoAsS	6.3
··	5.5–6	Arsenopyrite	FeAsS	6.1
··	5.5–6	Skutterudite series	$(CoNi)As_{3-x}$	6.1–6.
··	5.5–6	Allanite	$R_2^{+2}R_3^{+3}(SiO_4)_3(OH)$	3.0–4.
···	5.5–6.5	Magnetite	$FeFe_2O_4$	5.2
···	5.5–6.5	Franklinite	$(FeZnMn)Fe_2O_4$	5.1–5.
··	6–6.5	Rutile	TiO_2	4.2
··	6–6.5	Columbite-tantalite series	$(FeMn)(CbTa)_2O_6$	5.2–7.
··	6–6.5	Pyrolusite	MnO_2	5.0
···	6–7	Cassiterite	SnO_2	7.0

Quartz

Knife blade

Copper penny

424

ction B: Distinct Cleavage

Color	Streak	Remarks	Page
ay	Gray to black	Foliated; distinguished from graphite by green streak on glazed porcelain	247
eel gray to black	Black	Foliated, greasy feel	227
digo blue	Black to gray	Platy aggregates	238
ay	Gray	Columnar, black tarnish	242
ad gray	Lead gray	Foliated or fibrous	242
rk lead gray	Black and shining	Sectile	230
d	Red	Subsectile, often earthy	239
ad gray	Lead gray	Cubic crystals and cleavage	233
ep red	Red	Translucent	251
ay black	Gray black	Plumose, iridescent tarnish	255
ay to black	Gray to black	Wheel-like twins	254
pper red	Gray black	"Peacock" tarnish	232
ack	Black	Bladed aggregates	253
ass yellow	Greenish black	Capillary crystals	237
n white	Gray	Dark gray tarnish, concentric layers	224
ack to brown	Brown to yellow	Common sulfide, resinous luster	234
ght bronze yellow	Yellow brown	Octahedral parting, with pyrrhotite	232
rk red	Brown red	Highly lustrous octahedra	263
onze yellow	Black	Weakly magnetic	236
ack	Brown	Prismatic crystals, with other Mn oxides	283
ack to brown black	Black to brown black	Sometimes weakly magnetic	319
own	Brownish yellow	Common mineral, colloform	281
ack to red	Black to reddish to yellow	Sometimes weakly magnetic, massive	268
ver white	Gray-black	Pink alteration "bloom"	244
ver white	Black	Prismatic crystals, common	246
ver white to silver gray	Black	Cubic or octahedral crystals	248
own to black	Grayish brown	Accessory in granitic rocks, usually radioactive	400
ack	Black	Common mineral, strongly magnetic	274
ack	Brown	With willemite and zincite, weakly magnetic	274
d to black	Pale brown	Prismatic crystals, highly lustrous	269
ack to brown black	Dark red to black	In granitic pegmatites	276
eel gray	Black	Pulvurent forms may stain fingers, crystals hard	270
own or black	White to brown	In greisen, highly lustrous	271

Hardness 1 2 3 4 5 6 7 8 9 10	Hardness Range	Mineral Name	Formula	Specifi Gravi
	1	Carnallite	$KCl \cdot MgCl_2 \cdot 6 H_2O$	1.6
	1–3	Bauxite	Mixture of Al hydroxides	2.0–2
	1–5.5	Limonite	$FeO(OH) \cdot nH_2O$	3.6–4
	1.5	Ice	H_2O	0.9
	2–2.5	Cinnabar	HgS	8.1
	2–3	Cerargyrite	$AgCl$	5.5
	2–3	Garnierite	$(NiMg)(SiO_3) \cdot nH_2O$	2.5
	2–4	Chrysocolla	$CuSiO_3 \cdot nH_2O$	2.3
	2–5	Collophane	$Ca_3(PO_4)_2 \cdot H_2O$	2.6–2
	2.5	Cryolite	Na_3AlF_6	3.0
	2.5–5.5	Serpentine	$Mg_6(Si_4O_{10})(OH)_8$	2.6
	3	Vanadinite	$Pb_5(VO_4)_3Cl$	6.7–7
	3–3.5	Greenockite	CdS	4.9
	3.5–4	Pyromorphite series	$Pb_3[(PAs)O_4]_3Cl$	6.5–7
	5–5.5	Analcite	$Na(AlSi_2O_6) \cdot H_2O$	2.5
	5–5.5	Datolite	$CaBSiO_4(OH)$	2.9–3
	5–5.5	Lazurite	$Na_5(AlSiO_4)_3S$	2.4–2
	5–5.5	Lazulite	$MgAl_2(PO_4)_2(OH)_2$	3.0–3.
	5–6	Uraninite	UO_2	10.8 (less
	5–6	Turquois	$Al_2PO_4(OH)_3 \cdot H_2O+xCu$	2.6–2.
	5–6	Hematite	Fe_2O_3	5.3
	5–6	Opal	$SiO_2 \cdot nH_2O$	1.9–2.
	5.5–6	Leucite	$K(AlSi_2O_6)$	2.5
	5.5–6	Allanite	$R_2^{+2}R_3^{+3}(SiO_4)_3(OH)$	3.0–4.
	6–6.5	Humite group	$xMg_2(SiO_4) \cdot Mg(OH,F)_2$	3.1–3.
	6–7	Cassiterite	SnO_2	7.0
	6.5	Vesuvianite	$Ca_{10}(MgFe)_2Al_4(Si_2O_7)_2(SiO_4)_5(OH)_4$	3.4
	6.5–7	Olivine series	$(MgFe)_2(SiO_4)$	3.3–3.
	6.5–7.5	Garnet group	$R_3^{+2}R_2^{+3}(SiO_4)_3$	3.5–4.
	7	Chalcedony	SiO_2	2.6
	7	Quartz	SiO_2	2.6
	7	Cristobalite	SiO_2	2.3
	7	Dumortierite	$(AlFe)_7BSi_3O_{18}$	3.3–3.
	7	Danburite	$CaB_2Si_2O_8$	3.0
	7–7.5	Tourmaline series	$(NaCaLi)(MgFe)_3B_3Al_3(Al_3Si_6O_{27})(OH,F)_4$	3.0–3.
	7.5–8	Spinel	$MgAl_2O_4$	3.6
	7.5–8	Beryl	$Be_3Al_2(SiO_3)_6$	2.8
	9	Corundum	Al_2O_3	4.0

Quartz
Knife blade
Copper penny

Color	Streak	Remarks	Page
ite to reddish	White	In salt beds, bitter taste	258
ite, stained gray	White	Often pisolitic	282
ellow, red			
wn to black	Yellow brown	Alteration of iron bearing minerals	281
orless to white	White	Melts at 0°	264
rk red	Red	Subsectile, earthy	239
ay to green	White	Texture of horn, color deepens on exposure to light	259
een to white	White	Unctuous, earthy	379
een to brown	White	Encrustations and fillings, enamel-like	378
ite, gray, brown	White	Colloform	313
ite	White	Pseudocubic parting, low refractive index	
een	White	Smooth or greasy feel, common alteration product	365
d to yellow	White to yellowish	Hollow prisms	315
ange to yellow	Orange to red	Incrusting, often with sphalerite	
een, brown, yellow	White	Hexagonal prisms, often barrel-shaped	314
ite	White	Trapezohedra	345
ite to green	White	Equant crystals or massive and porcelain-like	
ue	White	In limestones near granite contacts	340
ue	White	Loses color when heated	
ack	Brownish black	Radioactive	272
ue to green	White or greenish	Turns brown when heated	316
d-brown to black	Brick red	Common mineral	267
rious	White	Milky or opalescent, never in crystals	331
ite or gray	White	Pseudotrapezohedra, in silica-poor igneous rocks	343
own to black	Grayish brown	Accessory in granitic rocks, usually radioactive	400
llow, brown, red, or white	White	In ancient dolomitic marbles	399
own or black	White to brown	Highly lustrous, in greisen	271
own to green	White	Columnar aggregates, in metamorphic rocks	391
een to brown	White	Rock forming mineral, in mafic rocks	393
d, brown, green	White	Dodecahedra or trapezohedra	395
rious	White	Often banded	330
ite	White	Common rock forming mineral, glassy	329
lorless to white	White	In siliceous volcanic rocks	330
olet, blue, pink	White	In pegmatites and crystalline metamorphic rocks, fibrous	
lorless to yellow	White	Orthorhombic crystals	
ack, green, red	White	Spherical triangle cross section	383
rious	White	Octahedra	273
ue to green	White	Hexagonal prisms in pegmatite	385
own, pink, blue	White	Good parting, in metamorphic rocks	266

Hardness 1 2 3 4 5 6 7 8 9 10	Hardness Range	Mineral Name	Formula	Speci Gravi
•	1	Montmoril-lonite series	$X(AlMg)_2[(AlSi)_4O_{10}](OH)_2$	2.0–2
••	1–1.5	Talc	$Mg_3(Si_4O_{10})(OH)_2$	2.7
•••	1–2	Pyrophyllite	$Al_2(Si_4O_{10})(OH)_2$	2.8
•••	1–2	Graphite	C	2.2
•••	1–2	Carnotite	$K_2(UO_2)_2(VO_4)_2 \cdot nH_2O$	4–5
•	1.5	Vermiculite	$Mg_3(Si_4O_{10})(OH)_2 \cdot nH_2O$	2.4
••	1.5–2	Orpiment	As_2S_3	3.5
••	1.5–2	Vivianite	$Fe_3(PO_4)_2 \cdot 8\ H_2O$	2.6–2
•	2	Gypsum	$Ca(SO_4) \cdot 2H_2O$	2.3
••	2–2.5	Kaolinite	$Al_2(Si_2O_5)(OH)_4$	2.6
••	2–2.5	Chlorite group	$(MgFeAl)_6[(AlSi)_4O_{10}](OH)_8$	2.7
••	2–2.5	Autunite	$Ca(UO_2)_2(PO_4)_2 \cdot 8\ H_2O$	3.1
••	2–2.5	Sericite	$KAl_2(AlSi_3O_{10})(OH)_2$	2.7–3.
••	2–2.5	Torbernite	$Cu(UO_2)_2(PO_4)_2 \cdot 8\ H_2O$	3.2
•	2.5	Brucite	$Mg(OH)_2$	2.4
••	2.5–3	Muscovite	$KAl_2(AlSi_3O_{10})(OH)_2$	2.8–3.
••	2.5–3	Biotite	$K(MgFe)_3(AlSi_3O_{10})(OH)_2$	2.7–3.
••	2.5–3	Phlogopite	$KMg_3(AlSi_3O_{10})(OH)_2$	2.8
•••	2.5–3.5	Gibbsite	$Al(OH)_3$	2.4
•••	2.5–3.5	Jarosite	$KFe(SO_4)_3(OH)_6$	2.9–3.
••••	2.5–4	Lepidolite series	$K_2Li_2Al_3(AlSi_7O_{20})(OH,F)_4$	2.9
•	3	Wulfenite	$Pb(MoO_4)$	6.5–7.
••	3–3.5	Barite	$Ba(SO_4)$	4.5
•	3.5	Arsenic	As	5.7
••	3.5–4	Heulandite	$Ca(Al_2Si_6O_{16}) \cdot 5\ H_2O$	2.2
••••	3.5–5	Margarite	$CaAl_2(Al_2Si_2O_{10})(OH)_2$	3.0
••	4–4.5	Zincite	ZnO	5.4–5.
••	4.5–5	Apophyllite	$KCa_4(Si_4O_{10})_2F \cdot 8H_2O$	2.3–2.
••	6–6.5	Albite	$Na(AlSi_3O_8)$	2.6

Quartz

Knife blade

Copper penny

ction B: Distinct Cleavage

ular or micaceous.)

Color	Streak	Remarks	Page
ite or gray	White	Unctuous feel, earthy smell when wet	353
een to white	White	Greasy feel, plastic cleavage folia	355
ite	White	Greasy feel, plastic cleavage folia	354
el gray to black	Black	Greasy feel	227
llow	Pale yellow	Radioactive, in sandstones	317
llow to brown	White	Expands when heated	362
llow	Yellow	Sectile, melts at 300°	241
lorless, blue, green	White to bluish	Color darkens with oxidation, flexible folia	
ite, gray, brown	White	Common mineral, plastic	307
ite, often stained	White	Unctuous when wet, earthy	352
rk green	White	Common alteration product, flexible cleavage folia	357
llow	Yellow	Tabular crystals, radioactive	317
lorless	White	Very fine scales with a silky luster	361
een	Green	Tabular crystals, radioactive	317
ite or pale tints	White	In veins in Mg-rich metamorphic rocks	279
lorless or pale ints	White	Common rock forming mineral, elastic cleavage folia	361
ack or brown-lack	White	Common rock forming mineral, elastic cleavage folia	362
own	White	Rare in igneous rocks, elastic cleavage folia	363
ite, often stained	White	Earthy smell when wet, in bauxite deposits and talc schists	280
llow to brown	Pale yellow	Crusts and coatings	310
k, violet, white	White	Elastic cleavage folia, in pegmatites	364
ange to yellow	White	Square tablets	322
ite	White	Often tinted yellow, red, green, or blue, tabular crystals	303
white	Gray	Dark gray tarnish, concentric layers	224
ite to reddish	White	A zeolite	346
k to white	White	Brittle cleavage folia, in chlorite schists	358
d to orange-yellow	Orange-yellow	With franklinite and willemite	
ite to gray	White	In mafic volcanics	
ite	White	A plagioclase	337

Part 2: Nonmetallic Lust

(Cleavage fragme

Hardness 1 2 3 4 5 6 7 8 9 10	Hardness Range	Mineral Name	Formula	Speci Gravi
••	1.5–2	Soda niter	$Na(NO_3)$	2.2–2.
•	2	Gypsum	$Ca(SO_4) \cdot 2H_2O$	2.3
•	2	Halite	$NaCl$	2.2
•	2	Sylvite	KCl	2.0
••	3–3.5	Calcite	$Ca(CO_3)$	2.7
••	3–3.5	Celestite	$Sr(SO_4)$	4.0
•	3.5	Anhydrite	$Ca(SO_4)$	3.0
••	3.5–4	Sphalerite	ZnS	3.9–4.
••	3.5–4	Rhodochrosite	$Mn(CO_3)$	3.7
••	3.5–4	Dolomite	$CaMg(CO_3)_2$	2.9
••	3.5–4	Cuprite	Cu_2O	6.1
•••	3.5–4.5	Siderite	$Fe(CO_3)$	4.0
•	4	Magnesite	$Mg(CO_3)$	3.0
•	4	Fluorite	CaF_2	3.2
••	4–4.5	Smithsonite	$Zn(CO_3)$	4.4
•••	4–5	Chabazite	$(CaNaK)_7[Al_{12}(AlSi)_2Si_{26}O_{80}] \cdot 40H_2O$	2.1
•••	5–6	Cancrinite	$Na_3Ca(Al_3Si_3O_{12})CO_3(OH)_2$	2.5
••	5.5–6	Sodalite	$Na_4(Al_3Si_3O_{12})Cl$	2.1–2.
	10	Diamond	C	3.5

Part 2: Nonmetallic Lust

(Colorless or lightly tinted minerals; cleava

Hardness 1 2 3 4 5 6 7 8 9 10	Hardness Range	Mineral Name	Formula	Speci Gravi
••	1.5–2	Mirabilite	$Na_2(SO_4) \cdot 10\ H_2O$	1.5
•	2	Gypsum	$Ca(SO_4) \cdot 2H_2O$	2.3
••	2–2.5	Borax	$Na_2B_4O_7 \cdot 10H_2O$	1.7
••	2–2.5	Epsomite	$Mg(SO_4) \cdot 7H_2O$	1.7
••	2.5–3	Anglesite	$Pb(SO_4)$	6.4
••	2.5–3	Kernite	$Na_2B_4O_7 \cdot 4H_2O$	1.9
••	3–3.5	Witherite	$Ba(CO_3)$	4.3
••	3–3.5	Cerussite	$Pb(CO_3)$	6.6
••	3–3.5	Celestite	$Sr(SO_4)$	4.0
••	3–3.5	Barite	$Ba(SO_4)$	4.5
•	3.5	Strontianite	$Sr(CO_3)$	3.8
••	3.5–4	Aragonite	$Ca(CO_3)$	2.9

Quartz
Knife blade
Copper penny

ection C: Distinct Cleavage

e polyhedral.)

Color	Streak	Remarks	Page
hite to brown, gray, yellow	White	Rhombs, cool taste	287
hite, gray, brown	White	Flattened rhombohedra, plastic	307
olorless or white	White	Cubes, salty taste, often tinted	257
hite to bluish or reddish	White	Cubes, bitter taste	258
olorless or white	White	Rhombs, often colored, very common	286
olorless to pale blue	White	Oblongs, in sedimentary rocks	304
olorless or blue-white	White	Oblongs, often tinted	306
ellow, brown, black	White, yellow, brown	Dodecahedra, resinous luster	234
nk	White	Rhombs	290
hite	White	Rhombs, common sedimentary rock forming mineral	296
ed	Brown red	Octahedra, highly lustrous	263
rown	White	Rhombs	289
olorless or white	White	Rhombs, as alteration of Mg-rich rock	288
olet, green, white	White	Octahedral cleavage, cubic crystals, often fluorescent	260
hite, green	White	Rhombs, usually colloform, variously colored	291
esh red to white	White	Rhombs, in cavities in mafic lavas	347
ellow	White	Rhombs, in silica-poor igneous rocks, variously colored	344
ue	White	Rhombs, in silica-poor igneous rocks, variously colored	340
ack, bluish, yellow	None	Octahedra	226

ection D: Distinct Cleavage

agments are not micaceous, tabular, or polyhedral.)

Color	Streak	Remarks	Page
hite	White	Cool then bitter taste	307
olorless to white, gray, brown	White	Common mineral, plastic	307
olorless to white	White	Sweetish taste, in evaporites, tinted gray, blue, or green	300
olorless to white	White	Bitter taste, tinted pink or green	309
olorless to white	White	Alteration of galena, tinted gray, yellow, green, blue	305
olorless to white	White	Long splintery cleavage fragments	300
olorless to white	White	Tinted yellow, brown, or green	293
olorless to white	White	Reticulated aggregates, tinted gray, blue, or green, very brittle	295
olorless to pale blue	White	In sedimentary rocks, tinted red or green	304
olorless to white	White	Tinted yellow, brown, red, gray, green, or blue, tabular crystals	303
olorless to gray	White	Columnar or fibrous, tinted yellow, green, or red	294
olorless to white	White	Columnar or fibrous	292

Part 2: Nonmetallic Lust

(Colorless or lightly tinted mineral

Hardness	Hardness Range	Mineral Name	Formula	Specif Gravit
1 2 3 4 5 6 7 8 9 10				
••	3.5–4	Stilbite	$(CaNaK)_3[Al_5(AlSi)Si_{14}O_{40}]$ · 15 H_2O	2.2
••	3.5–4	Wavellite	$Al_3(PO_4)_2(OH)_3$ · 5 H_2O	2.3
•	4	Alunite	$KAl_3(SO_4)_2(OH)_6$	2.6–2.8
••	4–4.5	Colemanite	$Ca_2B_6O_{11}$ · 5 H_2O	2.4
••	4.5–5	Scheelite	$Ca(WO_4)$	6.1
••	4.5–5	Wollastonite	$Ca(SiO_3)$	2.8
••	4.5–5	Hemimorphite	$Zn_4(Si_2O_7)(OH)_2$ · H_2O	3.5
• •	4.5,6.5	Kyanite	$Al_2(SiO_4)O$	3.6
•	5	Pectolite	$Ca_2NaH(SiO_3)_2$	2.8
•	5	Melilite series	$Ca_2(MgAl)[(AlSi)_2O_7]$	3.0
••	5–5.5	Natrolite	$Na_2(Al_2Si_3O_{10})$ · 2 H_2O	2.2
••••	5–6	Nepheline	$Na(AlSiO_4)$	2.6
•••	5–6	Tremolite series	$Ca_2(MgFe)_5(Si_8O_{22})(OH)_2$	3.0–3.3
••••	5–6	Diopside series	$Ca(MgFe)(Si_2O_6)$	3.2–3.6
••••	5–6.5	Scapolite series	$(NaCa)_4[Al(AlSi)Si_2O_8]_3$ (Cl,CO_3)	2.6–2.8
••	5.5–6	Amblygonite series	$LiAl(PO_4)(OH,F)$	3.1
••	5.5–6	Leucite	$K(AlSi_2O_6)$	2.5
•	6	Sanidine	$(KNa)(AlSi_3O_8)$	2.6
•	6	Orthoclase	$K(AlSi_3O_8)$	2.6
•	6	Adularia	$K(AlSi_3O_8)$	2.6
••	6–6.5	Microcline	$K(AlSi_3O_8)$	2.6
••	6–6.5	Zoisite	$Ca_2Al_3(SiO_4)_3(OH)$	3.3
••	6–6.5	Plagioclase series	$(CaNa)[(AlSi)_4O_8]$	2.6–2.7
••	6–6.5	Prehnite	$Ca_2Al(AlSi_3O_{10})(OH)_2$	2.9
••	6–6.5	Humite group	$xMg_2(SiO_4)$ · $Mg(OH,F)_2$	3.1–3.3
•••	6–7	Sillimanite	$AlAl(SiO_4)O$	3.2
••	6.5–7	Diaspore	$α-AlO(OH)$	3.4
••	6.5–7	Spodumene	$LiAl(Si_2O_6)$	3.2
•	7.5	Zircon	$Zr(SiO_4)$	4.7
•	7.5	Andalusite	$AlAl(SiO_4)O$	3.2
•	8	Topaz	$Al_2(SiO_4)(OH,F)_2$	3.5

Quartz
Knife blade
Copper penny

avage fragments are not micaceous, tabular, or polyhedral.)

Color	Streak	Remarks	Page
ite to brownish	White	Sheaf-like aggregates, in cavities in basalt	346
ite to yellow, green, gray, or brown	White	Radiated globular aggregates	316
ite to gray or pink	White	Alteration of salic volcanics	310
lorless to white	White	In stratified lake deposits, tinted yellow or gray	301
lorless to white	White	Blue fluorescence, tinted yellow, gray, green, or red	320
ite	White	In contact metamorphic limestones, tinted gray, yellow, or brown	380
een-white	White	Tinted blue or brown	390
e-white	White	Bladed crystals in metamorphic rocks	406
ite	White	Fibrous radiating masses in mafic lavas	381
ite	White	Tinted yellow, green, red, or brown	389
lorless to white	White	Radiating acicular crystals, tinted green, yellow, or red	348
lorless to white	White	In silica-poor igneous rocks, tinted yellow, green, gray, or red	339
ay to white	White	Prismatic crystals, in contact metamorphic zones	370
ite to green	White	Stubby prismatic crystals	375
ite or gray	White	Square prisms with a woody surface, colored green, blue, red	341
ite	White	In pegmatites or greisen, tinted yellow, pink, green, blue, or gray	316
ite or gray	White	Pseudotrapezohedral crystals, in silica-poor igneous rocks	343
assy	White	In salic extrusives	336
ite to flesh pink	White	Common rock-forming mineral	336
lorless	White	Pseudoorthorhombic crystals, often opalescent	336
ite to cream to red	White	Common rock-forming mineral, distinguished from orthoclase only by fine twinning striations on basal plane	336
ay to green or red	White	Vertically striated prisms	400
ite or gray	White	Common rock-forming mineral, polysynthetic twinning	337
ght green to white	White	Colloform with a crystalline surface	359
llow, brown, white	White	In ancient dolomitic marbles	399
own, green, white	White	Fibrous groups in metamorphic rocks	405
lorless or white	White	Platy crystals, very brittle	282
ite	White	In pegmatites, tinted green, gray, yellow, purple, or pink	376
own to colorless	White	Square prisms, tinted gray, green, red	397
ite, rose, green	White	Maltese cross on (001) section, in metamorphic rocks	403
lorless to white	White	Highly modified prisms, tinted green, blue, or red	401

Hardness 1 2 3 4 5 6 7 8 9 10	Hardness Range	Mineral Name	Formula	Specifi Gravit
	1.5–2	Realgar	AsS	3.6
	2–2.5	Proustite	Ag_3AsS_3	5.6
	2.5	Pyrargyrite	Ag_3SbS_3	5.8
	2.5–3	Polyhalite	$K_2Ca_2Mg(SO_4)_4 \cdot 2H_2O$	2.8
	2.5–3	Crocoite	$Pb(CrO_4)$	5.9–6.
	2.5–3.5	Jarosite	$KFe(SO_4)_3(OH)_6$	2.9–3.⬛
	3.5–4	Sphalerite	ZnS	3.9–4.
	3.5–4	Cuprite	Cu_2O	6.1
	4	Manganite	MnO(OH)	4.3
	4	Riebeckite	$Na_4Fe_6Fe_4(Si_{16}O_{44})(OH)_4$	3.4
	4–4.5	Wolframite series	$(MnFe)(WO_4)$	7.3
	4–4.5	Zincite	ZnO	5.4–5.⬛
	5	Apatite series	$Ca_5(PO_4)_3(F,Cl,OH)$	3.1
	5–5.5	Goethite	α-FeO(OH)	3.3–4.⬛
	5–5.5	Monazite	$(CeLaDy)(PO_4)$	5.1
	5–5.5	Sphene	$CaTi(SiO_4)O$	3.5
	5–6	Ilmenite series	$(FeMgMn)TiO_3$	4.7
	5–6	Hornblende series	$Ca_4Na_2(MgFe)_8(AlFe)_2 (Al_4Si_{12}O_{44})(OH,F)_4$	2.9–3.⬛
	5–6	Augite	$Ca(MgFeAl)[(AlSi)_2O_6]$	3.2–3.
	5–6	Enstatite series	$(MgFe)_2(Si_2O_6)$	3.1–3.⬛
	5–6	Hematite	Fe_2O_3	5.3
	5–6.5	Scapolite series	$(NaCa)_4[Al(AlSi)Si_2O_8]_3 (Cl,CO_3)$	2.6–2.⬛
	5.5–6	Allanite	$R_2^{+2}R_3^{+3}(SiO_4)_3(OH)$	3.0–4.⬛
	5.5–6	Anthophyllite series	$(MgFeAl)_7[(AlSi)_8O_{22}](OH)_2$	2.8–3.⬛
	5.5–6.5	Rhodonite	$Mn(SiO_3)$	3.4–3.⬛
	6	Arfvedsonite	$Na_6Mg_8Al_2(Si_{16}O_{44})(OH,F)_4$	3.4
	6	Orthoclase	$K(AlSi_3O_8)$	2.6
	6–6.5	Microcline	$K(AlSi_3O_8)$	2.5–2.⬛
	6–6.5	Rutile	TiO_2	4.2
	6–6.5	Columbite-tantalite series	$(FeMn)(CbTa)_2O_6$	5.2–7.⬛
	6–6.5	Humite group	$xMg_2(SiO_4) \cdot Mg(OH,F)_2$	3.1–3.⬛
	6–6.5	Acmite	$NaFe(Si_2O_6)$	3.5
	6–7	Cassiterite	SnO_2	7.0
	6.5–7	Axinite	$H(CaMnFe)_3Al_2B(SiO_4)_4$	3.3
	7–7.5	Staurolite	$FeAl_4(SiO_4)_2O_2(OH)_2$	3.7
	7.5	Zircon	$Zr(SiO_4)$	4.7
	9	Corundum	Al_2O_3	4.0

Quartz

Knife blade

Copper penny

Section E: Distinct Cleavage

(Fragments are not micaceous, tabular, or polyhedral.)

Color	Streak	Remarks	Page
...ed to orange-yellow	Orange to yellow	Melts at 310°	240
...ed	Red	With pyrargyrite	251
...eep red	Red	Translucent	251
...ght to dark red	White	Bitter taste	258
...ed	Orange	Secondary mineral in lead deposits	312
...own to yellow	Pale yellow	Crusts and coatings	310
...ack, brown, yellow	Brown, yellow, white	Resinous luster	234
...ark red	Brown-red	Octahedra, highly lustrous	263
...ack	Brown	Prismatic crystals, with other Mn oxides	283
...ark blue to black	White	In NaFe rich igneous rocks	371
...ack to brown-black	Brown-black	Sometimes weakly magnetic	319
...ed to orange-yellow	Orange-yellow	With franklinite and willemite	
...ark red-brown	White	Hexagonal prisms	313
...own	Brownish yellow	Common mineral, colloform	281
...own	White	Usually radioactive, accessory in salic igneous rocks	312
...own, red, black	White	Wedge-shaped crystals	407
...ack, brown, red	Black, brown, yellow	Common mineral, sometimes weakly magnetic	268
...ack	White	Common rock forming mineral	371
...ack to dark green	White	Common rock forming mineral, cleavage at right angles	375
...own	White	Common rock forming minerals in mafic rocks	374
...ack to red-brown	Brick red	Common mineral, good parting	267
...ed, gray	White	Square prisms with a woody surface	341
...own to black	Gray-brown	Accessory in granitic rocks, usually radioactive	400
...own	White or gray	Lamellar or fibrous, in crystalline schists	369
...ed or pink	White	Black surface stains	377
...ack	Bluish gray	In NaFe rich igneous rocks	371
...ed or pink	White	Common rock forming mineral	336
...ed to pink	White	Common rock forming mineral, distinguished from orthoclase only by fine twinning striations on basal plane	336
...lack to red	Pale brown	Prismatic crystals, highly lustrous	269
...lack to brown-black	Dark red to black	In granitic pegmatites	276
...rown, red	White	Formless grains in dolomitic marble	399
...rown to green	Yellowish gray	In NaFe rich igneous rocks	375
...rown or black	White to brown	Highly lustrous, in greisen	271
...rown, gray, blue	White	In igneous contact zones	
...rown to black	White	Distinct crystals in metamorphic rocks	408
...rown	White	Square prisms	397
...rown	White	In metamorphic rocks	266

Part 2: Nonmetallic Lus*

(Orange, yellow, green, blue, and violet minerc

Hardness 1 2 3 4 5 6 7 8 9 10	Hardness Range	Mineral Name	Formula	Specif Gravi*
	1.5–2	Orpiment	As_2S_3	3.5
	1.5–2	Realgar	AsS	3.6
	1.5–2.5	Sulfur	S	2.1
	2	Melanterite	$Fe(SO_4) \cdot 7\,H_2O$	1.9
	2	Glauconite	$K_2(MgFe)_2Al_6(Si_4O_{10})_3(OH)_{12}$	2.3
	2.5	Chalcanthite	$Cu(SO_4) \cdot 5\,H_2O$	2.1–2.
	2.5–3	Wulfenite	$Pb(MoO_4)$	6.5–7.
	2.5–3.5	Jarosite	$KFe(SO_4)_3(OH)_6$	2.9–3.
	2.5–5.5	Serpentine	$Mg_6(Si_4O_{10})(OH)_8$	2.6
	2.5–5.5	Chrysotile	$Mg_6(Si_4O_{10})(OH)_8$	2.2
	3.5–4	Malachite	$Cu_2(CO_3)(OH)_2$	4.1
	3.5–4	Azurite	$Cu_3(CO_3)_2(OH)_2$	3.8
	4	Fluorite	CaF_2	3.2
	4	Riebeckite	$Na_4Fe_6Fe_4(Si_{16}O_{44})(OH)_4$	3.4
	4.5, 6.5	Kyanite	$Al_2(SiO_4)O$	3.6
	5	Apatite series	$Ca_5(PO_4)_3(F,Cl,OH)$	3.1
	5	Melilite series	$Ca_2(MgAl)[(AlSi)_2O_7]$	3.0
	5–5.5	Monazite	$(CeLaDy)(PO_4)$	5.1
	5–5.5	Lazurite	$Na_5(AlSiO_4)_3S$	2.4–2.
	5–5.5	Lazulite	$MgAl_2(PO_4)_2(OH)_2$	3.0–3.
	5–6	Cancrinite	$Na_3Ca(Al_3Si_3O_{12})CO_3(OH)_2$	2.5
	5–6	Actinolite	$Ca_2(MgFe)_5(Si_8O_{22})(OH)_2$	3.0–3.
	5–6	Hornblende series	$Ca_4Na_2(MgFe)_8(AlFe)_2 (Al_4Si_{12}O_{44})(OH,F)_4$	2.9–3.
	5–6	Enstatite series	$(MgFe)_2(Si_2O_6)$	3.1–3.
	5–6	Diopside series	$Ca(MgFe)(Si_2O_6)$	3.2–3.
	5–6	Turquois	$Al_2PO_4(OH)_3 \cdot H_2O + xCu$	2.6–2.
	5–6.5	Scapolite series	$(NaCa)_4[Al(AlSi)Si_2O_8] (Cl,CO_3)$	2.6–2.
	5.5	Willemite	$Zn_2(SiO_4)$	3.9–4.
	5.5–6	Anthophyllite series	$(MgFeAl)_7[(AlSi)_8O_{22}] (OH)_2$	2.8–3.
	5.5–6	Sodalite	$Na_4(Al_3Si_3O_{12})Cl$	2.1–2.
	6–6.5	Prehnite	$Ca_2Al(AlSi_3O_{10})(OH)_2$	2.9
	6–6.5	Humite group	$xMg_2(SiO_4) \cdot Mg(OH,F)_2$	3.1–3.
	6–6.5	Glaucophane	$Na_4Mg_6Al_4(Si_{16}O_{44})(OH,F)_4$	3.0–3.
	6–6.5	Microcline	$K(AlSi_3O_8)$	2.5–2.
	6–7	Sillimanite	$AlAl(SiO_4)O$	3.2
	6–7	Epidote series	$Ca_2(AlFeMn)_3(SiO_4)_3(OH)$	3.2–3.
	6.5–7	Jadeite	$NaAl(Si_2O_6)$	3.3–3.
	6.5–7	Axinite	$H(CaMnFe)_3Al_2B(SiO_4)_4$	3.3
	7	Dumortierite	$(AlFe)_7BSi_3O_{18}$	3.3–3.
	7–7.5	Cordierite	$Mg_2Al_3(AlSi_5O_{18})$	2.6
	8.5	Chrysoberyl	Al_2BeO_4	3.7–3.
	9	Corundum	Al_2O_3	4.0

Quartz

Knife blade

Copper penny

ction F: Distinct Cleavage

(...avage fragments are not micaceous, tabular, or polyhedral.)

Color	Streak	Remarks	Page
...llow	Yellow	Sectile, melts at 300°	241
...ange-yellow to red	Orange-yellow to red	Sectile, melts at 310°	240
...llow	White	Melts and burns at 113°	225
...ie or Green	White	Sweetish taste	308
...ll green	White	Pellets in sedimentary rocks	366
...ie	White	Metallic taste	
...ange to yellow	White	Square tablets	322
...llow to brown	Pale yellow	Crusts and coatings	310
...een	White	Smooth to greasy feel	365
...een	White	Asbestiform	365
...een	Green	Colloform	297
...ie	Blue	Encrusting	298
...een or violet	White	Cubic crystals with octahedral cleavage, frequently fluorescent	260
...rk blue to black	White	In NaFe-rich igneous rocks	371
...ie-white	White	Bladed crystals in metamorphic rocks	406
...rk green	White	Hexagonal crystals	313
...llow or green to white	White	In silica-poor igneous rocks	389
...llow-brown	White	Usually radioactive	312
...ie	White	In limestones near granite contacts	340
...ie	White	Loses color when heated	
...llow, green, blue	White	In silica-poor igneous rocks	344
...een	White	In contact metamorphic zones	370
...rk green	White	Common rock forming mineral	371
...eenish white	White	Common rock forming mineral in mafic rocks	374
...een to white	White	Common mineral, in mafic and metamorphic rocks	375
...ie to green	White or greenish	Turns brown when heated	316
...een or blue	White	Square prisms with a woody surface	341
...een to brown or white	White	With other zinc minerals, fluorescent	
...een	White to grayish	In crystalline schists	369
...ie, green	White	In silica-poor igneous rocks	340
...ght green	White	Colloform with a crystalline surface	359
...llow to white	White	Formless grains in dolomitic marble	399
...ie	Grayish blue	In metamorphic rocks	371
...een	White	In siliceous igneous rocks and pegmatites	336
...ay-green to white	White	Fibrous groups in metamorphic rocks	405
...een	White	Common mineral	400
...een	White	Compact and tough	375
...ie, yellow, colorless	White	In igneous contact zones	
...olet, blue, pink	White	In pegmatites and crystalline metamorphic rocks, fibrous	
...ie to green	White	In metamorphic rocks	387
...een	Colorless	Tabular crystals in pegmatite or crystalline schist	394
...ie	White	Good parting, in metamorphic rocks	266

MINERAL INDEX

Entries in boldface type refer to minerals described in Part II.

SUBJECT INDEX